1961: International Atom

Element	Symbol	Number	Weight
Mercury	Hg	80	200.59
Molybdenum	Mo	42	95.94
Neodymium	Nd	60	144.24
Neon	Ne	10	20.183
Neptunium	Np	93	[237]
Nickel	Ni	28	58.71
Niobium	Nb	41	92.906
Nitrogen	N	7	14.0067
Nobelium	No	102	[254]
Osmium	Os	76	190.2
Oxygen	O	8	15.9994
Palladium	Pd	46	106.4
Phosphorus	P	15	30.9738
Platinum	Pt	78	195.09
Plutonium	Pu	94	[242]
Polonium	Po	84	[210]
Potassium	K	19	39.102
Praseodymium	Pr	59	140.907
Promethium	Pm	61	[147]
Protactinium	Pa	91	[231]
Radium	Ra	88	[226]
Radon	Rn	86	[222]
Rhenium	Re	75	186.2
Rhodium	Rh	45	102.905
Rubidium	Rb	37	85.47
Ruthenium	Ru	44	101.07
Samarium	Sm	62	150.35
Scandium	Sc	21	44.956
Selenium	Se	34	78.96
Silicon	Si	14	28.086
Silver	Ag	47	107.870
Sodium	Na	11	22.9898
Strontium	Sr	38	87.62
Sulfur	S	16	32.064
Tantalum	Ta	73	180.948
Technetium	Tc	43	[99]
Tellurium	Te	52	127.60
Terbium	Tb	65	158.924
Thallium	Tl	81	204.37
Thorium	Th	90	232.038
Thulium	Tm	69	168.934
Tin	Sn	50	118.69
Titanium	Ti	22	47.90
Tungsten	W	74	183.85
Uranium	U	92	238.03
Vanadium	V	23	50.942
Xenon	Xe	54	131.30
Ytterbium	Yb	70	173.04
Yttrium	Y	39	88.905
Zinc	Zn	30	65.37
Zirconium	Zr	40	91.22

introduction to qualitative analysis

INTRODUCTION *to*

QUALITATIVE

ANALYSIS

Durward C. Layde Associate Professor
of Chemistry, University of Wisconsin — Milwaukee

Boston   *Allyn and Bacon, Inc.*

First printing: April, 1961
Second printing: November, 1961
Third printing: February, 1963

Library of Congress Catalog Card Number: 61–11869

Printed in the United States of America

Preface

This book is intended as a laboratory introduction to equilibrium and solution chemistry, along with the reactions of the familiar cations and anions. The use of qualitative analysis as the basis of the laboratory consideration of these topics in the second semester of freshman chemistry is so widely favored that it needs no further justification.

Like most manuals of qualitative analysis, this book contains a considerable amount of material to supplement the textbook of general chemistry with which it is used. For example, included in the theoretical material of Part One is a discussion of modern inorganic nomenclature, a subject which is neglected in some excellent general chemistry texts. The attempt has been made to keep the discussions of ionization constants, solubility product, hydrolysis, and complex ions as simple as possible while presenting the essential material. The problems at the ends of the chapters range in difficulty from easy to moderately hard, with answers for enough of them to assure the student that he is working them correctly. The discussion of metals in Part Two should help the student to understand the reactions of the metal ions which he has observed in the laboratory.

The coordination of laboratory and lecture material in qualitative analysis is something of a problem. It is of course desirable to present the descriptive chemistry of each metal while the student is working with the ions of the metal in the laboratory; the advantages of arranging the sequence of discussions of the elements in accordance with the periodic table are also evident. Unfortunately a group separation in qualitative analysis is based on only a single property of an ion, so some of the groups are not homogeneous. If the laboratory material is begun with Groups 4 and 5, followed by Groups 3, 2, and 1, it is possible to use the periodic table as a basis for the discussion of the metals. This arrangement is favored by the simple chemistries of the alkali and alkaline earth metals and by the fact that many general chemistry texts begin the discussion of the metals with them. With this in mind, the procedures of Groups 4 and 5, as well as those of Group 1, are addressed to the beginning student, with terms carefully explained and operations described in detail.

In this book all equations are of the net ionic type. The Brönsted concept of acid-base reactions is used consistently, and the hydronium ion is never represented merely as H^+. Thus the ionization of acetic acid is given as

$$H_2O + HC_2H_3O_2 \rightleftharpoons H_3O^+ + C_2H_3O_2^-$$

to emphasize that ionization involves *a reaction* with the solvent.

Durward C. Layde

Contents

PART TWO / THE METALS

PART THREE / THE LABORATORY

PART FOUR / APPENDIX

part ONE

THEORY

A Few Words of Introduction
to the Student

1

Chemistry has grown into a vast science with many branches and divisions. One of the oldest of these is *Qualitative Analysis*: the study of what substances are present in a sample. (*Quantitative Analysis* is then used to determine how much of each component is present.) In the early days of chemistry, qualitative analysis was a most important branch of the subject. As soon as there was some understanding of what elements were, chemists busied themselves analyzing minerals of all sorts to find what elements they contained and trying to find new elements. Many ingenious methods of analysis were developed, and as early as 1840, Fresenius, a German chemist, developed what is essentially the system of analysis in general use today. However, systematic qualitative analysis as used in this book has limited practical importance nowadays. A chemist desiring to know the composition of an unknown substance is more likely to resort to instrumental analysis using a spectrograph, a mass spectrometer, or the like. Or, particularly if he has some idea of what may be present, and he usually does, he may try some specific chemical tests with small amounts of the material on a spot plate. Or, he may use chromatography—a method in which a solution of unknown composition is allowed to flow through a column of insoluble adsorbent material or to diffuse on filter paper. If the components of the solution are adsorbed at different rates, they will separate into bands which can be observed by color-producing reagents.

Systematic qualitative analysis is used at present mainly just as we will use it, as a convenient way to study the chemistry of the metals and as a way of illustrating some principles that govern certain chemical reactions and processes, especially equilibrium reactions in solution.

Perhaps you are wondering what exactly is meant by the term "Systematic Qualitative Analysis." If your only knowledge of analytical procedures had been obtained by watching movie or TV chemists you might think that a chemist (dressed in a neat white coat, though perhaps somewhat wild of eye) analyzes a completely unknown substance by putting a pinch of it in a test tube, adding some dark liquid, and holding it up to the light to watch it fizz. (The dark liquid is probably Coca-Cola.) Then, he peers at it through a microscope and announces in a firm voice, "This ore assays fifteen pounds of uranium to the ton," or, "The victim was given a lethal dose of 37 grains of strychnine one hour and eighteen minutes before he died."

The reality is quite different. We cannot take small portions of an unknown and apply to one portion a test for actinium, to another a test for aluminum, and so on through the alphabetical list of elements. There are few reagents available that will give tests with one specific substance regardless of what else is present. It is necessary to use reagents that will react with certain ions in such a way that they may be separated from other substances present, forming a conveniently small "group." This group can then be separated further into individual ions and the presence of each ion verified by subjecting it to some characteristic reaction or "confirmatory test." Most of the confirmatory tests are effective only on fairly pure substances. As an example, let us consider the test you will use for the Fe^{+3} ion. It is one of the better tests, very sensitive and easily observed, and it is not affected by impurities of the sort that might be present with the Fe^{+3} after you have separated it first as a member of a group and then as a single cation. But the test for iron could not be applied to an original substance because it is interfered with by both Hg^{+2} and Cu^{+2}.

Most of the operations of qualitative analysis are carried on in what is called the "wet way," that is, in a solution of which water is the principal solvent. In order to isolate an individual ion, we have various ways of removing ions from solution. There are four methods which are especially suited for this course:

1. Precipitation
2. Oxidation-reduction reactions
3. Formation of complex ions
4. Formation of covalent, or only slightly ionized, compounds

Of these, precipitation is by far the most important, since it is the only method on which separations are actually based. The others are useful for separations only when they are used in conjunction with precipitation for the purpose of changing some of the ions into forms that are easier or more difficult to precipitate. In a separation, the insoluble material is removed from the rest by decanting, that is, by carefully pouring off, the supernatant liquid, that is, the liquid that floats on top, or by withdrawing it with a pipette. This process is easier if the precipitate is first made more compact by centrifuging.

Some other techniques for removing ions from a solution that are of less value in this course but are useful for various purposes include:

5. Distillation
6. Solvent extraction
7. Ion exchange

Some of these you will use in a few separations, especially in the analysis of anions.

Atoms and Valence:
A Quick Review

2

2.1 / THE STRUCTURE OF THE ATOM

Three fundamental particles are needed to explain the makeup of the atom: the *electron*, with mass of about $\frac{1}{1850}$ on the atomic weight scale and 1 unit of negative charge; the *proton*, with mass of about 1 and 1 positive charge; and the *neutron* with mass of 1 and no electrical charge. The protons and neutrons, which comprise almost all of the mass, are concentrated in the center of the atom in a very small *nucleus*, which has a radius about $\frac{1}{10,000}$ that of the whole atom. The number of protons in an atom equals its nuclear charge or *atomic number*; the total number of protons and neutrons gives the *mass number* of the atom. Outside the nucleus there are electrons equal in number to the protons within, so the atom is electrically neutral.

2.2 / THE ELEMENTS

The simplest atom is that of hydrogen. Most of the hydrogen atoms in nature have a nucleus composed of just a single proton; the atomic number and the mass number are both 1. Another species of hydrogen atom contains 1 proton and 1 neutron in its nucleus. The atomic number of this atom is 1, also, but its mass number is 2. It is much less abundant since only one in about 6000 atoms of hydrogen is of this type. There is also a third kind of hydrogen atom, very rare in nature, which has 1 proton and 2 neutrons in its nucleus. It must have the same atomic number of 1 but the mass number is 3. Atoms of the same element which have different mass numbers are called *isotopes*. The familiar solar system diagrams of the three isotopes of hydrogen are shown in Figure 2.1.

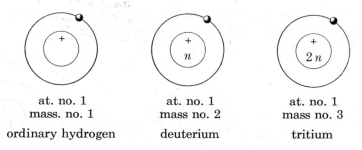

at. no. 1	at. no. 1	at. no. 1
mass. no. 1	mass no. 2	mass no. 3
ordinary hydrogen	deuterium	tritium

FIGURE 2.1

Since the electron is not restricted to a definite orbit in its motion, such a diagram might be thought of as representing only a highly probable path of the electron. A better representation of the hydrogen atom would show the nucleus surrounded by an "electron cloud" whose density at any point represents the likelihood that the electron is at that point at any one instant. The electron travels so rapidly around the nucleus that it effectively fills all the volume within a distance of about 10^{-8} cm (1 Å) from the nucleus. In other words, 2 hydrogen atoms can be brought together until their centers are about 2 Å apart. Half that distance, or 1 Å, is considered the radius of the hydrogen atom.

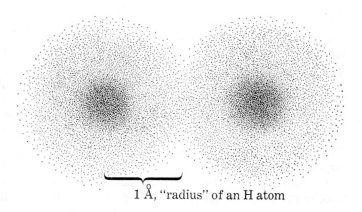

FIGURE 2.2   1 Å, "radius" of an H atom

After hydrogen, the simplest atom is that of helium, which has 2 protons in its nucleus. The only common type of helium atom has 2 neutrons; the mass number is therefore 4 and the atomic number 2. Both electrons are found in the same energy level or shell. But lithium, the element with atomic number 3, must begin to use the second level for its extra electron as is shown graphically in the diagrams of Figure 2.3.

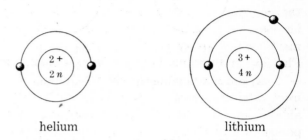

FIGURE 2.3   helium   lithium

The configuration of the first 20 elements is given in Table 2.1.

TABLE 2.1 / THE ELECTRON ARRANGEMENT OF THE FIRST 20 ELEMENTS

Element	At. no.	1st level	2nd	3rd	4th
Hydrogen	1	1			
Helium	2	2			
Lithium	3	2	1		
Beryllium	4	2	2		
Boron	5	2	3		
Carbon	6	2	4		
Nitrogen	7	2	5		
Oxygen	8	2	6		
Fluorine	9	2	7		
Neon	10	2	8		
Sodium	11	2	8	1	
Magnesium	12	2	8	2	
Aluminum	13	2	8	3	
Silicon	14	2	8	4	
Phosphorus	15	2	8	5	
Sulfur	16	2	8	6	
Chlorine	17	2	8	7	
Argon	18	2	8	8	
Potassium	19	2	8	8	1
Calcium	20	2	8	8	2

2.3 / THE INERT GAS STRUCTURE

The table of electron distributions of the elements shows 2 electrons as the maximum in the first level, 8 in the second, and 8 in the third. In heavier elements, however, in which it is not the outermost level, as many as 18 electrons can be added to the third level. It will be noticed that each outermost level has become complete at an inert gas: helium, neon, or argon. Since the elements on either side of the inert gases happen to be familiar ones, we know that lithium, sodium, and potassium are active metals which always show a valence of +1 in their compounds. Fluorine and chlorine are non-metals which show a valence of −1; oxygen is a non-metal which exhibits a valence of −2. The inert gases themselves, however, do not react at all. It is reasonable to explain these facts by assuming that the inert gases possess a preferred type of electron configuration. Sodium, for instance, could achieve the neon structure by giving up 1 electron. Since it would then have 11 protons and only 10 electrons, it would become a positive ion, Na$^+$. Chlorine could achieve the argon structure by acquiring an electron. This would give it 18 electrons and 17 protons so it too would become an ion, the negatively charged Cl$^-$, as represented diagrammatically by Figure 2.4.

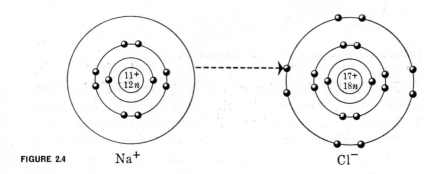

FIGURE 2.4   Na$^+$ Cl$^-$

Although the diagrams in Figure 2.4 show all the electrons of the atoms and ions, only the electrons of the outermost levels, the *valence electrons*, were involved in the formation of NaCl. A simpler way to show what takes place is to let the symbol of an element stand for the nucleus and the inner shells, and to use dots around the symbol for the valence electrons:

$$\text{Na} \cdot + \cdot \ddot{\underset{\cdot\cdot}{Cl}} : \rightarrow \text{Na}^+ + \overset{\cdot\cdot}{\underset{\cdot\cdot}{Cl}} :^-$$

The sodium ions and the chloride ions attract one another because of their opposite electrical charge, but they do not show a tendency to gather together simply in pairs. Instead they stack together in larger aggregates in which each sodium ion is surrounded by, and is attracted equally to, 6 neighboring chloride ions (one in each direction—north, south, east, west, up and down). Similarly, each chloride ion is in the center of 6 sodium ions and this arrangement continues throughout the whole crystal. A small part of a sodium chloride crystal is shown in Figure 2.5.

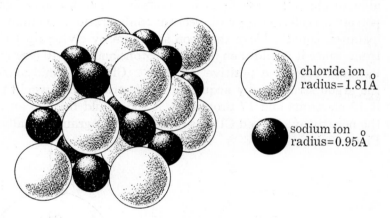

chloride ion radius = 1.81Å

sodium ion radius = 0.95Å

FIGURE 2.5 / CRYSTAL STRUCTURE OF SODIUM CHLORIDE

Because the formation of the compound NaCl involves a transfer of electrons, the attractive force is termed *electrovalence*. It is also called *ionic valence*. Both names are logical and descriptive, and both are used. Sodium chloride, a typical ionic compound, is also a typical salt. Other compounds that are considered salts are also ionic, and the ionic composition explains those properties that are recognized as characteristics of salts, such as hardness, brittleness, high melting point, and high electrical conductivity of the molten substance. Hence the modern definition of a *salt: any substance whose crystal is made up of ions.*

2.4 / COVALENCE

Electrovalence accounts for the formation of compounds between elements that have only a very few electrons in their outer levels and those that require only a few more electrons to fill up their outer levels to an inert gas conformation. Another explanation is needed for the existence of substances like nitrogen trichloride, water, or the chlorine molecule. *Covalence,* or the sharing of pairs of electrons, provides the answer in such cases.

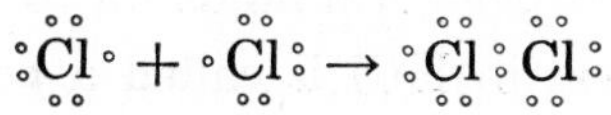

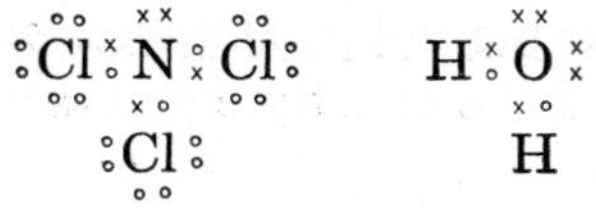

$$:\!\ddot{Cl}\cdot \; + \; \cdot\ddot{Cl}: \; \rightarrow \; :\!\ddot{Cl}:\!\ddot{Cl}:$$

$$:\!\ddot{Cl}\!:\!\ddot{N}\!:\!\ddot{Cl}: \qquad\qquad H\!:\!\ddot{O}\!:$$
$$:\!\ddot{Cl}: \qquad\qquad\qquad H$$

Please note that we may use x's or o's instead of dots whenever we think it helps to clarify the electron arrangement. Usually, but not always, the outer energy levels are brought up to 8 (2 for hydrogen) by the shared electrons. There are plenty of exceptions; for example:

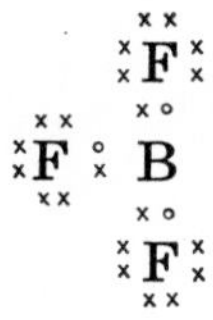

$$\underset{x\,F\,x}{\overset{x\,F\,x}{x\,F\,x\,B\,x\,F\,x}} \qquad\text{and}\qquad \underset{F\;F}{\overset{F\;F}{F\,S\,F}}$$

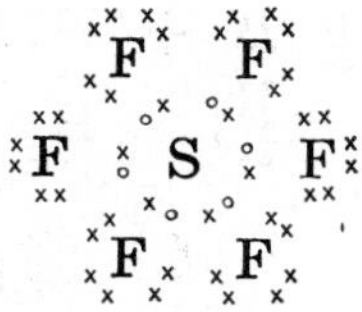

Boron has only 6 electrons in its outer level in BF_3, and sulfur in SF_6 has 12.

More than one pair of electrons may be shared between two atoms so we have double and triple bonds. Examples are:

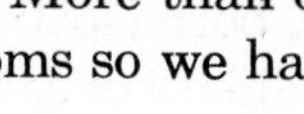

$:\!\ddot{O}\!:\!C\!:\!\ddot{O}\!:$, usually written $:\!\ddot{O}\!::\!C\!:\!\ddot{O}:$ which is easier to set in type or to write on a typewriter, and $H:C:::C:H$.

Many chemists like to use a dash to represent the electron pair bond, often omitting non-bonding electrons, so some of the formulas above might be written

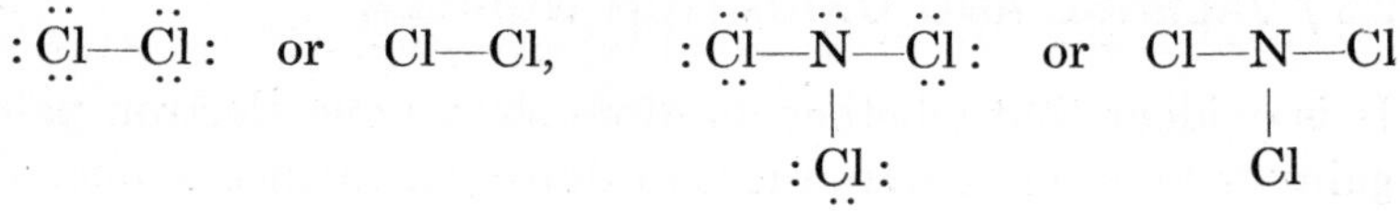

$$:\!\ddot{Cl}\!-\!\ddot{Cl}: \quad\text{or}\quad Cl\!-\!Cl, \qquad :\!\ddot{Cl}\!-\!\ddot{N}\!-\!\ddot{Cl}: \quad\text{or}\quad Cl\!-\!N\!-\!Cl$$
$$\qquad\qquad\qquad\qquad\qquad\qquad |\qquad\qquad\qquad |$$
$$\qquad\qquad\qquad\qquad\qquad\qquad :\!\ddot{Cl}: \qquad\qquad Cl$$

$$H\!-\!\overset{..}{O}\!: \quad \text{or} \quad H\!-\!O, \qquad H\!-\!C\!\equiv\!C\!-\!H, \qquad O\!=\!C\!=\!O$$
$$|\qquad\qquad\qquad|$$
$$H\qquad\qquad\quad H$$

Polar bonds. In the $:\overset{..}{\underset{.}{C}}l:\overset{..}{\underset{.}{C}}l:$ molecule we should certainly expect the bonding electron pair to be shared equally by the two chlorine atoms. In $H:\overset{..}{\underset{.}{C}}l:$ the electron pair, however, is attracted more strongly to the chlorine than to the hydrogen, but, unlike sodium in $Na^+, :\overset{..}{\underset{.}{C}}l:^-$, the hydrogen still holds on to the electrons. The unequally shared bond in HCl is called a *polar covalent bond.* Aside from bonds between 2 atoms of the same element, most covalent bonds show some polar character since we cannot expect dissimilar atoms to have exactly equal attraction for the bonding electrons.

Coordinate covalence. In the examples of covalence used so far, each of the atoms has contributed one electron to the shared pair, but that is not a necessity as these reactions show:

$$\begin{array}{ccc}
\overset{\circ\circ}{:\!F\!:} & H & \overset{\circ\circ}{:\!F\!:}H \\
\overset{\circ\circ}{:\!F\!:}B & +\ \overset{x}{:}\!N\overset{x}{:}H \rightarrow & \overset{\circ\circ}{:\!F\!:}B\overset{x}{:}N\overset{x}{:}H \\
\overset{\circ\circ}{:\!F\!:} & H & \overset{\circ\circ}{:\!F\!:}H
\end{array}$$

$$\begin{array}{cc}
& H \\
H\overset{xx}{:}N\overset{x}{:}H + H\overset{\circ\circ}{:}O\overset{\circ\circ}{:} \rightleftharpoons & H\overset{xx}{:}N\overset{x}{:}H^+ + \overset{\circ\circ}{:}O\overset{\circ\circ}{:}^- \\
H & H \qquad H \qquad H
\end{array}$$

It is easy to spot the *coordinate covalent* bonds, both electrons of which came from the same atom. Once a coordinate covalent bond is formed, it is just like any other bond. In the NH_4^+ ion the hydrogen atom which was the latecomer·is joined in exactly the same way as the others; and if the reaction is reversed the chances of any one of the hydrogen atoms being the one to leave the ammonium ion are identical.

2.5 / VALENCE AND OXIDATION NUMBER

It is evident that whether an atom shares one electron pair or gains or loses one electron it is exhibiting a valence of one. The atoms in a molecule of fluorine are held together by a single valence bond; those in a nitrogen molecule, $: N : : : N :$, are held together by a triple bond. We find, though, that valence is not always so easily determined as in these examples, and it is of less practical importance than the *oxidation number*. The oxidation number might be defined as the *effective valence*, or the charge the atoms would have if we assigned all the shared electrons completely to the atom that has greater affinity for them. Even if we do not assign these electrons correctly, the values we get for the oxidation numbers will be useful if we consistently follow certain arbitrary rules:

1. The oxidation number of a free element is zero.
2. The sum of the oxidation numbers in a neutral molecule is zero. The sum of the oxidation numbers in an ion equals the charge on the ion.
3. Hydrogen in compounds is commonly +1, oxygen in compounds is commonly −2.
4. The metals of Periodic Group Ia show a valence of +1, the metals of Periodic Group IIa show a valence of +2.
5. Halogens in binary compounds commonly show a valence of −1.

A few examples will suffice to illustrate these rules:

In $KMnO_4$, $K = +1$ and $O = -2$, so $Mn = +7$ to make the sum of the oxidation numbers zero.

In NH_4^+, $H = +1$, so $N = -3$.

And in $Cr_2O_7^{-2}$, $O = -2$, so $Cr = +6$ to make the sum of the oxidation numbers equal the charge on the ion.

Questions and problems

1. Give the oxidation numbers of each of the elements in the following substances:

   a. $NaClO_3$

   b. Mn^{+2}

   c. PCl_3

   d. $H_2AsO_4^-$

   e. $Sn(OH)_6^{-2}$

   f. H_2O_2

   g. Sb_2S_3

   h. $N_2H_5^+$

2. What is meant by the "radius" of an atom? What are isotopes?

3. Explain the difference between mass number and atomic weight.

4. By means of dotted symbols, show the arrangement of valence electrons in:

   a. BF_3 d. ClO_3^-

   b. C_2H_4 e. H_3PO_4

   c. N_2O_4 f. N_2H_4

Nomenclature

3

The basic system of naming inorganic compounds was devised by Lavoisier and his fellows in 1787. It is, then, about as old as the American Constitution, and like the Constitution it has served excellently as a fundamental framework, although also like the Constitution it has required some amendments from time to time and the addition of various rules to make it fit problems which could not be foreseen at the time of its origin. Of course, the original rules, written for the French language, have had to be modified to adjust to English or other languages. In recent years some of the original rules of nomenclature have been changed, partly to simplify the system, partly to get rid of some indefinite or confusing names, and partly to make distinctive names available for many newly discovered compounds.

3.1 / BINARY COMPOUNDS

For binary electrovalent compounds, the positive ion is named first, then the negative ion with the ending "-ide"; for example,

KCl   Potassium chloride
CaO   Calcium oxide

The names of covalent binary compounds are similar, with the more electropositive element given first, followed by the more electronegative element as in the examples

HF   Hydrogen fluoride
OF_2 Oxygen fluoride
Cl_2O Chlorine monoxide

To be sure, we may sometimes not know offhand which is the more electronegative element; that is, which element in the compound has the greater attraction for electrons. Moreover, chemists do not completely agree on the order of electronegativity of the elements, since different methods of measuring this property have been used. Sometimes, as in the case of nitrogen triiodide, the elements are written in the order to which chemists have become accustomed, even though the first element is decidedly more electronegative. The order of increasing electronegativity of non-metallic elements which has been suggested is

Sb, As, B, Si, H, C, P, Te, Se, S, I, Br, Cl, N, O, F

However, the order of these elements is not ordinarily a problem because as familiarity with chemical formulas increases, writing them in the preferred order becomes habitual.

When two elements combine in different ratios to form more than one compound, several methods are available for distinguishing the compounds. The system favored in modern writing is that adopted by the International Union of Chemistry, the I.U.C. A Roman numeral in parenthesis following immediately after the name of the more electropositive element designates its valence; for example,

$FeCl_2$	Iron(II) chloride
Cu_2O	Copper(I) oxide
$TiCl_3$	Titanium(III) chloride

Many authors still use the older method of distinguishing between two valence states of the more electropositive element by adding to the name of the element the suffix "-ous" to designate the lower valence and "-ic" for the higher valence, and of course this system is used almost exclusively in the vast body of older chemical literature. We must be prepared to recognize the older names as well as the new as shown in the following table:

$FeSO_4$	Ferrous sulfate as well as	Iron(II) sulfate
AgO	Argentic oxide	Silver(II) oxide
Fe_3O_4	Ferroso-ferric oxide	Iron(II,III) oxide
$CrBr_3$	Chromic bromide	Chromium(III) bromide

Note that Latin names are used with the suffixes "-ous" and "-ic" for some elements which have been known for a long time. This is not a point to endear the older terminology to the student. Also, we have the interesting case of those chemists who write "iron(II) chloride" but say "ferrous chloride" because the latter sounds more euphonious (or because, let us admit, we have the habit of thinking of $FeCl_2$ as "ferrous chloride").

The fact that some elements have three or more valences is one of the reasons for the adoption of the I.U.C. system. If $TiCl_4$ is titanic chloride and $TiCl_3$ is titanous chloride, what shall we call $TiCl_2$? But if $TiCl_4$ and $TiCl_3$ are titanium(IV) chloride and titanium(III) chloride, $TiCl_2$ is titanium(II) chloride.

Even the use of Roman numerals to indicate oxidation states does not always give us simple distinctive names for all known or possible compounds. The use of Greek numerical prefixes* to indicate the number of atoms of each element present may then be preferable:

P_4S_3	Tetraphosphorus trisulfide
P_4S_7	Tetraphosphorus heptasulfide
Si_2Br_6	Disilicon hexabromide
NO_2	Nitrogen dioxide
N_2O_4	Dinitrogen tetraoxide (or tetroxide)

The prefix "mono-" is not used unless it is needed to remove uncertainty.

Binary compounds of hydrogen. Compounds of hydrogen with metals (especially compounds containing the H^- ion) are called *hydrides*, as would be expected. Compounds of hydrogen with the more electronegative elements are given "hydrogen .....-ide" or "hydro......-ic acid" names, as in *hydrogen bromide* for HBr, or *hydrobromic acid* if it is dissolved in an ionizing solvent. Special names are often used for some well-known compounds of hydrogen, particularly those with the non-metallic elements toward the middle of the periodic table:

---

*The Greek numerical prefixes are, in order: mono-, di-, tri-, tetra-, penta-, hexa-, hepta-, octa-.

The corresponding Latin prefixes are uni-, bi-, ter-, quadri-, quinque-, sexi-, septi-, octa-. These should be used in combination with words of Latin origin; for example, with words like "valence" to make "univalence."

NaH	Sodium hydride
CaH_2	Calcium hydride
HI	Hydrogen iodide or hydriodic acid
H_2S	Hydrogen sulfide or hydrosulfuric acid
B_2H_6	Diborane
CH_4	Methane
SiH_4	Silane
Si_2H_6	Disilane
NH_3	Ammonia
N_2H_4	Hydrazine
PH_3	Phosphine
AsH_3	Arsine
SbH_3	Stibine
BiH_3	Bismuthine
H_2O	Water
H_2O_2	Hydrogen peroxide

Compounds named like binary compounds. The names of certain negative radicals end in "-ide," so the names of their compounds are similar to those of binary compounds. Some of the common radicals of this type are

CN^-	Cyanide	N_3^-	Azide
CN_2^{-2}	Cyanamide	NH_2^-	Amide
OH^-	Hydroxide	NH^{-2}	Imide
O_2^{-2}	Peroxide	SH^-	Hydrosulfide

But the compound NH_2OH which might be considered either a hydroxide or, preferably, an amide, is called *hydroxylamine.*

In addition to the very familiar ammonium ion, there are other common positive radicals; for example,

NH_4^+	Ammonium	H_3O^+	Hydronium
NH_3OH^+	Hydroxylammonium	PH_4^+	Phosphonium

A compound of one of these radicals is named like a compound of an electropositive element. For example, NH_4I is ammonium iodide, and phosphonium cyanide, PH_4CN, containing four elements, has a name formed in the same way as that of a binary compound like sodium chloride.

3.2 / OXYGEN-CONTAINING ACIDS AND THEIR SALTS

The familiar names of the ternary oxygen acids and their salts have proved so satisfactory they have not needed to be changed. These acids are formed of a central atom to which are attached hydroxyl groups and sometimes oxygen atoms. The acid is named for the central atom, with prefixes and suffixes to indicate the oxidation state of this atom.

If the central element has only a single oxidation state, the ending "-ic" is used for the acid and "-ate" for the salts, as in *boric acid* and *sodium borate*. If there are two oxidation states known, these endings are used for the higher oxidation state; the acid for the lower oxidation state is given the suffix "-ous," and the corresponding salt ends in "-ite." If more oxidation states are known, the prefix "hypo-" is added to the name of the "-ous" acid to indicate a still lower oxidation state, and the prefix "per-" is added to the "-ic" acid to indicate a still higher oxidation state. Using chlorine as an example, the names of all the oxyacids are: "*perchloric*," "chlor*ic*," "chlor*ous*," and "*hypo*chlor*ous*" acids in order of descending oxidation states of the chlorine: $+7$, $+5$, $+3$, and $+1$.

Oxidation states of the central atom change by two units between successive members of a series. Some names of compounds illustrating the system are given in the following list:

H_2CO_3	Carbonic acid	Na_2CO_3	Sodium carbonate
H_3AsO_4	Arsenic acid	Na_3AsO_4	Sodium arsenate
H_3AsO_3	Arsenious acid	Na_3AsO_3	Sodium arsenite
HNO_3	Nitric acid	$NaNO_3$	Sodium nitrate
HNO_2	Nitrous acid	$NaNO_2$	Sodium nitrite
$H_2N_2O_2$	Hyponitrous acid	$Na_2N_2O_2$	Sodium hyponitrite
$HClO_4$	Perchloric acid	$NaClO_4$	Sodium perchlorate
$HClO_3$	Chloric acid	$NaClO_3$	Sodium chlorate
$HClO_2$	Chlorous acid	$NaClO_2$	Sodium chlorite
$HClO$	Hypochlorous acid	$NaClO$	Sodium hypochlorite

Ortho-, pyro-, and meta-acids. More than one oxygen acid exists for the same oxidation state of some elements, the difference being due to the replacement of two hydroxyl groups by a single oxygen atom, or an apparent difference in the degree of dehydration. Phosphoric acid, for example, might be written H_3PO_4, $H_4P_2O_7$, $H_5P_3O_{10}$ or HPO_3, the phosphorus having an oxidation state of $+5$ in each case. The prefix "ortho-" is used in naming the acid which has the greatest known number of hydroxyl groups, or for which corresponding compounds are known, as in

H_3BO_3	Orthoboric acid
H_4SiO_4	Orthosilicic acid
H_3PO_4	Orthophosphoric acid

In the case of H_4SiO_4, the existence of the ortho-acid has been doubted, but the structure of compounds like the mineral zircon, which is $ZrSiO_4$, zirconium orthosilicate, is well authenticated.

If an ortho-acid is dehydrated by removing one molecule of water from two molecules of the ortho-acid, a "pyro-" acid is obtained:

$H_4P_2O_7$	Pyrophosphoric acid
$H_4P_2O_5$	Pyrophosphorous acid
$H_2S_2O_7$	Pyrosulfuric acid

If one molecule of water is removed from each molecule of ortho-acid, a "meta-" acid results:

HPO_3	Metaphosphoric acid
HBO_2	Metaboric acid
$NaAsO_2$	Sodium metaarsenite

When dehydration of an ortho-acid results in condensation to more complex compounds than the prefixes "pyro-" and "meta-" indicate, the number of atoms of the central element may be indicated by a Greek numerical prefix:

$H_5P_3O_{10}$	Triphosphoric acid
$Na_2B_4O_7$	Sodium tetraborate

Thio-acids: The prefix "thio-" indicates that one or more atoms of oxygen in an oxy-acid or its salt have been replaced by sulfur:

Na_2SO_4	Sodium sulfate
$Na_2S_2O_3$	Sodium thiosulfate
AsO_2^-	Metaarsenite ion
AsS_2^-	Metadithioarsenite ion
CH_3CONH_2	Acetamide
CH_3CSNH_2	Thioacetamide

3.3 / MIXED SALTS

If a salt has two or more cations, the more electropositive one is named first:

$KMgCl_3$ Potassium magnesium chloride

Na_3AlF_6 Sodium aluminum fluoride (or, better, sodium hexafluoroaluminate, as AlF_6^{-3} is a complex ion)

In *acid salts* the hydrogen is named last of the positive constituents; thus,

$NaHSO_4$ Sodium hydrogen sulfate (*not* sodium bisulfate, and *certainly not* sodium acid sulfate)

NaH_2PO_4 Sodium dihydrogen phosphate

If a salt contains two or more anions, they are simply placed in alphabetical order, as relative electronegativity may not be easily decided:

$KCl \cdot K_2SO_4$ Potassium chloride sulfate.

But if one of the anions is oxide or hydroxide (as in basic salts) it is written "oxy-" or "hydroxy-" before any other anion:

$SbOCl$ Antimony oxychloride

$ZrOBr_2$ Zirconium(IV) oxybromide

Sometimes "-yl" is used to indicate oxygen, though it is properly used only if the group was obtained from an oxygen acid:

$NOCl$ Nitrosyl chloride derived from HNO_2 by replacing the OH^- group with Cl^-

CrO_2Cl_2 Chromyl chloride derived from H_2CrO_4

but

$BiOCl$ Bismuth oxychloride

3.4 / TRIVIAL NAMES

In serious chemical writing, we should consistently use the best name of any substance, while being prepared for the use by others of some less desirable name. So let us refer to $HgCl_2$ only as "mercury(II) chloride," but let us not be upset if it is referred to by someone else as "mercuric chloride." What about names like "corrosive sublimate" or "bichloride of mercury" or just "bichloride"? Bichloride of mercury does not conform to any of the accepted usages in nomenclature but it could hardly be called wrong or misleading. At worst, it is old-fashioned. If a druggist or a physician wishes to use the term we shall have no trouble understanding it, but let us never repeat it. The name "corrosive sublimate" gives us no clue to the composition of the substance. Like "red lead," "oil of vitriol," and "laughing gas" it is a *trivial* name (from a Latin word for crossroads or market-place, it means a name used by non-scientists). Many trivial names have interesting historical connotations or like "corrosive sublimate" are commonly used in commerce, so they are part of our vocabularies to be used when they seem appropriate. The same substance which in this book is called "sodium chloride" is properly referred to only as "salt" at the dining table. In a few cases, the trivial name is the accepted scientific name; no one would think of calling H_2O by any such systematic name as "dihydrogen monoxide" nor is NH_3 ever called anything but "ammonia."

3.5 / WHEN IN DOUBT, USE THE FORMULA

Even with the improvements the I.U.C. rules have made in nomenclature, the names of some compounds are clumsy and confusing. This situation seems likely to become worse rather than better, as chemists seem to be more ingenious at discovering new compounds than at inventing names to describe them systematically. Rather than try to find words to designate properly such a substance as $K_2SO_3 \cdot 2NO$ or $N_4S_4H_4$ or $(NH_4)_3PO_4Mo_{12}O_{36}$, it is better and simpler to use the formula.

Questions and problems

1. Give chemical formulas of the following substances:
    a. Iron(III) sulfate
    b. Copper(I) oxide
    c. Barium perchlorate trihydrate
    d. Vanadium(II) bromide

    e. Titanium(IV) chloride
    f. Phosphonium iodide
    g. Trilead tetroxide
    h. Potassium metadithioantimonite
    i. Dihydrogen orthophosphate ion
    j. Dioxochromium(VI) ion

2. Give systematic names for the following substances:
    a. $Ti_3(PO_4)_4$
    b. N_2O
    c. NO_2
    d. $NaHSO_4$
    e. $Fe_2(SO_4)_3 \cdot 9\,H_2O$
    f. $BiONO_3$
    g. $K_2Mg(SO_4)_2$
    h. KHF_2
    i. BrO_3^-
    j. VO^+

3. Give formulas and I.U.C. systematic names for the following substances which are listed by old style or trivial names:
    a. Cupric sulfate
    b. Ferrous carbonate
    c. Mercurous chloride
    d. Sodium bicarbonate
    e. Sodium acid sulfate
    f. Blue vitriol
    g. Copperas
    h. Stannous chloride
    i. Litharge
    j. Borax

Chemical Equations

4

4.1 / CHEMICAL CHANGE

In a chemical change, atoms combine with one another, or the groupings of atoms are rearranged or broken down. We may use various methods of expressing the changes that take place. The burning of hydrogen might be described in words:

hydrogen + oxygen → water

Or if our interest is in the chief product of a reaction we might write

$$H_2 \xrightarrow{O_2} H_2O$$

as is often done in organic chemistry. But if we wish to express the quantitative relationships we would write

$$2H_2 + O_2 \rightarrow 2H_2O$$

Only this last formulation is a true chemical equation. It tells us that two molecules of hydrogen, each consisting of two atoms of the element, unite with one diatomic molecule of oxygen to give two molecules of water, each consisting of two atoms of hydrogen and one of oxygen. Since this equation describes the way this reaction always proceeds, the weight relationships of the atoms and the volume relationships of gaseous substances can be derived from it. In general, the simpler operations applicable to mathematical equations may be applied to it: terms may be added to both sides or subtracted from both sides; all terms may be multiplied or divided by the same number, and it can be combined with other chemical equations by addition or subtraction. However, the right and left sides cannot be freely transposed, since the arrow separating them (to be read "yields") indicates that the reaction is proceeding in a definite direction.

4.2 / NET EQUATIONS

Depending on the purposes a chemist has in mind, he may write different types of chemical equations to describe the same reaction. A certain neutralization reaction might be written

$$HCl + NaOH \rightarrow NaCl + H_2O$$

if the purpose is to show the weight of sodium hydroxide to be put into solution to react with a definite amount of hydrochloric acid. Such an equation is called a *molecular* equation. Since we know that NaOH and NaCl are always ionic, never molecular, we would usually do better to try to show exactly what species are present:

$$H_3O^+ + Cl^- + Na^+ + OH^- \rightarrow Na^+ + Cl^- + 2H_2O$$

Sometimes those ions which came into the reaction together are indicated by brackets:

$$[H_3O^+ + Cl^-] + [Na^+ + OH^-] \rightarrow Na^+ + Cl^- + 2H_2O$$

Either way, this is an *ionic* equation. However, two of the ions, Na^+ and Cl^-, actually took no part in the proceedings; they merely stood around and watched. Therefore, they are called *spectator* ions. To be sure, their presence was required; the OH^- ion could not have been added without a suitable positive ion accompanying it, and the H_3O^+ ion required a negative companion of some sort. In a somewhat different sense, a Major League baseball team would not play a game without the spectators being present, yet the names of the spectators do not appear in the box score. If we leave the spectators out of our box score, we will have

$$H_3O^+ + OH^- \rightarrow 2H_2O$$

This is called a *net ionic* equation. Only the formulas of the substances that actually react are given, and their formulas are presented in the way that seems to represent the best combination of correctness and simplicity.

Thermochemical equations may also be used. For the reaction of sodium hydroxide with hydrochloric acid (or any strong base with a strong acid), the thermochemical equation would be

$$H_3O^+ + OH^- \rightarrow 2H_2O + 13.8 \text{ kcal}$$

The combustion of hydrogen would be shown by

$$2H_2 + O_2 \rightarrow 2H_2O + 137 \text{ kcal}$$

Like the other components of a chemical equation, the heat term may be handled like a member of an algebraic equation:

$$3O_2 \rightarrow 2O_3 - 68 \text{ kcal}$$
$$3O_2 + 68 \text{ kcal} \rightarrow 2O_3$$
$$\tfrac{3}{2}O_2 \rightarrow O_3 - 34 \text{ kcal}$$

4.3 / OXIDATION-REDUCTION REACTIONS

In Chapter 2, page 13, the rules for determining the oxidation number were given. It was pointed out that this value represents the charge on an atom due to electrons gained or lost, with the understanding that electrons shared by two atoms are counted as belonging completely to the atom with greater electronegativity. An oxidation-reduction reaction is any reaction that involves a change in oxidation number. This may correspond to an actual transfer of electrons, as in

$$2\text{Na}^\cdot + :\ddot{\text{Cl}}:\ddot{\text{Cl}}: \; \rightarrow \; 2\text{Na}^+ + 2:\ddot{\text{Cl}}:^-$$

If there is merely a change in covalent bonds, the result would be only a formal reassignment of the shared electrons:

$$
\begin{array}{ccc}
\text{H} & & \text{H} \\
\text{H}:\overset{\cdot}{\underset{\cdot}{\text{C}}}:\text{H} + :\ddot{\text{Cl}}:\ddot{\text{Cl}}: & \rightarrow & \text{H}:\overset{\cdot}{\underset{\cdot}{\text{C}}}:\ddot{\text{Cl}}: + \text{H}:\ddot{\text{Cl}}: \\
\text{H} & & \text{H}
\end{array}
$$

If we rewrite this second equation linearly with the oxidation numbers above each element, we have

$$\overset{-4\ +1}{\text{CH}_4} + \overset{0}{\text{Cl}_2} \; \rightarrow \; \overset{-2\ +1\ -1}{\text{CH}_3\text{Cl}} + \overset{+1\ -1}{\text{HCl}}$$

Although no atom has gained or lost electrons, there have been changes in the oxidation numbers.

Because carbon is more electronegative than hydrogen, all cf the shared electrons of methane are assigned to it; in CH_3Cl, carbon is assigned the 3 pairs of electrons shared with atoms of hydrogen, but the pair shared with the atom of chlorine is assigned to the chlorine, as the sketches of Figure 4.1 seek to represent.

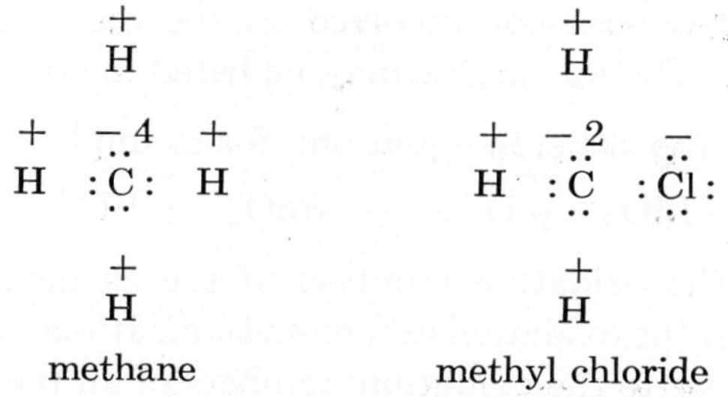

$$
\begin{array}{ccc}
+ & & + \\
H & & H \\
& & \\
+ \quad -4 \quad + & & + \quad -2 \quad - \\
H \;\; :\overset{..}{\underset{..}{C}}: \;\; H & & H \;\; :\overset{..}{\underset{..}{C}} \;\; :\overset{..}{\underset{..}{Cl}}: \\
& & \\
+ & & + \\
H & & H \\
\text{methane} & & \text{methyl chloride}
\end{array}
$$

FIGURE 4.1 / REPRESENTATION OF THE ASSIGNMENT OF ELEC-TRONS BETWEEN ATOMS OF DIFFERENT ELECTRONEGATIVITY. *Though one atom may have only slightly greater affinity for electrons, we pretend that it has sole possession of the bonding electrons.*

Oxidation we will define as loss of electrons, whether the loss is actual and complete, as in the change from Na· to Na⁺, or only a matter of a lessened degree of attraction for the electron pair that makes up a covalent bond. Since electrons lost by an atom that is oxidized must go somewhere, oxidation must always be accompanied by a gain of electrons, or reduction, of some other atom. The term *redox* is often used as a telescoped form of *red*uction plus *ox*idation.

4.4 / BALANCING OXIDATION-REDUCTION EQUATIONS

Some oxidation-reduction reactions are rather difficult to balance unless some systematic procedure is followed. The number of electrons lost by each atom of the element which is oxidized may not be the same as the electron gain per atom of the element which is reduced. Or the elements involved may be contained in complex ions or in covalent compounds. Since in such cases, the inspection, or "hit-and-miss," methods of balancing may not be very effective, some arithmetical device for equalizing the number of electrons lost and gained is useful. Two different approaches are used: the *electron-change* method and the *ion-electron* method.

The electron-change method. First, the skeleton equation is written out and the electron transfers necessary to bring about the desired changes in oxidation number are equalized; then the other substances not involved in the oxidation-reduction are balanced. The operations may be listed in six steps:

1. Write out the skeleton equation; for example

$$Mn^{+2} + BiO_3^- + H_3O^+ \rightarrow MnO_4^- + Bi^{+3} + H_2O$$

2. Write in the oxidation numbers of the elements that were involved in the oxidation and reduction. It may be necessary at first to write the oxidation numbers of all the elements:

$$\overset{+2}{Mn}{}^{+2} + \overset{+5\ -2}{BiO_3^-} + \overset{+1\ -2}{H_3O^+} \rightarrow \overset{+7\ -2}{MnO_4^-} + \overset{+3}{Bi}{}^{+3} + \overset{+1\ -2}{H_2O}$$

However, you soon acquire the knack of identifying those elements whose oxidation numbers are changed in the reaction:

$$\overset{+2}{Mn}{}^{+2} + \overset{+5}{BiO_3^-} + H_3O^+ \rightarrow \overset{+7}{MnO_4^-} + \overset{+3}{Bi}{}^{+3} + H_2O$$

3. Indicate the number of electrons lost by each atom of the element that was oxidized and the number of electrons gained by each atom of the element that was reduced:

loss of 5e per atom

$$Mn^{+2} + BiO_3^- + H_3O^+ \rightarrow MnO_4^- + Bi^{+3} + H_2O$$

gain of 2e per atom

4. Balance the loss and gain of electrons by taking the proper numbers of atoms of the elements oxidized and reduced. The total number of electrons transferred equals the least common multiple of the number of electrons lost and the number of electrons gained. In this example, in which 5 electrons were lost per atom and 2 were gained, the total number transferred is 10:

2 (loss of 5e per atom)

$$Mn^{+2} + BiO_3^- + H_3O^+ \rightarrow MnO_4^- + Bi^{+3} + H_2O$$

5 (gain of 2e per atom)

Then write in the coefficients to provide the proper number of atoms:

$$\overset{\overset{\text{2 (loss of 5e per atom)}}{\boxed{}}}{2Mn^{+2} + 5BiO_3^- + H_3O^+} \rightarrow 2MnO_4^- + 5Bi^{-3} + H_2O$$

$$\underset{\underset{\text{5 (gain of 2e per atom)}}{\boxed{}}}{}$$

5. Balance the equation electrically by putting in the proper coefficients for the ions that were not involved in the oxidation and reduction. Ordinarily these are either hydronium or hydroxide ions.

$$\underset{\underset{\text{Total 1}-}{\underset{4+ \qquad + \qquad 5-}{}}}{2Mn^{+2} + 5BiO_3^-} + H_3O^+ \rightarrow \underset{\underset{\text{Total 13}+}{2- \qquad + \qquad 15+}}{2MnO_4^- + 5Bi^{+3}} + H_2O$$

14 H_3O^+ ions are required to provide electrical balance:

$$2Mn^{+2} + 5BiO_3^- + 14H_3O^+ \rightarrow 2MnO_4^- + 5Bi^{+3} + H_2O$$

6. Balance any other elements in accordance with the law of conservation of matter. Usually only hydrogen and oxygen are still left unbalanced at this point. Balance the hydrogens first and then check the oxygens. If the oxygens are balanced, the equation may be presumed to be correctly balanced. To balance the hydrogens in this equation 21 H_2O molecules are required on the right side of the equation:

$$2Mn^{+2} + 5BiO_3^- + 14H_3O^+ \rightarrow 2MnO_4^- + 5Bi^{+3} + 21H_2O$$

A count of the oxygens shows 29 atoms on each side. No further check should be necessary; the equation is presumed to be correct.

Let us go through the procedure again, this time balancing the equation for the reduction of nitrate ion to nitrogen by aluminum in alkaline solution.

1. Write the skeleton equation:

$$Al + NO_3^- + OH^- + H_2O \rightarrow Al(OH)_4^- + N_2$$

2. Put in the oxidation numbers of the elements whose oxidation numbers have changed:

$$\overset{0}{Al} + \overset{+5}{N}O_3^- + OH^- + H_2O \rightarrow \overset{+3}{Al}(OH)_4^- + \overset{0}{N_2}$$

3. Indicate the loss and gain of electrons:

loss of 3e per atom

$$Al + NO_3^- + OH^- + H_2O \rightarrow Al(OH)_4^- + N_2$$

gain of 5e per atom

4. Balance the loss and gain of electrons:

5 (loss of 3e per atom)

$$Al + NO_3^- + OH^- + H_2O \rightarrow Al(OH)_4^- + N_2$$

3 (gain of 5e per atom)

This gives us the number of atoms of Al and N required to balance the transfer of electrons, but 3 atoms of N correspond to $1\frac{1}{2}$ molecules:

5 (loss of 3e per atom)

$$5Al + 3NO_3^- + OH^- + H_2O \rightarrow 5Al(OH)_4^- + 1\tfrac{1}{2}N_2$$

3 (gain of 5e per atom)

Since we want only integral coefficients, multiply by 2 the coefficients that have been put in:

2 × 5 (loss of 3e per atom)

$$10Al + 6NO_3^- + OH^- + H_2O \rightarrow 10Al(OH)_4^- + 3N_2$$

2 × 3 (gain of 5e per atom)

5. Balance electrically: there are 10 negative ions on the right, 6 negative ions on the left, so 4 OH^- ions are needed:

$$10Al + 6NO_3^- + 4OH^- + H_2O \rightarrow 10Al(OH)_4^- + 3N_2$$

6. Balance the hydrogens: there are 4 hydrogen atoms on the left and 40 on the right, so the proper coefficient for H_2O is 18:

$$10Al + 6NO_3^- + 4OH^- + 18H_2O \rightarrow 10Al(OH)_4^- + 3N_2$$

Count the oxygens: there are $(6 \times 3) + 4 + 18 = 40$ atoms on the left and $4 \times 10 = 40$ atoms on the right. The equation is balanced.

The ion-electron method. The electron-change method is the practical way to balance a redox equation if the reactants and products are known. The ion-electron method is often favored because it gives some insight into the mechanisms of oxidation and reduction and also because it makes it easier to predict whether a reaction will take place and what the products will be. The part of the reaction in which the electrons are lost and the part in which the electrons are gained are considered separately as *half-reactions*, and the two half-reactions are added together algebraically to give the final equation.

1. Write the skeleton equation:

$$Mn^{+2} + PbO_2 + H_3O^+ \rightarrow MnO_4^- + Pb^{+2} + H_2O$$

2. Write oxidation numbers over the symbols of the elements to help in determining which element is oxidized and which is reduced. Or, with practice, you will usually be able to select the proper elements by inspection:

$$\overset{+2}{Mn}{}^{+2} + \overset{+4 \ -2}{PbO_2} + \overset{+1 \ -2}{H_3O^+} \rightarrow \overset{+7 \ -2}{MnO_4^-} + \overset{+2}{Pb}{}^{+2} + \overset{+1 \ -2}{H_2O}$$

3. Select the element which is being oxidized. Write a half-reaction showing the element in the original ion or compound on the left and the product on the right, together with the number of electrons lost:

$$Mn^{+2} \rightarrow MnO_4^- + 5e$$

4. Since the original skeleton equation (or our knowledge of the conditions of this reaction) tells us that the reaction was carried on in acid solution, H_3O^+ ion and H_2O are used as needed to balance the charges and to provide the necessary hydrogen and oxygen atoms. (Had the specified conditions been basic, OH^- ion and H_2O would be used.) In the oxidation of manganese

$$\underset{2+}{Mn^{+2}} \rightarrow \underset{1-}{MnO_4^-} + \underset{+5-}{5e}$$

there are 2 positive charges on the left and 6 negative charges on the right; add $8H_3O^+$ to the right for electrical balance and $12H_2O$ to the left to balance the hydrogens and oxygens:

$$Mn^{+2} + 12H_2O \rightarrow MnO_4^- + 8H_3O^+ + 5e$$

5. Write the electron change for the reduction:

$$PbO_2 + 2e \rightarrow Pb^{+2}$$

6. Balance the half-reaction with H_3O^+ and H_2O:

$$PbO_2 + 4H_3O^+ + 2e \rightarrow Pb^{+2} + 6H_2O$$

7. Multiply the equations for the two half-reactions by whatever numbers make the electron changes equal. The least common multiple obtained by multiplying the equation obtained in Step 4 by 2 and that obtained in Step 6 by 5 gives 10 electrons in each. Then add the two equations, canceling terms that appear on both sides:

$$2Mn^{+2} + 24H_2O \rightarrow 2MnO_4^- + 16H_3O^+ + 10e$$

$$\frac{5PbO_2 + 20H_3O^+ + 10e \rightarrow 5Pb^{+2} + 30H_2O}{2Mn^{+2} + 5PbO_2 + 4H_3O^+ \rightarrow 2MnO_4^- + 5Pb^{+2} + 6H_2O}$$

4.5 / OXIDATION POTENTIALS

In the ion-electron method we wrote separate equations for the parts of the reaction in which electrons were lost and gained. If the oxidation and reduction can be separated from one another, the electrons being lost in the oxidation can be forced to travel along a wire before being used in the reduction. The electrical pressure which forces the electrons along the wire can be measured by inserting a voltmeter in the circuit.

If we write the half-reactions for the displacement of copper(II) ion by metallic zinc, we have

$$Zn^0 \rightarrow Zn^{+2} + 2e, \text{ the oxidation}$$

$$Cu^{+2} + 2e \rightarrow Cu^0, \text{ the reduction}$$

One arrangement to separate these reactions in space is shown in Figure 4.2. In one beaker, a strip of zinc is dipped in a solution containing zinc ion, and in another a strip of copper in a solution of copper(II) ion, with the two beakers connected by a *salt bridge*—an inverted U-tube containing a solution of some electrolyte such as KCl. When the circuit is completed by a wire from zinc electrode to copper electrode, zinc ions are able to go into solution, leaving electrons behind. The electrons flow through the wire as an electric current to the copper strip where they combine with copper ions to form a deposit of metallic copper. Ions diffusing through the salt bridge will keep the solutions in the two beakers electrically neutral.

Each electrode and its surrounding solution make up a *half-cell*. The whole arrangement is a *cell*. The electrode—copper,

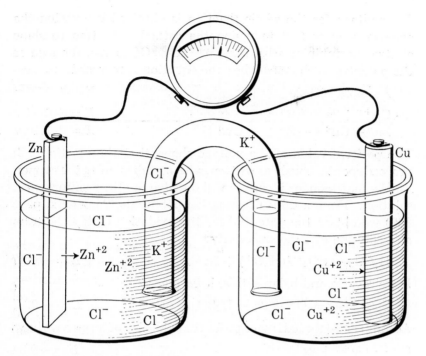

FIGURE 4.2 / AN ELECTROCHEMICAL CELL

in this case—where electrons enter the cell is the *cathode*, and the one where electrons leave the cell is the *anode*. If a cell is made up carefully with pure electrodes and solutions of known strength, the voltage or *electromotive force* produced will be a definite reproducible value. For purposes of comparison, the voltage obtained from a cell composed of the half-cell being studied and a half-cell utilizing the reaction

$$H_2 + 2H_2O \rightleftharpoons 2H_3O^+ + 2e$$

is used. The *hydrogen electrode* is arbitrarily taken as zero so the potential of such a cell is attributed entirely to whatever half-cell is joined to it. Customarily, all solutions are made up to an effective concentration of 1 molar, and measurements are made at 25°C. For the two half-reactions involved here, the voltages with respect to the hydrogen electrode are

$$Zn \rightarrow Zn^{+2} + 2e \qquad\qquad E = +0.76 \text{ v}$$
$$Cu \rightarrow Cu^{+2} + 2e \qquad\qquad E = -0.34 \text{ v}$$

The voltage for the whole reaction is obtained by adding the equations, after first reversing the cathode equation to show electrons combining with the Cu^{+2} ion. Of course, the sign of the potential is changed when the equation is reversed:

$$Zn \rightarrow Zn^{+2} + 2e \qquad\qquad E = +0.76 \text{ v}$$
$$\underline{Cu^{+2} + 2e \rightarrow Cu^0 \qquad\qquad E = +0.34 \text{ v}}$$
$$Zn^0 + Cu^{+2} \rightarrow Zn^{+2} + Cu^0 \qquad\qquad E = +1.10 \text{ v}$$

The positive value of the voltage shows that the reaction will proceed spontaneously as written, with zinc displacing the copper.

We may wonder if copper will dissolve in dilute sulfuric acid solution. From a table of oxidation potentials (Appendix, page 338) we obtain the potential for the oxidation of H_2SO_3 in an acid solution of 1 molar activity:

$$H_2SO_3 \rightarrow SO_4^{-2}(H_3O^+) + 2e \qquad\qquad E = -0.17$$

If we reverse and balance this, it becomes

$$SO_4^{-2} + 4H_3O^+ + 2e \rightarrow H_2SO_3 + 6H_2O \qquad\qquad E = +0.17$$

Adding this to the half reaction for the oxidation of copper, we have

$$Cu \rightarrow Cu^{+2} + 2e \qquad\qquad E = -0.34$$
$$SO_4^{-2} + 4H_3O^+ + 2e \rightarrow H_2SO_3 + 6H_2O \qquad\qquad E = +0.17$$
$$Cu + 4H_3O^+ + SO_4^{-2} \rightarrow Cu^{+2} + H_2SO_3 + 6H_2O \qquad\qquad E = -0.17$$

The value of E is negative, showing that the reaction does not take place under these conditions.

It is also possible to predict what products will be obtained from the reaction of a particular combination of oxidant and reductant by reference to the table. For example, consider the probable products resulting from the addition of HClO to an acid solution containing Br^- ion. We find two likely half reactions listed:

$$Cl^- \rightarrow HClO + 2e \text{ in acid sol.} \qquad\qquad E = -1.49$$
$$2Br^- \rightarrow Br_2 + 2e \qquad\qquad E = -1.07$$

If we write these in the proper form and add, we obtain

$$HClO + H_3O^+ + 2e \rightarrow Cl^- + 2H_2O \qquad\qquad E = +1.49$$
$$\underline{2Br^- \rightarrow Br_2 + 2e \qquad\qquad E = -1.07}$$
$$HClO + 2Br^- + H_3O^+ \rightarrow Cl^- + Br_2 + 2H_2O \qquad\qquad E = +0.42$$

so the reaction should occur as written.

A prediction of this sort must be accepted with some reservations, however. A reaction that has been shown to be possible may take place only very slowly, or some other more likely reaction may have been overlooked. But if the voltage obtained is negative, the reaction will not take place under the conditions listed.

Questions and problems

1. Write net ionic equations to represent the reactions described in the following molecular equations:

   a. $NaOH + HCl \rightarrow NaCl + H_2O$

   b. $2KOH + H_2SO_4 \rightarrow K_2SO_4 + 2H_2O$

   c. $NaHCO_3 + HNO_3 \rightarrow NaNO_3 + H_2O + CO_2$

   d. $2KMnO_4 + 10FeSO_4 + 9H_2SO_4 \rightarrow$
   $$2KHSO_4 + 2MnSO_4 + 5Fe_2(SO_4)_3 + 8H_2O$$

   e. $3CuS + 8HNO_3 \rightarrow 3Cu(NO_3)_2 + 4H_2O + 3S + 2NO$

2. Using either the electron-change or the ion-electron method as you prefer, or as you are instructed, balance the following:

   a. $Zn + H_3O^+ + NO_3^- \rightarrow Zn^{+2} + H_2O + NH_4^+$

   b. $I^- + ClO^- + H_2O \rightarrow I_2 + Cl^- + OH^-$

   c. $Zn + H_3O^+ + As_2O_3 \rightarrow Zn^{+2} + AsH_3 + H_2O$

   d. $H_3PO_2 + MnO_4^- + H_3O^+ \rightarrow Mn^{+2} + H_2PO_4^- + H_2O$

   e. $PbO_2 + Pb + H_3O^+ + SO_4^{-2} \rightarrow PbSO_4 + H_2O$

   f. $MnO_4^{-2} + ClO_3^- + H_3O^+ \rightarrow MnO_4^- + Cl_2 + H_2O$

3. The following skeleton equations are for redox reactions which will take place in acid solutions. Add hydronium ions and water molecules wherever necessary and balance:

   a. $Cu + NO_3^- \rightarrow Cu^{+2} + NO$

   b. $ClO_3^- + Mn^{+2} \rightarrow \underline{MnO_2} + ClO_2$

   c. $VO_2^+ + Cr^{+2} \rightarrow V^{+2} + Cr^{+3}$

   d. $Bi_2S_3 + NO_3^- \rightarrow Bi^{+3} + \underline{S} + NO$

   e. $Al + NO_3^- \rightarrow Al(H_2O)_6^{+3} + N_2$

4. The following skeleton equations represent reactions that will take place in alkaline solutions. Add hydroxide ions and water molecules as necessary and balance:

   a. $ClO^- + I_2 \rightarrow Cl^- + IO_3^-$

   b. $Zn + ClO_3^- \rightarrow Zn(OH)_4^{-2} + Cl^-$

   c. $Mn(OH)_2 + H_2O_2 \rightarrow \underline{MnO_2} + H_2O$

   d. $MnO_4^- + Fe^{+2} \rightarrow \underline{MnO_2} + Fe^{+3}$

   e. $NiO_2 \cdot 2H_2O + Fe \rightarrow Ni(OH)_2 + Fe(OH)_2$

5. With the aid of the table of oxidation potentials in the Appendix determine the truth of the following statements:

   a. Metallic iron reduces Fe^{+3} to Fe^{+2} in an acid solution.

   b. Metallic copper reduces Cu^{+2} to Cu^+ in an acid solution.

   c. Iron(III) iodide is unstable because I^- is oxidized by Fe^{+3} ion.

   d. Copper metal dissolves in HNO_3 solution, evolving H_2 gas.

   e. Cadmium metal can be used to reduce Fe^{+3} to Fe^{+2}.

Solutions

5

5.1 / REVIEW OF DEFINITIONS

Since almost all reactions in qualitative analysis are carried out in solution, we ought to review some commonly used terms. A *solution* may be defined as a *homogeneous body composed of two or more substances which are not readily interconvertible and whose proportions are variable.* The phrase "readily interconvertible" must be put in to exclude a combination like H_2O, H_3O^+, and OH^-, unless we wish to consider ordinary water as a solution. Also, we understand that the proportions of the components may be varied continuously within certain limits determined by the solubility and that for miscible substances the limits become infinity. The component of a solution that does the dissolving is called the *solvent*; the one that is dissolved is called the *solute*. This distinction is sometimes not easily made; if the two components are present in approximately equal amounts the classification may be quite arbitrary. The more active component might then be called the solute, and the inert one the solvent. Thus in a 50-50 mixture of sulfuric acid and water, the water would probably be regarded as the solvent and the H_2SO_4 as the solute. Or, if only one of the components is of the same physical state as the solution, it is called the solvent. For example, in a solution containing 75 grams of lithium acetate and 25 grams of water, the water is regarded as the solvent.

The concentration of a solution may be expressed in various ways: percentage, weight of solute per volume of solvent, weight of solute per weight of solvent, or weight of solute per volume of solution. In qualitative analysis, we almost invariably refer to concentration in terms of molarity.

Molarity. A *molar* solution contains one mole of solute in one liter of solution.

A *mole* is a *gram-formula weight* of a substance.

For a covalent substance like glucose, $C_6H_{12}O_6$, where the formula represents the composition of a molecule, the gram-formula weight is also the gram-molecular weight, in this case 180 g. But, for an ionic substance like sodium sulfate which never occurs in molecular form, we cannot properly speak of a gram-molecular weight. The gram-formula weight, of course, refers to the sum of the atomic weights of the atoms in the formula of a substance. The formula may represent the composition of a molecule, as it does in a covalent compound, or merely the simplest atomic ratio of the different elements in the compound, as it does in an ionic substance. (Some chemists prefer to speak of a solution containing one gram-formula weight of solute in a liter of solution as a *formal* solution.)

As an illustration, one liter of $1M$ NaCl contains 58.448 g of sodium chloride. To prepare one liter of $1M$ Na_2CO_3 solution, we could weigh out either 105.993 g of Na_2CO_3 or 286.153 g of $Na_2CO_3 \cdot 10H_2O$, depending on whether we choose the anhydrous salt or the decahydrate as our source of Na_2CO_3.

Example: How much $CuSO_4 \cdot 5H_2O$ would be required to pre-
         pare 230 ml of $0.12M$ $CuSO_4$ solution?

Solution: The gram-formula weight of $CuSO_4 \cdot 5H_2O$ is
         $63.54 + 32.066 + 64 + (5 \times 18.016) = 249.686$
                                             or 249.69 g

Then: 1 liter of $1M$ $CuSO_4$ contains 249.69 g.
         1 liter of $0.12M$ $CuSO_4$ contains 0.12×249.69 g
         0.230 liter of $0.12M$ $CuSO_4$ contains 0.230×0.12
                              $\times 249.69$ g $= 6.8914$ g

Normality. A *normal* solution contains one gram-equivalent weight of solute in a liter of solution.

A simple, practical definition of the *gram-equivalent weight* is that it is the weight in grams of a substance that is equivalent to 1.008 g of hydrogen or 8.000 g of oxygen. For neutralization reactions, the gram equivalent weights are obtained by dividing the gram-formula weight of the acid by the number of replace-able hydrogens in the molecule and the gram-formula weight of the base by the number of reacting hydroxide groups. For an oxidation-reduction reaction, the gram-equivalent weight of a reactant is obtained by dividing its gram-formula weight by the number of electrons it is considered to gain or lose in the reaction.

Often the term gram-equivalent weight is shortened to *gram-equivalent* or *equivalent*. If a liter of a normal solution contains one equivalent of solute, then 1 milliliter of a normal solution contains one *milliequivalent (meq)*. Since, in laboratory work, volumes are usually measured in milliliters rather than liters, milliequivalents are perhaps of more general utility than are equivalents.

Normal solutions are useful because equivalent weights of two substances A and B will react exactly with one another. If a certain volume of a solution of A is required to react with a volume of B, the number of milliequivalents in the two volumes is known to be equal. Since the number of milliequivalents in a solution is the product of the normality of the solution and its volume in milliliters,

$$\text{volume}_A \times \text{normality}_A = \text{volume}_B \times \text{normality}_B$$

In the branch of quantitative analysis known as volumetric analysis, the number of equivalents of a substance present is determined by titrating it against a solution of known normality; that is, a *standard solution*.

In our course, as you will observe, molarity is a more useful concept than normality, so we will consistently express concentrations in molarity both in theoretical discussions and in laboratory instructions.

5.2 / FACTORS INFLUENCING SOLUBILITY

The wide differences of solubility of one substance in another depend on a number of factors: the nature of the solute and solvent, the temperature, the pressure, and the presence of other substances. In the majority of cases, increased temperature means greater solubility. However, some solute-solvent combinations show virtually no temperature effect, and many cases exist of greatly diminished solubility with increased temperature, especially in solutions of gases in liquids. Pressure is also an important factor when the solutes are gases but is not of much significance otherwise. The effect of a third substance on the solubility of a particular solute in a solvent may mean that it reacts with either the solute or the solvent in such a way as to produce an altered solution system. Or, there may be special considerations, such as "common ion effect" and "salt effect," which we are going to take up later.

The general rule is that substances which are chemically similar are likely to be soluble in one another. Thus ethyl alcohol, C_2H_5OH, is similar in its molecular configuration to both water, HOH, and ether, $C_2H_5OC_2H_5$, and is miscible with both. Water and ether are less closely related and are not very soluble in one another. Sodium chloride and silver chloride are miscible in all proportions, both as liquids and solids. NaCl and AgCl certainly resemble one another, but the nature of the similarity between two mutually soluble substances is not always so clear. We do not understand, for example, why silver is completely miscible with palladium in both liquid and solid states, but completely immiscible with vanadium. The best generalization we have is that non-polar substances are apt to be soluble in one another but not in polar substances, while polar and ionic substances are apt to be soluble in polar solvents. Since so many organic compounds are non-polar, the organic chemist uses non-polar solvents like carbon tetrachloride, ether, and benzene. In qualitative analysis, and in inorganic chemistry generally, most solutes are ionic or polar; water, therefore, is the outstanding solvent.

5.3 / WATER AS A POLAR SUBSTANCE

The water molecule is usually represented as

$$H : \overset{..}{\underset{..}{O}} :$$
$$H$$

This representation shows the arrangement of valence electrons and the approximate relative positions of the hydrogen atoms. A better picture is shown in Figure 5.1.

The angle formed by the lines drawn from the two hydrogen nuclei to the oxygen nucleus is about 105° or slightly greater than

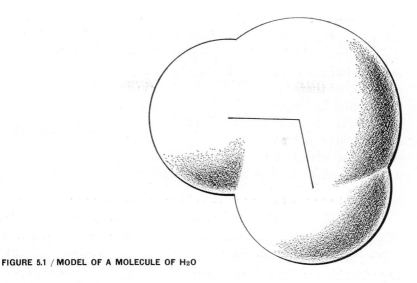

FIGURE 5.1 / MODEL OF A MOLECULE OF H_2O

a right angle. Since the oxygen atom is much more electronegative than the hydrogens, the bonding electrons are drawn
toward the oxygen. Therefore the center of negative charge
does not coincide with the positive center of the molecule, as
shown in Figure 5.2, so water is a dipole, behaving effectively
as shown in B of Figure 5.2.

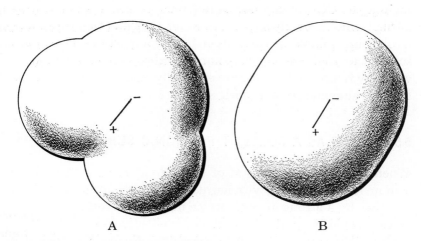

A   B

FIGURE 5.2 / DIPOLE CHARACTER OF THE WATER
MOLECULE, A, AND SIMPLIFIED REPRESENTATION
TO SHOW THE EFFECTIVE DIPOLE CHARACTER
OF WATER OR ANY OTHER POLAR MOLECULE, B.

A strong attraction exists between the molecules of a polar substance, the negative end of one molecule being attracted to the positive end of another. In water there is an additional effect due to *hydrogen bonds*. Remember that, aside from a valence electron, all there is to a hydrogen atom is a single proton. The proton of a hydrogen atom belonging to one water molecule can be attracted to an electron pair of the oxygen atom of a neighboring water molecule, forming a weak link between the molecules. Especially at low temperatures, a fairly large group of water molecules may be weakly chained together in this way:

$$H : \overset{..}{\underset{..}{O}} : \cdots \cdot H : \overset{..}{\underset{..}{O}} : \cdots \cdot H : \overset{..}{\underset{..}{O}} : \cdots \cdot H : \overset{..}{\underset{..}{O}} : \cdots \cdot$$
$$\quad H \qquad\qquad H \qquad\qquad H \qquad\qquad H$$

The unusual properties of water, such as its high melting and boiling points, high specific heat, and large heats of fusion and vaporization are due to its polar nature and its hydrogen bonding.

5.4 / WATER AS A SOLVENT FOR POLAR SUBSTANCES

Because of the great attraction of water molecules for one another and their slight attraction for non-polar molecules, water is a poor solvent for a substance such as CCl_4. We may think of the water molecules as crowding toward one another and squeezing out the CCl_4 molecules. A different situation is found with alcohol which is nearly as polar as water. We find that water and alcohol are soluble in each other in all proportions. Covalent substances that are highly polar and that can also join with water by hydrogen bonding are especially soluble. Examples are alcohol, ammonia, and sulfuric acid.

5.5 / WATER AS A SOLVENT FOR IONIC SUBSTANCES

When we consider a crystal of sodium chloride, with positive sodium ions alternating with negative chloride ions so all are held together by a strong attraction, we might well wonder how any solvent could break it down. Water is effective for two reasons, both of them due to its dipole character. Figure 5.3 illustrates these two effects. First, the water hydrates the ions, the negative ends of the water molecules being attracted to the sodium ions and the positive ends to the chloride ions. The attraction of an ion to its surrounding water molecules is comparable in amount to its attraction to oppositely charged ions in the crystal. Second, the polar water molecules tend to line up between the dissolved sodium and chloride ions, insulating them from one another. We say that water has a high *dielectric* or insulating value.

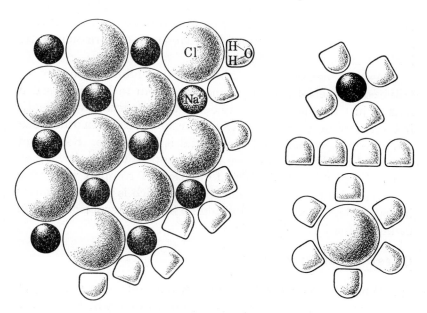

FIGURE 5.3 / SOLUTION OF A SALT IN WATER
Hydration of ions in a crystal of NaCl and insulating effect of polar water molecules between two dissolved ions.

The extent to which a particular ionic substance will dissolve in water is, however, impossible to predict. There are a number of factors that determine the solubility of a salt. Some of these have not been measured with great precision; we cannot predict how much each will influence a given case; and we cannot even be sure we know all the factors involved.

The forces that hold the crystal together are measured as its *lattice energy*. Large, loosely packed ions can attract each other less strongly than small, closely packed ones, because the attracting forces must operate over greater distances. Ions of high charge should attract each other more than do singly charged ions. Also, when we compare salts of K^+ with those of Ag^+ or salts of Ca^{+2} with those of Zn^{+2}, we observe that ions that have only eight electrons in the outer energy level (the inert gas structure) show less attraction than those with more electrons. The same factors that make for high lattice energy, however, also contribute to high heat of hydration. Small ions having high ionic charges are most effective in attracting water molecules. The situation resulting from the interplay of these various forces is therefore too complex for quantitative expression on the basis of our present knowledge.

Cases of unexpected solubility or insolubility may be attributed to special causes. Some salts seem to be composed of ions of just the right size and charge to fit together very neatly in their crystals, giving an unusually insoluble salt. In other cases the fit is not as good, and the crystal is less stable. Some compounds, like $HgCl_2$, which we might suppose to be salts, are actually largely covalent. The formation of complex ions often affects solubility; for example, $HgCl_2$, which is not very soluble in water alone, becomes quite soluble in the presence of Cl^- ion, owing to the formation of $HgCl_4^{-2}$.

Questions and problems

1. Which do you think a solution resembles more closely, a mixture or a compound? List some ways in which a solution is like a mixture. Make another list of ways in which a solution is like a compound.

2. Define *solution* in your own words. Do it if possible without using any of the important words (nouns or adjectives) of the book definition.

3. Without any help from books or friends, make a list of ten substances you consider insoluble in water and ten you consider soluble.

4. How do you account for the fact that when calcium chloride is added to water, heat is evolved, while ammonium nitrate and water show a cooling effect?
    Hint: Think in terms of lattice energy and heat of hydration.

5. Express the following quantities in grams:
   a. 1.250 moles of $AgNO_3$
   b. 0.34 mole of $K_4Fe(CN)_6 \cdot 3H_2O$
   c. 11.2 millimoles of Na_2CO_3
   d. 3.33 milliequivalents of $Ba(OH)_2$

6. What weight of solute would be contained in each of these solutions?
   a. 2500 ml of $1.4M$ H_2SO_4 solution
   b. Six drops (0.3 ml) of $3M$ HNO_3 solution
   c. 55 ml of $0.25M$ Na_2HPO_4 solution
   d. 1.0 ml of $0.1M$ H_2S solution

7. What is the molarity of concentrated nitric acid which contains 69.8 per cent HNO_3 and has a specific gravity of 1.42?

8. Concentrated hydrochloric acid is approximately $12M$ and has a specific gravity of 1.19. What percentage HCl does it contain?

9. What is the molarity of the following solutions?
   a. 12.5 ml of a solution containing 0.165 g $(NH_4)_2SO_4$
   b. 19.0 ml of a solution containing 3.61 g $Pb(C_2H_3O_2)_2 \cdot 3H_2O$
   c. The solution prepared by diluting 12 ml of $0.5M$ KCNS to 60 ml
   d. The solution prepared by boiling down 75 ml of $0.1M$ NaCl to 20 ml

10. What volume of each of the following solutions will contain 4.0 moles of solute?
    a. $18M$ H_2SO_4 solution
    b. $0.2M$ $AgNO_3$ solution
    c. $3M$ HCl solution
    d. $0.02M$ $KMnO_4$ solution

Equilibrium

6

6.1 / STATIC AND DYNAMIC EQUILIBRIUM

The Statue of Liberty in New York Harbor is certainly in equilibrium; that is, it is balanced. It has no tendency to tip over or fly away. But we do not ordinarily think of it as exchanging any of its matter with the air around it or with the island on which it is placed. It just stands there. We consider that it is in a state of *static equilibrium*. On the other hand, we are used to thinking of a lump of salt in a saturated salt solution as being in *dynamic equilibrium* with its surroundings. We realize that sodium ions and chloride ions from the crystal are constantly going into solution and being replaced by other ions which are deposited from the solution at exactly the same rate. We can even observe the results of this interchange. If an irregularly shaped crystal of salt is dropped into a saturated solution of the same substance, its shape gradually becomes more regular though its weight remains the same. Such a dynamic equilibrium in which two opposing processes go on at equal rates is customary in nature. Chemical equilibrium systems are all of this type, with two opposing chemical reactions proceeding constantly at equal rates.

6.2 / FACTORS AFFECTING RATE OF A REACTION

We shall consider four factors which determine the velocity of a chemical reaction: the nature of the reacting substances, the temperature, the presence of a catalyst, and the concentration of the reactants.

The nature of the reacting substances. The fact that different sets of reactants vary in their reaction rates is well known to all of us. Sodium reacts with hydrochloric acid violently, magnesium reacts vigorously, tin slowly, and gold not at all.

Temperature. The faster rate of reactions at higher temperature is also appreciated by everyone. We can readily understand that at higher temperatures there will be more collisions between molecules that have sufficient energy to react. For a large number of reactions the velocity can be approximately doubled by raising the temperature 10°C.

Catalyst. The presence of an effective catalyst also speeds up a reaction. Sometimes we can observe a definite relationship between the amount of catalyst added and the extent by which a reaction is accelerated, but the situation is frequently too complex for such relationships to be apparent. A reaction catalyzed by one of its own products is *autocatalytic.* Such a reaction, once started, may accelerate to explosive speed as more and more catalyst becomes present. Acetanilid is used as a preservative for hydrogen peroxide solutions because it reacts with and destroys various substances that would catalyze the decomposition of H_2O_2. Acetanilid is then said to be an *inhibitor.* An inhibitor can also function in other ways. Lead tetraethyl, for example, interrupts a chain reaction to prevent the gasoline-air mixture from exploding or knocking in an automobile engine.

Concentration of the reactants. The amount of material that is available to react at a particular instant also affects the rate of a reaction.

In a *heterogeneous reaction* involving two or more phases, the reaction takes place at the surfaces between the phases. The reaction can be made more rapid by increasing the area of contact of the phases. For example, a boy scout makes his fire burn more rapidly by chopping his wood to kindling; he uses a whole log to burn slowly through the night. Mossy zinc—irregular pieces with large surface area—is reacted with acid to prepare hydrogen in the laboratory. Solid chunks would react too slowly; zinc dust, too rapidly.

Reactions of gases and those of substances dissolved in liquid solvents are examples of *homogeneous reactions*. The reaction of hydrogen with iodine is often used as an illustration, as the reaction rate can be easily measured by the rate at which the violet color of iodine vapor disappears. It is found that the reaction becomes more rapid as the concentration of either reactant is increased, while at very low pressures of hydrogen and iodine the reaction is quite slow. Two Norwegian chemists, Guldberg and Waage, first stated the generalization that covers the effect of concentration on reaction rate, the *law of mass action*. One way of stating this law is: *The rate of a chemical reaction is dependent on the molecular concentration of each of the reactants.*

6.3 / CONCENTRATION AND REACTION RATE

We can write the equation for the reaction between any two substances A and B in the following way:

$$A + B \rightarrow C + D$$

The law of mass action and our own observations tell us that the rate of the reaction increases as the concentration of substance A increases, or, expressed in mathematical symbols,

$$r_1 \propto [A]$$

The term $[A]$ is to be read "the molecular concentration of A." Also, of course,

$$r_1 \propto [B]$$

and

$$r_1 \propto [A] \cdot [B]$$

That is, the rate of the reaction of substance A with substance B varies as the product of the molecular concentrations of A and B. This may be written as a mathematical equation:

$$r_1 = k_1[A][B]$$

This seems reasonable, and a simple device will convince us of its truth. If in a certain volume there were 1 molecule of A ready to react and 1 molecule of B, there would be one possibility of a reaction occurring within a certain period of time. If in the same volume there were 2 molecules of A and 1 of B, there would be two possibilities of a reaction occurring within that same period of time, as either molecule of A might react with the 1 molecule of B. If there were 2 molecules of A and 3 of B were present, there would be six chances for a reaction to take place, as shown in Figure 6.1.

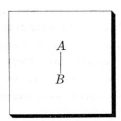 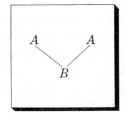 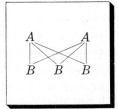

FIGURE 6.1 / CONCENTRATIONS OF REACTANTS AND POSSIBILITIES OF REACTION

In the reaction

$$2HI \rightarrow H_2 + I_2$$

for the decomposition of hydrogen iodide (the reverse of the homogeneous reaction mentioned earlier), the A and B terms of the general equation are identical:

$$HI + HI \rightarrow H_2 + I_2$$

Therefore,

$$r_1 = k_1[HI][HI]$$

or

$$r_1 = k_1[HI]^2$$

The coefficient in the chemical equation has become the power to which the concentration was raised in the expression of the rate of reaction. In general for the reaction

$$nA + mB \rightarrow xC + yD$$
$$r_1 = k_1[A]^n[B]^m$$

We can now give a more complete statement of the law of mass action as applied to a homogeneous reaction: *The rate of a chemical reaction is directly proportional to the product of the molecular concentrations of the reactants raised to the power corresponding to the coefficient of each reactant in the chemical equation.*

In chemical kinetics, that is, in studies of chemical reaction rates, it is usually found that reactions are not so simple as they appear. What we write as a single reaction may take place in several steps, each proceeding at its own velocity. If one of these steps proceeds more slowly than the others, its rate determines the rate of the over-all reaction. If we don't know the step-by-step course of the reaction nor which is the slowest step, we won't be able to give a correct form to the rate expression. In kinetics studies, the form of the rate expression that agrees best with experimental work often gives a clue to the rate-determining step in a reaction. For calculating the equilibrium constant, however, it is the rate expression for the over-all reaction that is useful, not that for one of the steps.

6.4 / THE EQUILIBRIUM CONSTANT

It is assumed by chemists that all chemical changes can be reversed, though some less easily than others. Sodium and chlorine combine with the evolution of much energy; a corresponding amount of energy in the form of electricity is needed to electrolyze the molten salt. The thermal decomposition of steam takes place to a considerable extent at 3000°C. Many reactions, however, are much more easily reversible; most of those of interest in qualitative analysis are noticeably reversible under ordinary conditions of temperature and concentration.

The general equation for a reversible reaction may be written

$$nA + mB \underset{r_2}{\overset{r_1}{\rightleftharpoons}} xC + yD$$

The rate expression for the reaction proceeding to the right has been given as

$$r_1 = k_1[A]^n[B]^m$$

Similarly, the rate expression for the reaction proceeding to the left is

$$r_2 = k_2[C]^x[D]^y$$

If substances A and B are put into a flask to react, r_1 is at first at a maximum, then gradually diminishes as the quantities of A and B are used up. The reverse reaction rate, r_2, on the other hand, is initially zero, but as soon as some C and D are produced, r_2 increases until eventually it becomes equal to r_1 and a dynamic equilibrium is established between the two. (How long it will take before equilibrium is established varies widely for different systems. It may require a fraction of a second or thousands of years, but equilibrium is usually attained rather quickly in an ionic reaction.)

At equilibrium the two reaction rates are equal; that is,

$$r_1 = r_2$$

Therefore we can substitute the rate expression for each reaction:

$$k_1[A]^n[B]^m = k_2[C]^x[D]^y$$

Rearranging to collect the constant terms,

$$\frac{k_1}{k_2} = \frac{[C]^x[D]^y}{[A]^n[B]^m}$$

When one constant is divided by another constant, the quotient is also a constant; therefore,

$$K = \frac{[C]^x[D]^y}{[A]^n[B]^m}$$

where K is the *equilibrium constant* of the reaction. The inverted form of this formula would be equally correct, of course, but it is the accepted convention to write the equilibrium constant formula as shown: the concentrations of the substances at the left of the double arrows are placed in the denominator; and the concentrations of those at the right, in the numerator. The equilibrium constant then must be accompanied by the chemical equation if it is to be interpreted correctly. For the equation

$$N_2 + 3H_2 \rightleftharpoons 2NH_3$$

the equilibrium constant is written

$$K = \frac{[NH_3]^2}{[N_2][H_2]^3}$$

But if the equation for the reaction is written

$$2NH_3 \rightleftharpoons N_2 + 3H_2$$

the equilibrium constant is

$$K = \frac{[N_2][H_2]^3}{[NH_3]^2}$$

The numerical values of equilibrium constants may range from very small to very large numbers, as illustrated in Table 6.1. A very small number indicates that the equilibrium mixture consists mainly of those substances on the left of the equation as written. If the value of K is large, the equilibrium mixture contains more of the substances on the right.

TABLE 6.1 / EQUILIBRIUM CONSTANTS

Equation	Formula for equilibrium constant	Value
$N_2 + 3H_2 \rightleftharpoons 2NH_3$ at 350°	$K = \dfrac{[NH_3]^2}{[N_2][H_2]^3}$	2.66×10^{-2}
$N_2 + 3H_2 \rightleftharpoons 2NH_3$ at 450°	$K = \dfrac{[NH_3]^2}{[N_2][H_2]^3}$	6.59×10^{-3}
$N_2 \rightleftharpoons 2N$ at 1000°	$K = \dfrac{[N]^2}{[N_2]}$	1.3×10^{-31}
$H_2 + I_2 \rightleftharpoons 2HI$ at 350°	$K = \dfrac{[HI]^2}{[H_2][I_2]}$	66.9
$2HI \rightleftharpoons H_2 + I_2$ at 350°	$K = \dfrac{[H_2][I_2]}{[HI]^2}$	1.49×10^{-2}
$Ag(NH_3)_2{}^+ \rightleftharpoons Ag^+ + 2NH_3$ at 25°	$K = \dfrac{[Ag^+][NH_3]^2}{[Ag(NH_3)_2{}^+]}$	6.8×10^{-8}

The value of the equilibrium constant of a particular reaction stays the same as long as the temperature remains unchanged. The addition of a catalyst does not affect the value of K, since, whenever it speeds up a reaction, it also speeds up the reverse reaction equally. (A little thought will convince you that if this were not so, a perpetual motion machine would be possible.) Hydrogen is sometimes transported as liquid ammonia, which is more convenient to handle than hydrogen under high pressure. The same catalyst that was used to produce the ammonia is used to decompose it and liberate the hydrogen.

If the amount of one of the reactants of an equilibrium system is changed, the constant is not changed. Rather, the equilibrium adjusts itself to agree with the constant. Thus if to the H_2, I_2, HI system in equilibrium at 350° we add some extra hydrogen, the reaction to produce HI will be speeded up; then as more HI is formed, its decomposition will be accelerated in turn, until a new equilibrium is established. In the new equilibrium, although the concentrations of HI, H_2, and I_2 will be different from those in the original mixture, the ratio of $[HI]^2$ to $[H_2][I_2]$ will be the same.

The effect of changes in the concentration of reactants on the equilibrium system is included in the generalization known as the *Principle of Le Châtelier: If a stress is applied to a system in equilibrium, the equilibrium is displaced in such a way as to lessen the stress.* In the example given, the increase in concentration of H_2 is considered a stress. So is a change in temperature: if the temperature is increased, the equilibrium is displaced in the direction that absorbs heat; if the temperature is lowered the equilibrium is displaced in the direction that evolves heat. In other words, a higher temperature favors the reaction in the direction which is endothermic.

Examples

1. An equilibrium mixture of hydrogen, steam, carbon monoxide, and carbon dioxide at 986°C has been determined to consist of 0.6 mole of H_2, 1.44 moles of H_2O, 0.4 mole of CO and 0.6 mole of CO_2 in a liter container. What is the equilibrium constant at this temperature for the system

$$CO + H_2O \rightleftharpoons CO_2 + H_2$$

Solution: For the equation as written, the equilibrium constant has the form

$$K = \frac{[CO_2][H_2]}{[CO][H_2O]}$$

Substituting molar concentrations as given,

$$K = \frac{[0.6][0.6]}{[0.4][1.44]} = 0.625 \qquad\qquad Answer$$

2. If 3 moles of H_2 and 1 mole of CO_2 are mixed at 986°C, what would the molar proportion of each component be after equilibrium is reached? Use the same equation and equilibrium constant as in Example 1:

$$CO + H_2O \rightleftharpoons CO_2 + H_2$$

$$K = \frac{[CO_2][H_2]}{[CO][H_2O]} = 0.625$$

Solution: In the attainment of equilibrium, of course, a certain amount of CO_2 would have to react with H_2 to produce CO and H_2O. Since all the coefficients in the equation are 1, for x moles of CO_2 reacting, x moles of H_2 are also required and x moles of CO and H_2O are formed. The equilibrium amounts then are $(3 - x)$ moles of H_2, $(1 - x)$ moles of CO_2, and x moles each of CO and H_2O. Substituting these terms in the equilibrium constant expression

$$K = \frac{[CO_2][H_2]}{[CO][H_2O]}$$

we get

$$0.625 = \frac{(1 - x)(3 - x)}{x^2}$$

Rearranging and solving for x, using the quadratic formula, we get $x = 0.812$. Therefore the concentrations at equilibrium are

CO_2	0.188 mole
H_2	2.188 moles
CO	0.812 mole
H_2O	0.812 mole

Answer

6.5 / SIGNIFICANCE OF THE EQUILIBRIUM CONSTANT

This brief introduction to the subject of reaction rates and equilibrium constants must have suggested the importance of the field. Knowledge of chemical kinetics is important in such diverse projects as devising new rocket fuels and studying digestive processes. Equilibrium studies have led to the Haber synthesis of ammonia and to improved blast furnace operation. To the student, a knowledge of the principles of equilibrium constants and reaction rates is useful in three ways: it helps him to get better results in the laboratory, it helps him to understand why he got better results, and it helps him to realize why he performed the experiment in the first place.

Methods of making a reaction go to completion. Even if we assume that all chemical reactions are reversible, we know that in a practical sense we may cause many of them to go nearly to completion or we may at least increase the yield of a desired product.

1. We may perform a reaction at a temperature at which the equilibrium is largely displaced in the desired direction. Reference to Le Châtelier's principle tells us that if the desired product is obtained by an exothermic reaction, the yield is best at a low temperature; if the desired product is obtained by the reaction in the direction that is endothermic, the yield is best at as high a temperature as is feasible.
2. We may adjust the concentrations of reactants to favor the yield of the desired product.
3. We may remove one of the products from the scene of the reaction.

The N_2, H_2, NH_3 equilibrium system is a good example to use to show how the equilibrium may be shifted to give a good yield of the desired product, ammonia:

$$N_2 + 3H_2 \rightleftharpoons 2NH_3 + 22 \text{ kcal}$$

Since the reaction in the direction to produce NH_3 is the exothermic one, the yield is greater at a low temperature. At a low temperature, however, the reactions are *very* slow. At a temperature of about 500°C, equilibrium is reached quickly and a reasonably good yield, about 15 per cent, can be obtained if the pressure is as high as 200 atmospheres. In terms of Le Châtelier's principle, we say that a high pressure is a stress that is lessened if the equilibrium is displaced in the direction of smaller volume. Since 4 molecules of reactants produce 2 molecules of products, the stress is lessened by the formation of ammonia. If the concentration of either N_2 or H_2 alone were increased, the effect would be the same—a greater yield of NH_3. In the Haber process, the ammonia produced is constantly removed by condensation to a liquid, the unreacted N_2 and H_2 being recycled over the catalyst. The removal of the product from the scene of the reaction exemplifies the third method of making a reaction go toward completion.

Homogeneous and heterogeneous equilibria. So far we have considered only instances of equilibrium in homogeneous reactions; that is, those in which the reaction system involves only gases or a single liquid or solid phase.* We will use the principles of homogeneous equilibrium in subsequent chapters in studying such things as the ionization of weak acids and bases and the formation of complex ions.

A heterogeneous equilibrium involving more than one phase is not necessarily more difficult to deal with, and indeed, may lend itself to a simpler treatment than we have used so far. If one of the phases in an equilibrium is a pure solid or a pure liquid, its concentration is constant and cannot be changed so long as the temperature remains the same. The reasonableness of this statement becomes apparent if we consider a simple case.

Figure 6.2 shows water in equilibrium with its vapor in containers of various shapes and sizes.

FIGURE 6.2 / AN EXAMPLE OF HETEROGENEOUS EQUILIBRIUM
At a given temperature the concentration of water vapor at equilibrium is constant regardless of the amount of water or the surface area exposed.

The equilibrium as illustrated in the figure is

water (liquid) $\rightleftharpoons$ water (vapor)

We know that at a given temperature the concentration in moles per liter of water vapor in air must be the same in all containers. Therefore, the concentration of the liquid phase is the same in each case, regardless of its total volume or surface area. The

---

*Phases are homogeneous portions of a system, separated from each other by physical boundaries; for example, liquid and gas, precipitate and solution, or two immiscible liquids.

reaction to the right (evaporation) of course takes place more rapidly if the surface is greater, so the reaction to the left (condensation) must be speeded to the same extent.

The heterogeneous equilibria of chief interest to us are those involving saturated solutions and precipitates.

Questions and problems

1. Describe three heterogeneous chemical equilibrium systems, giving the equations for the reversible reactions.

2. The directions on a package of cake mix recommend baking 40 minutes at 350°F. If the oven thermostat is improperly adjusted so the actual temperature is 332°F when it reads 350°, what would be the effect on the baking time?

3. Explain in terms of the factors listed as affecting reaction rates why water is a good fire extinguishing agent.

4. Derive the equilibrium constant expression for the following equilibrium reactions:

   a. $Cu(NH_3)_4^{+2} \rightleftharpoons Cu^{+2} + 4NH_3$
   b. $3Fe(s) + 4H_2O \rightleftharpoons Fe_3O_4(s) + 4H_2$
   c. $FeO(s) + CO \rightleftharpoons Fe(s) + CO_2$
   d. $4NH_3 + 5O_2 \rightleftharpoons 4NO + 6H_2O$
   e. $4HCl + O_2 \rightleftharpoons 2H_2O + 2Cl_2$
   f. $2BaO_2(s) \rightleftharpoons 2BaO(s) + O_2$

5. What is the effect on each of the following equilibrium systems when conditions are changed as listed?

   a. $N_2 + 3H_2 \rightleftharpoons 2NH_3 + 22$ kcal
      Increasing the pressure
   b. $N_2 + 3H_2 \rightleftharpoons 2NH_3 + 22$ kcal
      Decreasing the temperature
   c. $H_2 + I_2 \rightleftharpoons 2HI + 12$ kcal
      Increasing the pressure
   d. $H_2 + I_2 \rightleftharpoons 2HI + 12$ kcal
      Increasing the temperature
   e. $CaCO_3(s) \rightleftharpoons CaO(s) + CO_2$
      Increasing the pressure of CO_2

   f. $CaCO_3(s) \rightleftharpoons CaO(s) + CO_2$
      Adding more $CaCO_3$

   g. $HC_2H_3O_2 + H_2O \rightleftharpoons H_3O^+ + C_2H_3O_2^-$
      Adding $KC_2H_3O_2$

   h. $HC_2H_3O_2 + H_2O \rightleftharpoons H_3O^+ + C_2H_3O_2^-$
      Adding NaOH

   i. $2H_2 + O_2 \rightleftharpoons 2H_2O + 137$ kcal
      Adding Pt catalyst

6. List as many examples as you can from everyday life of reactions which are made to go faster by increasing the reacting surface.

7. True homogeneous reactions are rarer than you may think. The reactants must be homogeneously dispersed throughout one another when reaction takes place. Is the combustion at the tip of a bunsen burner a homogeneous reaction? How about the combustion of gasoline in the cylinder of an automobile engine?

8. Give three different ways in which the yield of Cl_2 may be increased in the equilibrium system

$$4HCl + O_2 \rightleftharpoons 2H_2O + 2Cl_2 + 28 \text{ kcal}$$

9. It was stated on page 52 that if the catalyst that speeds up a reaction did not speed up the reverse reaction equally, a perpetual motion machine would be possible. Try to prove that this is so by designing a perpetual motion machine that would operate if the same catalyst that is used to speed up the reaction

$$N_2 + 3H_2 \rightleftharpoons 2NH_3 + 22 \text{ kcal}$$

had no effect on the reverse reaction.

Ionization Constants of
Acids and Bases

7

7.1 / IONS IN SOLUTION

Two different types of substances are able to provide ions in solution. *Salts*, as we have seen, are ionic substances. In crystal form they are composed of ions; when melted, their liquid states are made up of ions; and they dissolve only in highly polar solvents like water, giving solutions that contain ions. When a salt is dissolved, the ions that were present all the time are pulled apart by the action of the solvent in the process called *dissociation*.

Many covalent substances can also give ions in solution, in this case by *ionization*; that is, the ions are produced by reaction between the solute and the solvent. For example,

$$HCl + H_2O \rightleftharpoons H_3O^+ + Cl^-$$

Although water is the best (and cheapest) ionizing solvent, there are many others, such as H_2SO_4:

$$HClO_4 + H_2SO_4 \rightleftharpoons H_3SO_4^+ + ClO_4^-$$

It has been mentioned (page 44) that $HgCl_2$ is not a salt but a covalent compound. There are other substances, like $CdCl_2$ and Al_2Br_6, that appear to be covalent in their anhydrous forms, but whose solutions conduct electricity and otherwise behave like solutions of ionic substances, and whose hydrated crystals seem to be ionic. We usually express the ionization reaction like this:

$$Al_2Br_6 + 12H_2O \rightarrow 2Al(H_2O)_6^{+3} + 6Br^-$$

showing hydrated cations and anions produced by the reaction between water and the covalent molecules.

The picture is often complicated by partial ionization or by combinations between cation and anion. Evidence has been adduced for the existence in solution of such species as $CdCl^+$, $PbC_2H_3O_2{}^+$, $Pb(C_2H_3O_2)_2$, $Pb(C_2H_3O_2)_3{}^-$, $Pb(C_2H_3O_2)_4{}^{-2}$, and more complex forms.

Those substances whose water solutions conduct electricity are called *electrolytes*. A fairly sharp distinction can be made between strong and weak electrolytes, depending on how well a substance conducts, considering its concentration. Thus, since $BaSO_4$ is very insoluble, a strongly conducting solution cannot be made. But when allowance is made for the diluteness of the solution, $BaSO_4$ rates as a strong electrolyte like NaCl. Besides the true salts, strong electrolytes include many of the ionizable covalent compounds of metals and also the strong acids such as HCl and HNO_3. Other covalent compounds of metals, for instance $HgCl_2$, must be classed as weak electrolytes, along with the weaker acids and bases.

Since strong electrolytes are those that are either always in ionic form or for which the ionization reactions go practically to completion, there is nothing to be gained by studying them from the standpoint of equilibrium. The later sections of this chapter, therefore, will apply principally to weak electrolytes.

7.2 / ACIDS AND BASES

An example of a typical, simple acid-base reaction is that between ammonia and hydrogen chloride with nothing else present, when the reaction takes place either between the two gases or in liquid ammonia below 33°C:

$$HCl + NH_3 \rightarrow NH_4{}^+ + Cl^-$$

Or, using dotted symbols,

$$H : \overset{..}{\underset{..}{Cl}} : + \; H : \overset{..}{\underset{H}{N}} : H \; \rightarrow \; H : \overset{H}{\underset{H}{N}} : H^+ + : \overset{..}{\underset{..}{Cl}} : ^-$$

Interpreting this in terms of the Brönsted-Lowry acid-base theory, we say that the reaction has involved the transfer of a proton (H^+), that the HCl molecule has given up a proton, becoming a Cl^- ion, and that the NH_3 molecule has taken on the proton, becoming an NH_4^+ ion. We can list herewith our definiticrs:

    Acid: A proton donor.

    Base: A proton acceptor.

Let us understand from the start that these definitions refer to the particular reaction being considered. If, in another reaction, NH_3 gives up a proton, in that reaction NH_3 is an acid. Two definitions of secondary importance are:

    Conjugate base: What is left after an acid has given up a proton. In the example, the conjugate base of HCl is Cl^-.

    Conjugate acid: What is formed when a base takes on a proton. In the example, it is NH_4^+.

In the reverse reaction, the conjugate acid acts as the proton donor, and the conjugate base as the proton acceptor. Listing HCl and its conjugate base Cl^- as substance 1 and NH_3 and its conjugate acid NH_4^+ as substance 2, we have

$$HCl + NH_3 \rightleftharpoons NH_4^+ + Cl^-$$
   Acid 1   Base 2   Acid 2   Base 1

Table 7.1 lists a number of familiar acid-base reactions, identifying the acids and bases and their respective conjugates in this way.

TABLE 7.1 / SOME ACID-BASE REACTIONS

Acid 1		Base 2		Acid 2		Base 1
$HClO_4$	+	H_2O	$\rightleftharpoons$	H_3O^+	+	ClO_4^-
H_2SO_4	+	H_2O	$\rightleftharpoons$	H_3O^+	+	HSO_4^-
H_3O^+	+	$H_2PO_4^-$	$\rightleftharpoons$	H_3PO_4	+	H_2O
HSO_4^-	+	HSO_3^-	$\rightleftharpoons$	H_2SO_3	+	SO_4^{-2}
$Al(H_2O)_6^{+3}$	+	NH_3	$\rightleftharpoons$	NH_4^+	+	$Al(H_2O)_5OH^{+2}$
H_2O	+	S^{-2}	$\rightleftharpoons$	HS^-	+	OH^-
NH_3	+	O^{-2}	$\rightleftharpoons$	OH^-	+	NH_2^-

Notice again that not only the familiar reagent acids but any molecule or cation or anion that can give up a proton in a particular reaction is an acid, and that any molecule or ion that can function as a base in a reaction is a base. A substance like H_2O or HSO_3^- which is capable of either giving or accepting a proton is said to be *amphiprotic*. H_3PO_4 can give up as many as three protons; it is a *polyprotic* acid. CO_3^{-2} is a polyprotic base. The general term *protolysis* is often used to apply to any acid-base reaction.

7.3 / ACIDS AND BASES: THE LEWIS DEFINITION

If we refer again to our sample acid-base reaction in its dotted symbol form,

$$H : \overset{..}{\underset{..}{Cl}} : + H : \overset{..}{\underset{H}{N}} : H \rightarrow \left[H : \overset{H}{\underset{H}{N}} : H \right]^+ + : \overset{..}{\underset{..}{Cl}} : ^-$$

we see that while the HCl molecule provided the proton that was transferred, the NH_3 provided the equally essential electron-pair to which the proton migrated. On this basis, G. N. Lewis, as long ago as 1923, suggested these definitions:

Base: An electron-pair donor.

Acid: An electron-pair acceptor.

These definitions are broader than those of the Brönsted system but more cumbersome to use. The Lewis system includes reactions that we instinctively regard as acid-base reactions but that do not involve proton transfer, such as the reaction between CaO and SO_3:

$$Ca^{+2} + : \overset{..}{\underset{..}{O}} : ^{-2} + \overset{\overset{..}{O} :}{\underset{: \overset{..}{O} :}{S : \overset{..}{O} :}} \rightarrow Ca^{+2} + \left[\overset{\overset{..}{O} :}{\underset{: \overset{..}{O} :}{: \overset{..}{O} : S : \overset{..}{O} :}} \right]^{-2}$$

Also some reactions that we would not ordinarily consider acid-base reactions are explained. For example, $AlCl_3$ catalyzes many reactions that are catalyzed also by various acids. The electron configuration

$$\begin{array}{l} : \overset{..}{\underset{..}{Cl}} : \\ \overset{..}{\underset{..}{Al}} : \overset{..}{\underset{..}{Cl}} : \\ : \overset{..}{\underset{..}{Cl}} : \end{array}$$

shows that the Al atom has an incomplete octet. Therefore, $AlCl_3$ should be an electron-pair acceptor, or Lewis acid, and might be expected to act like other acids.

A Brönsted base, like a Lewis base, is always an electron pair donor, but Brönsted acids are limited to those that contain a proton. Although the Brönsted theory is thus a special case of the Lewis theory, it includes the most important acid-base phenomena: all those in which water is the solvent as well as many in non-aqueous media. Because it is usually necessary to write out electron-dot formulas in order to interpret Lewis acid-base reactions, many chemists prefer to use the Brönsted system most of the time, falling back on the Lewis concepts only when they have to.

7.4 / IONIZATION CONSTANTS OF WEAK ACIDS

Any weak acid undergoes an ionization, or protolytic, reaction to some extent when it is dissolved in water. Dilute solutions of such acids may be profitably studied from the equilibrium standpoint. Acetic acid is a good example; it is familiar to all of us, and plentiful data on its degree of ionization are available. With water, acetic acid reacts in accordance with the equation

$$HC_2H_3O_2 + H_2O \rightleftharpoons H_3O^+ + C_2H_3O_2^-$$

Therefore, the expression for the equilibrium constant is

$$K = \frac{[H_3O^+][C_2H_3O_2^-]}{[HC_2H_3O_2][H_2O]}$$

However, for dilute solutions of weak acids we can derive a simpler expression. Let us, for example, look at the ionization of acetic acid for one of the concentrations listed in Table 7.2. (The extent of ionization was determined by measurements of electrical conductivity.) In the 0.02 molar solution, we see that the extent of ionization as given in the second column is 2.98 per cent, which means there are 0.02×0.0298 or 0.000596 mole* of H_3O^+ and 0.000596 mole of $C_2H_3O_2^-$ per liter.

---

*One mole of H_3O^+ by definition (see p. 38) is 1 gram-formula weight or 19 grams. A mole of an ionic species is often referred to as a gram-ionic weight, abbreviated g-ion.

TABLE 7.2 / THE IONIZATION CONSTANT OF ACETIC ACID AT 25°C

Molarity	Per cent ionized	$[H_3O^+]$	$[HC_2H_3O_2]$	K_a
0.1000	1.35	0.00135	0.09865	1.85×10^{-5}
0.0500	1.90	0.000950	0.04905	1.84×10^{-5}
0.0200	2.98	0.000596	0.019404	1.83×10^{-5}
0.0100	4.16	0.000416	0.009584	1.81×10^{-5}
0.0050	5.84	0.000292	0.004708	1.81×10^{-5}
0.0010	12.48	0.000125	0.000875	1.78×10^{-5}

Also, of our original 0.02 mole of acetic acid, there must be 0.02 × (1 − 0.0298) or 0.019404 still left as un-ionized $HC_2H_3O_2$ molecules. There must also be 0.000596 mole of water reacted out of an original concentration of 55 moles per liter. (One liter of this solution at 25°C contains about 995 grams of water, molecular weight 18. Dividing 995 by 18 gives about 55 moles.) Listing these molar concentrations at equilibrium we have

$$[HC_2H_3O_2] = 0.02 - 0.000596 = 0.019404$$

$$[H_2O] = 55 - 0.000596 = 54.999404$$

$$[H_3O^+] = 0.000596$$

$$[C_2H_3O_2^-] = 0.000596$$

These numbers are carried out to far too many significant figures mainly to point out that there is practically no change in the molar concentration of water during the ionization reaction; that is, $[H_2O]$ stays constant at 55. Our equilibrium expression might be written

$$K = \frac{[H_3O^+][C_2H_3O_2^-]}{55[HC_2H_3O_2]}$$

or, since the number 55 is a constant, we ought to rearrange the expression to

$$55K = \frac{[H_3O^+][C_2H_3O_2^-]}{[HC_2H_3O_2]}$$

or

$$K_a = \frac{[H_3O^+][C_2H_3O_2^-]}{[HC_2H_3O_2]}$$

where K_a, *the ionization constant of a weak acid*, has a value about 55 times as large as K, the equilibrium constant. K_a is more convenient to use than K in dealing with the ionization of weak acids; tables of ionization constants of acids such as Table 7.3 and the larger table in the Appendix refer to K_a, rather than to K.

If we now substitute the values of the molar concentrations in the K_a expression, we obtain

$$K_a = \frac{[0.000596][0.000596]}{[0.0194]}$$
$$K_a = 0.0000183 \text{ or } 1.83 \times 10^{-5}$$

If necessary, see the Appendix for remarks on significant figures and exponential numbers. For most K_a problems, no more than two significant figures are justified.

TABLE 7.3 / IONIZATION CONSTANTS OF SOME WEAK ACIDS
(For a more complete list, see Appendix, page 339)

Acid	Formula of acid		K_a at 25°C
Acetic	$HC_2H_3O_2$		1.8×10^{-5}
Carbonic	H_2CO_3	K_1	4.2×10^{-7}
	HCO_3^-	K_2	4.8×10^{-11}
Hydrocyanic	HCN		4.0×10^{-10}
Hydrofluoric	HF		7.0×10^{-4}
Hydrosulfuric	H_2S	K_1	1.0×10^{-7}
	HS^-	K_2	1.2×10^{-15}
Hypochlorous	$HClO$		3.5×10^{-8}
Nitrous	HNO_2		4.4×10^{-4}

Solving problems involving K_a. There are two secrets* to the successful working of K_a problems:

1. Systematize your thinking.
2. Learn when you can simplify by approximations.

To help in the systematizing, *always* write out the chemical equation and the expression for K_a derived from it. If you keep in mind the number of significant figures you want to end up with, you will be able to simplify your arithmetic by dropping unnecessary digits.

---

*It is assumed that fifth-grade arithmetic is not a secret.

Examples

1. A $0.1M$ solution of HCN is ionized to the extent of 0.0064 per cent at 25°C. What is the K_a of HCN at this temperature? *Solution:* Write the chemical equation and put the molar concentrations either above each term of the equation or in a separate tabulation. (We do it both ways below.) Directly beneath the chemical equation, write the K_a expression.

$$\overset{(0.1-0.0000064)}{HCN} + H_2O \rightleftharpoons \overset{0.0000064}{H_3O^+} + \overset{0.0000064}{CN^-}$$

$$K_a = \frac{[H_3O^+][CN^-]}{[HCN]}$$

$[H_3O^+] = 0.0000064$ or 6.4×10^{-6}

$[CN^-] = 0.0000064$ or 6.4×10^{-6}

$[HCN] = (0.1 - 0.0000064)$—practically 0.1

Substitute in the ionization constant expression

$$K_a = \frac{(0.0000064)^2}{0.1} \quad \text{or} \quad \frac{(6.4 \times 10^{-6})^2}{0.1}$$

$$K_a = 4.1 \times 10^{-10} \hspace{4cm} \textit{Answer}$$

I'm sure no one doubts the legitimacy of using 0.1 rather than $(0.1 - 0.0000064)$ for the molar concentration of HCN, but you are welcome to test it. In the next example, the question of whether to simplify by approximation is not so easily answered.

2. The K_a of hydrofluoric acid is 7.0×10^{-4}. What is the hydronium ion concentration in a $0.200M$ HF solution? *Solution:* Proceed as before with the chemical equation, the K_a expression, and the molar concentration terms.

$$HF + H_2O \rightleftharpoons H_3O^+ + F^-$$

$$K_a = \frac{[H_3O^+][F^-]}{[HF]}$$

$[H_3O^+] = x$

$[F^-] = x$

$[HF] = (0.2 - x)$

Substituting in the ionization constant expression,

$$7.0 \times 10^{-4} = \frac{x^2}{(0.2 - x)}$$

This gives us a quadratic equation, a nuisance to work with. If we assume that x is much smaller than 0.2, however, we can use 0.2 as the approximate value of [HF] and get something easier to handle, though the result will be less accurate:

$$7.0 \times 10^{-4} = \frac{x^2}{0.2}$$

Then,

$$1.4 \times 10^{-4} = x^2$$
$$x = \sqrt{1.4 \times 10^{-4}}$$
$$x = 1.2 \times 10^{-2} \quad \text{or} \quad 0.012 \qquad \textit{Answer}$$

Now we should substitute our value for x in the original expression to see if the approximation was valid:

$$7.0 \times 10^{-4} = \frac{(0.012)^2}{0.2 - 0.012}$$

This works out to

$$7.0 \times 10^{-4} \simeq 7.7 \times 10^{-4}$$

The result is neither very good nor very bad. The value of the K_a of HF was given to two significant figures, implying that the second figure was doubtful. If there were a much greater discrepancy than this, we would want to use the quadratic formula. Ionization constant problems generally refer to weaker acids than HF, so the use of approximations of this kind is usually satisfactory.

7.5 / COMMON ION EFFECT

A solution of acetic acid that is 0.1 molar gives the red acid color to methyl orange, an indicator that changes color only in strongly acid solutions. If we add some sodium acetate to this solution, the indicator reverts to its yellow alkaline color. In terms of Le Châtelier's principle, we say we are adding a stress in the form of $C_2H_3O_2^-$ ions, the Na^+ ions being mere spectators in a dilute solution. The equilibrium

$$HC_2H_3O_2 + H_2O \rightleftharpoons H_3O^+ + C_2H_3O_2^-$$

is then displaced to the left to lessen the stress, that is, the excess $C_2H_3O_2^-$ concentration. The use of the ionization constant

$$K_a = \frac{[H_3O^+][C_2H_3O_2^-]}{[HC_2H_3O_2]}$$

permits a more exact analysis.
Originally,

$$[HC_2H_3O_2] = 0.1 - x \text{ or approximately } 0.1$$

$$[H_3O^+] = x$$

$$[C_2H_3O_2^-] = x$$

Using the value of K_a from Table 7.3,

$$1.8 \times 10^{-5} = \frac{x^2}{0.1}$$

$$x^2 = 1.8 \times 10^{-6}$$

$$x = 1.3 \times 10^{-3}$$

The hydronium ion concentration is large enough to give the acid color with methyl orange.

Now let us suppose we add sodium acetate so that the solution is 0.2 molar with respect to sodium acetate, and therefore also 0.2 molar with respect to the acetate ion. Now let

$$[H_3O^+] = y$$

Then, because the solution contains 0.2 mole of $C_2H_3O_2^-$ added as sodium acetate, besides any produced by the ionization of acetic acid,

$$[HC_2H_3O_2] = (0.1 - y)$$

$$[C_2H_3O_2^-] = (0.2 + y)$$

Substituting in the K_a expression,

$$1.8 \times 10^{-5} = \frac{y(0.2 + y)}{(0.1 - y)}$$

However, y is so small that $(0.1 - y)$ and $(0.2 + y)$ are very close to 0.1 and 0.2. Therefore,

$$1.8 \times 10^{-5} = \frac{y \cdot 0.2}{0.1}$$

$$y = 9 \times 10^{-6}$$

Since the value of y is small compared to 0.1 and 0.2, we were justified in dropping it from those terms.

The effect of the sodium acetate was to reduce the H_3O^+ concentration from 1.3×10^{-3} to 9×10^{-6}, or in decimal notation from 0.0013 to 0.000009. The name, *common ion effect*, is applied to this phenomenon because it was the acetate *ion*, *common* to both the equilibrium system and the added salt, that was effective. In the same way, we can regulate the sulfide ion concentration of the system

$$H_2S + 2H_2O \rightleftharpoons 2H_3O^+ + S^{-2}$$

by the addition of HCl which provides the common H_3O^+ ion.

7.6 / IONIZATION OF WEAK POLYPROTIC ACIDS

Hydrogen sulfide is typical of polyprotic acids in that the first proton is much more readily given up than the second:

$$H_2S + H_2O \rightleftharpoons H_3O^+ + HS^-$$

$$K_1 = \frac{[H_3O^+][HS^-]}{[H_2S]} = 1.0 \times 10^{-7}$$

$$HS^- + H_2O \rightleftharpoons H_3O^+ + S^{-2}$$

$$K_2 = \frac{[H_3O^+][S^{-2}]}{[HS^-]} = 1.2 \times 10^{-15}$$

Since the second ionization constant is so much smaller than the first, very little of the HS^- ion produced in the first reaction is used up in the second. It follows that in a solution of pure H_2S the H_3O^+ and HS^- concentrations are practically equal. Also, practically all the H_3O^+ ion present is produced in the first reaction.

The ionization constant for the over-all reaction

$$H_2S + 2H_2O \rightleftharpoons 2H_3O^+ + S^{-2}$$

is equal to the product of K_1 and K_2 as is readily seen.

$$K_a = \frac{[H_3O^+]^2[S^{-2}]}{[H_2S]}$$

And

$$K_1 \times K_2 = \frac{[H_3O^+][HS^-]}{[H_2S]} \times \frac{[H_3O^+][S^{-2}]}{[HS^-]} = \frac{[H_3O^+]^2[S^{-2}]}{[H_2S]}$$

So,

$$K_a = 1.0 \times 10^{-7} \times 1.2 \times 10^{-15} = 1.2 \times 10^{-22}$$

As was mentioned in the previous section, the concentration of sulfide ion can be adjusted by the addition of HCl. A saturated solution of H_2S in water is about 0.1 molar over a fairly wide range of temperature and acidity; therefore, we can calculate the S^{-2} concentration in a solution which is, for example, 0.4 molar with respect to HCl. In this solution

$$[H_2S] = 0.1$$

$$[H_3O^+] = 0.4$$

If we substitute these values in the K_a expression

$$K_a = \frac{[H_3O^+]^2[S^{-2}]}{[H_2S]}$$

we get

$$1.2 \times 10^{-22} = \frac{(0.4)^2[S^{-2}]}{0.1}$$

Solving this equation, we obtain $[S^{-2}] = 7.5 \times 10^{-23}$, which is an ample amount for the precipitation of many sulfides.

7.7 / IONIZATION OF WEAK BASES

Weak bases react with water just as do weak acids, except that in this case the water functions as a Brönsted acid. Ammonia is considered the typical weak base just as acetic acid is the typical weak acid; the ionization constants are about the same for the two substances. The ionization reaction of ammonia is

$$NH_3 + H_2O \rightleftharpoons NH_4^+ + OH^-$$

$$K_b = \frac{[NH_4^+][OH^-]}{[NH_3]} = 1.8 \times 10^{-5}$$

The small value of K_b shows that there are comparatively few NH_4^+ and OH^- ions in the equilibrium, and of course there are no ammonium hydroxide molecules. The name *ammonium hydroxide* applied to aqueous ammonia may be justified by the fact that many of the useful properties of ammonia solutions are due to the few NH_4^+ and OH^- ions present, but the real reason it is still used is probably that it is printed on all the reagent bottles, and no one wants to relabel them.

It is often said that there are not so many common bases as there are acids. In a sense this is true; we have many reagent acids on the shelf and only a few substances we think of as bases: NaOH, KOH, and a few other sources of OH^- ion, aqueous ammonia, and perhaps a few ammonia derivatives such as aniline, $C_6H_5NH_2$. However, we should remember that there is a conjugate base for every acid. The weaker the acid, the stronger is its conjugate base. Among the important bases of this type are $C_2H_3O_2^-$, CO_3^{-2}, HCO_3^-, PO_4^{-3}, and $H_2PO_4^-$. Some metal-oxide or -hydroxide groupings also are valuable bases; for example, BiO^+, Ag_2O, $Al(H_2O)_4(OH)_2^+$.

7.8 / LIMITATIONS OF THE IONIZATION CONSTANT

Although the K_a concept explains the behavior of dilute solutions of weak acids nicely, we must remember that it has very definite limitations.

1. It can be applied only to solutions of *weak acids*. In dilute solutions, the ionization of a strong acid like HCl proceeds to virtual completion; there is no point in treating it as a reversible reaction.

2. It applies only to *dilute solutions*. If an ionization equilibrium

$$HA + H_2O \rightleftharpoons H_3O^+ + A^-$$

is to be represented by the expression

$$K_a = \frac{[H_3O^+][A^-]}{[HA]}$$

the value of $[H_2O]$ must remain practically constant since it is included in the constant term. In a concentrated solution the HA may react with enough of the H_2O so that the $[H_2O]$ changes appreciably.

3. Another factor that can cause error in calculations for concentrated solutions is that some H_2O molecules are tied up as water of hydration of the dissolved ions and molecules and thus cannot be included in the value of $[H_2O]$. Although there is no way we can determine how much water is tied up in this way, in a dilute solution it is a negligible fraction of the water present.

4. It is also assumed that the ions have no effect on one another. In very dilute solutions the interionic attraction is slight. When the ionic concentration is greater, oppositely charged ions attract one another, slowing down their movement, and therefore making their effective concentration, or *activity*, less than their actual concentration. In more advanced work, whenever the solutions are concentrated enough that the activity is noticeably different from the concentration, a correction should be made.

5. If a strong electrolyte is present in the solution along with the weak acid being studied, even though there is no common ion, there are what are called *salt effects*. Interionic attraction between the hydronium ion and the anion of the salt, and between the acid anion and the cation of the salt, leads to a greater ionization of the acid. (To demonstrate this, dilute some acetic acid till it is just neutral to methyl orange, then add some NaCl. The indicator turns red, showing the increased concentration of H_3O^+ ions.) Also, an unknown amount of water is tied up hydrating the salt ions, and is unavailable for the ionization reaction.

Questions and problems

1. Solutions of NaCl and of HCl must both contain ions since they are both excellent conductors of electricity. What is the basic difference in the formation of these two ionic solutions?

2. Hydrochloric acid is classed as a strong electrolyte, acetic acid as a weak one. Can you justify this distinction?

3. Using a text of physical or inorganic chemistry as a reference, list four ionizing solvents other than water, giving the melting point, boiling point, and dielectric constant of each.

4. For each of the acid-base reactions in the following list, identify the acid, the base, the conjugate acid, and the conjugate base. (It is possible that not all the reactions listed are acid-base reactions.)

   a. $NH_3 + H_2SO_4 \rightarrow NH_4^+ + HSO_4^-$
   b. $HS^- + HSO_4^- \rightarrow H_2S + SO_4^{-2}$
   c. $4HCl + O_2 \rightarrow 2H_2O + Cl_2$

    d. $Cu(H_2O)_4^{+2} + OH^- \rightarrow Cu(H_2O)_3(OH)^+ + H_2O$

    e. $NH^{-2} + OH^- \rightarrow NH_2^- + O^{-2}$

    f. $HCO_3^- + HS^- \rightarrow CO_3^{-2} + H_2S$

    g. $HCO_3^- + HC_2H_3O_2 \rightarrow H_2CO_3 + C_2H_3O_2^-$

5. Referring only to the immediately preceding question, select
    a. Some substance that shows amphiprotic behavior
    b. A diprotic acid

6. Using electron-dot formulas as a guide, decide which of the following are acid-base reactions according to the Lewis definition, and pick out the Lewis acids and bases.

    a. $HCl + NH_3 \rightarrow NH_4^+ + Cl^-$

    b. $Cu^{+2} + 4NH_3 \rightarrow Cu(NH_3)_4^{+2}$

    c. $F^- + BF_3 \rightarrow BF_4^-$

    d. $HgCl_2 + 2Cl^- \rightarrow HgCl_4^{-2}$

    e. $Zn + 2HCl \rightarrow ZnCl_2 + H_2$

    f. $CaO + CO_2 \rightarrow Ca^{+2} + CO_3^{-2}$

    g. $Cl_2 + 2Na \rightarrow 2Na^+ + 2Cl^-$

7. Nitrous acid is a weak acid, a $0.1M$ solution being about 6.4 per cent ionized at 25°C. What is its K_a?

8. Since nitrous acid is unstable, the $0.1M$ solution referred to in the previous question is prepared by dissolving 0.1 mole of $NaNO_2$ and 0.1 mole of HCl in sufficient water to give a liter of solution. Will the presence of the Na^+ and Cl^- ions have any effect on the ionization equilibrium for nitrous acid?

9. What is the H_3O^+ concentration of a $0.5M$ solution of HClO? The K_a of HClO is 3.5×10^{-8}.

                                         Answer 1.3×10^{-4}

10. The K_a of formic acid, $HCHO_2$, is 2.1×10^{-4}. What is the H_3O^+ concentration of a $0.1M$ solution? What is the percentage ionization of this solution?

11. What is the H_3O^+ concentration of a solution containing 0.1 mole of HCNO and 0.3 mole of KCNO in a liter?

                                         Answer 6.7×10^{-5}

12. How many moles of sodium acetate would have to be added to a liter of $0.2M$ $HC_2H_3O_2$ to give a solution with H_3O^+ concentration of 1×10^{-5}?

13. Calculate the OH^- concentration of a $0.1M$ solution of NH_3.

       Answer 1.3×10^{-3}

14. If 0.05 mole of NH_4Cl were added to a liter of the $0.1M$ NH_3 solution of Problem 13, what would the OH^- concentration be?

15. Which solution would have the higher H_3O^+ concentration, $1M$ HCN or $0.001M$ HCNO?

       Answer $[H_3O^+]$ of $0.001M$ HCNO $= 4.4 \times 10^{-4}$
       that of $1M$ HCN $= 2 \times 10^{-5}$

16. Calculate the H_3O^+ concentration of a solution prepared by pouring 20 ml of $0.1M$ HF into 30 ml of $0.06M$ NaF solution in a polyethylene beaker.

17. What is the H_3O^+ concentration of a $0.003M$ H_2CO_3 solution? Use only the first ionization constant of H_2CO_3. Why is it unnecessary to take the second ionization constant into account?

Solubility Product

8

8.1 / EQUILIBRIUM BETWEEN SATURATED SOLUTION AND PRECIPITATE

An especially important type of equilibrium system in qualitative analysis is that between a slightly soluble solid substance and its saturated solution. As an example, consider the equilibrium existing in a saturated solution of silver chloride containing some excess solid. The equation for the equilibrium reaction is

$$AgCl\ (solid) \rightleftharpoons Ag^+ + Cl^-$$

with the expression for the equilibrium constant being

$$K = \frac{[Ag^+] \cdot [Cl^-]}{[AgCl]}$$

It was stated in Section 6.5 that if one of the phases in a heterogeneous equilibrium is a pure solid or pure liquid, its concentration is constant so long as the temperature remains the same. When we look at the flasks in Figure 8.1, it seems obvious that the addition of more solid silver chloride does not increase the concentration of ions in the already saturated solution. Careful experimental studies have confirmed that the concentration of a solid is constant whether a small or a large amount is present. If [AgCl(solid)] is a constant, we should rearrange our equilibrium constant expression to bring the constant terms together:

$$[AgCl]K = [Ag^+][Cl^-]$$

The product of the two constant terms is a constant; therefore, we may write

$$K_{sp} = [Ag^+][Cl^-]$$

The new constant, K_{sp}, is called the *solubility product constant*.

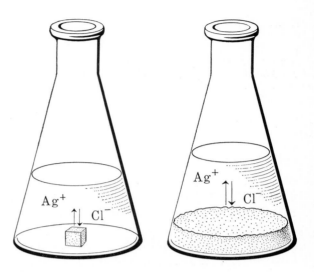

FIGURE 8.1 / HETEROGENEOUS EQUILIBRIUM IN A SATURATED SOLUTION

For any slightly soluble salt having the general formula A_nB_m, the equilibrium reaction in a saturated solution is

$$A_nB_m \rightleftharpoons nA^{+m} + mB^{-n}$$

and the solubility product expression is

$$K_{sp} = [A^{+m}]^n[B^{-n}]^m$$

Using $Pb_3(PO_4)_2$ as an example,

$$K_{sp} = [Pb^{+2}]^3[PO_4^{-3}]^2$$

Stated in words, the *solubility product constant of a substance is the product of the molar concentrations of its ions in a saturated solution, each raised to the appropriate power.* Subject to the limitations summarized in Section 8.5, the K_{sp} for a slightly soluble substance tells us the *maximum* concentrations of its ions that can exist together in solution or the *minimum* amount of a reagent necessary to initiate precipitation of an ion.

8.2 / CALCULATION OF THE SOLUBILITY PRODUCT

If the solubility of a substance is known, the numerical value of its K_{sp} may be obtained from the molar concentrations of its ions in a saturated solution.

Examples

1. The solubility of AgCl is 1.1×10^{-5} mole/l at 20°C. Calculate its K_{sp} at this temperature.

    Solution: Follow a procedure like that for K_a problems. Write out the chemical equation and the K_{sp} expression and tabulate the molar solubilities. Remember that it is a waste of time to carry more than three significant figures, if only two are to be used in the answer.

    $$AgCl \rightleftharpoons Ag^+ + Cl^-$$

    $$K_{sp} = [Ag^+][Cl^-]$$

    The solubility of AgCl $= 1.1 \times 10^{-5}$ mole/l. Since the chemical equation shows that 1 mole of AgCl yields 1 mole of Ag^+ ion and 1 mole of Cl^- ion,

    $$[Ag^+] = 1.1 \times 10^{-5}$$
    $$[Cl^-] = 1.1 \times 10^{-5}$$

    Substituting these values in the K_{sp} expression,

    $$K_{sp} = (1.1 \times 10^{-5})(1.1 \times 10^{-5})$$
    $$K_{sp} = 1.2 \times 10^{-10} \qquad\qquad Answer$$

2. It has been found that a solution which is 0.02 molar with respect to fluoride ion can hold a maximum of 2.4×10^{-7} mole of Ca^{+2} per liter before CaF_2 begins to precipitate. What is the K_{sp} of CaF_2?

    Solution: As in Example 1, write out the chemical equation and the K_{sp} expression and tabulate the molar solubilities:

    $$CaF_2 \rightleftharpoons Ca^{+2} + 2F^-$$

    $$K_{sp} = [Ca^{+2}][F^-]^2$$

    The molar concentrations of Ca^{+2} and F^- at saturation are given:

    $$[Ca^+] = 2.4 \times 10^{-7}$$
    $$[F^-] = 2 \times 10^{-2}$$

    Then substitute the molar solubilities in the K_{sp} expression:

    $$K_{sp} = (2.4 \times 10^{-7})(2 \times 10^{-2})^2$$
    $$K_{sp} = 9.6 \times 10^{-11} \qquad\qquad Answer$$

Since the formula of calcium fluoride contains two fluoride ions, the K_{sp} expression involves the square of the fluoride ion concentration. If we had a saturated solution of CaF_2 in pure water, the $[Ca^{+2}]$ and $[F^-]$ would be in a fixed ratio to each other, but we would treat them in the same way. Let's try it:

3. The solubility of CaF_2 at room temperature is 2.3×10^{-3} g/100 ml. Calculate the value of its K_{sp}.

   Solution: We may as well find the molar solubilities first. Summarizing the operation,

   Solubility of $CaF_2 = 2.3 \times 10^{-3}$ g/100 ml
   $$= 2.3 \times 10^{-2} \text{ g/l}$$

   Formula weight of $CaF_2 = 78$
   Molar solubility of $CaF_2 = 2.3 \times 10^{-2}/78 = 2.9 \times 10^{-4}$

   As the chemical equation shows, each mole of CaF_2 provides 1 mole of Ca^{+2} and 2 moles of F^-; therefore,

   $[Ca^{+2}] = 2.9 \times 10^{-4}$
   $[F^-] = 5.8 \times 10^{-4}$

   Now write out the chemical equation and the K_{sp} expression·

   $CaF_2 \rightleftharpoons Ca^{+2} + 2F^-$

   $K_{sp} = [Ca^{+2}][F^-]^2$

   Substitute the values for the molar solubilities:

   $K_{sp} = (2.9 \times 10^{-4})(5.8 \times 10^{-4})^2$
   $K_{sp} = 9.7 \times 10^{-11}$ *Answer*

In accordance with the expression $K_{sp} = [Ca^{+2}][F^-]^2$, we squared the value for the fluoride ion concentration in Example 3 just as in Example 2. The fact that in this case the concentration of fluoride ion happened to be just twice as large as the concentration of calcium ion did not change our method of working the problem. We simply substituted the values of $[Ca^{+2}]$ and $[F^-]$ in the K_{sp} expression to obtain the numerical value of the K_{sp}, exactly as before. (The two values for the K_{sp}, 9.6×10^{-11} and 9.7×10^{-11} are equal within the limits of precision usually possible in problems of this kind.)

TABLE 8.1 / SOLUBILITY PRODUCT CONSTANTS OF A FEW SLIGHTLY SOLUBLE SALTS
(See Appendix, page 340)

Salt	K_{sp} expression	K_{sp} value
$AgCl$	$[Ag^+][Cl^-]$	1.2×10^{-10}
Ag_3PO_4	$[Ag^+]^3[PO_4^{-3}]$	1.0×10^{-18}
$BaSO_4$	$[Ba^{+2}][SO_4^{-2}]$	1.1×10^{-10}
CaF_2	$[Ca^{+2}][F^-]^2$	9.6×10^{-11}
$Cu(IO_3)_2$	$[Cu^{+2}][IO_3^-]^2$	1.4×10^{-7}
Hg_2Cl_2	$[Hg_2^{+2}][Cl^-]^2$	1.3×10^{-18}
$Mg(OH)_2$	$[Mg^{+2}][OH^-]^2$	1.2×10^{-11}

8.3 / CALCULATION OF SOLUBILITIES FROM SOLUBILITY PRODUCTS

From known solubility products we can derive useful information on solubilities.

Examples

1. The K_{sp} of $BaSO_4$ is 1.1×10^{-10}. Calculate the molar solubility of barium sulfate.
Solution: First write out the chemical equation and the solubility product expression:

$$BaSO_4 \rightleftharpoons Ba^{+2} + SO_4^{-2}$$

$$K_{sp} = [Ba^{+2}][SO_4^{-2}]$$

Substitute the value of the K_{sp} from the table:

$$1.1 \times 10^{-10} = [Ba^{+2}][SO_4^{-2}]$$

From the chemical equation we see that for each mole of $BaSO_4$ that dissolves there is 1 mole of Ba^{+2} and 1 mole of SO_4^{-2} in solution; therefore,

$$x \text{ moles of } BaSO_4 \rightarrow x \text{ moles of } Ba^{+2} + x \text{ moles of } SO_4^{-2}$$

Then,

$$1.1 \times 10^{-10} = x \cdot x$$

$$x^2 = 1.1 \times 10^{-10}$$

$$x = \sqrt{1.1 \times 10^{-10}} = 1.05 \times 10^{-5} \text{ mole/l} \quad \textit{Answer}$$

The saturated solution of barium sulfate contains 1.05×10^{-5} mole of Ba^{+2} and 1.05×10^{-5} mole of SO_4^{-2} per liter and, therefore, 1.05×10^{-5} mole/l of $BaSO_4$.

If we wish to express the answer in grams per liter, we multiply the molar solubility by the formula weight:

Moles/liter $\times$ gram-formula weight $=$ grams/l

$1.05 \times 10^{-5} \times 233 = 2.45 \times 10^{-3}$ or 0.00245 grams $BaSO_4$/l

2. Calculate the maximum concentration of magnesium ion in milligrams per milliliter which may be dissolved in water that is kept at a pH of 9.0.

Solution: As we shall see in the next chapter, the hydroxide ion concentration of water with pH of 9.0 is 1×10^{-5}. Since $Mg(OH)_2$ is not very soluble, it precipitates easily from alkaline solutions of magnesium salts:

$Mg(OH)_2 \rightleftharpoons Mg^{+2} + 2OH^-$

$K_{sp} = [Mg^{+2}][OH^-]^2$

Of the terms in the solubility product expression, only $[Mg^{+2}]$ is not known. $[OH^-]$ is determined by the pH of 9.0, and K_{sp} of $Mg(OH)_2$ is listed in Table 8.1. Tabulating,

$[Mg^{+2}] = x$
$[OH^-] = 1 \times 10^{-5}$
$K_{sp} = 1.2 \times 10^{-11}$

Substituting in the solubility product expression,

$1.2 \times 10^{-11} = x(1 \times 10^{-5})^2$

$x = 1.2 \times 10^{-1} = 0.12$ mole/l, the maximum concentration of Mg^{+2} soluble at pH of 9.0. Multiplying this by the atomic weight of magnesium gives

0.12 mole/l $\times 24 = 2.9$ g Mg^{+2}/l $= 2.9$ mg/ml   *Answer*

8.4 / PRECIPITATION AND THE SOLUBILITY PRODUCT PRINCIPLE

In Example 1 of Section 8.2 we calculated the K_{sp} of AgCl from its molar solubility of 1.1×10^{-5}. In the saturated solution of silver chloride in water, we had

$[Ag^+] = [Cl^-] = 1.1 \times 10^{-5}$

When we precipitate silver ion in qualitative analysis, however, we would hardly expect to add an exactly equivalent amount of chloride ion. In practice, the best thing to do is to add a slight excess of chloride ion. The reason for adding a slight excess of reagent becomes clear if we consider the effect of adding just one drop of concentrated hydrochloric acid to 20 ml of saturated silver chloride solution. The drop of HCl would make the chloride ion concentration about 0.03 molar; so the precipitation equilibrium

$$AgCl \rightleftharpoons Ag^+ + Cl^-$$

would be displaced to the left to reduce the product of the concentrations of the ions to the solubility product value:

$$K_{sp} = [Ag^+][Cl^-] = 1.2 \times 10^{-10}$$

To find out how much silver ion would be left in the solution, substitute the known values in the K_{sp} expression:

$$1.2 \times 10^{-10} = [Ag^+](0.03)$$
$$[Ag^+] = 4.0 \times 10^{-9}$$

Thus a modest increase in the chloride ion concentration removes *most* of the silver ion from a saturated silver chloride solution:

$[Ag^+]$ in saturated AgCl solution	0.000011
$[Ag^+]$ left in $0.03M$ HCl solution	0.000000004
Moles of Ag^+ precipitated	0.000010996

This shows clearly the reason for adding a slight excess of reagent in a precipitation reaction.

If a slight excess of reagent is so helpful, why not use a large excess on the principle that "if a little is good, more is better"? There are several reasons, among them these:

1. It is not necessary. You can easily calculate that while the first drop of hydrochloric acid reduced the silver ion concentration of 20 ml of silver chloride solution by three thousand-fold, a second drop would precipitate only half of the very small amount of silver ion left. The point of diminishing returns is reached very quickly.
2. A high concentration of reagent may produce a soluble complex ion. In this case, a very large addition of hydrochloric acid causes the $AgCl_2^-$ ion to form, redissolving the silver

chloride. In some precipitations, complex ions form so easily that you will be warned to use special care in adding the reagent.

3. A large amount of reagent may give rise to salt effects referred to in Section 8.5.

4. If too much reagent is added, the K_{sp} may be exceeded for some substance other than the desired precipitate.

Chemists are often faced with the problem of separating an ion from a solution that contains several chemically related ions. The separation of Ba^{+2} from Sr^{+2} and Ca^{+2} in qualitative analysis is a typical example; any anion that precipitates one of them also precipitates the others. The method of fractional precipitation must then be used; that is, enough of the reagent is added to precipitate substantially all of one ion with very little of the others. Table 8.2 lists the solubility product constants of some of the slightly soluble compounds of calcium, strontium, and barium. These data make clear why chromate ion is almost always used to precipitate barium from the other ions of this group.

TABLE 8.2 / SOLUBILITY PRODUCT CONSTANTS OF SOME SLIGHTLY SOLUBLE SALTS OF CALCIUM, STRONTIUM, AND BARIUM

	Ca^{+2}	Sr^{+2}	Ba^{+2}
CO_3^{-2}	7.5×10^{-9}	1.0×10^{-9}	5.0×10^{-9}
CrO_4^{-2}	7.1×10^{-4}	3.6×10^{-5}	1.8×10^{-10}
$C_2O_4^{-2}$	2.0×10^{-9}	5.6×10^{-8}	1.7×10^{-7}
SO_4^{-2}	2.4×10^{-5}	3.0×10^{-7}	1.1×10^{-10}

If the concentrations of barium, strontium, and calcium ions are each originally 0.1 molar, the addition of chromate ion (as K_2CrO_4 solution) causes $BaCrO_4$ to precipitate first, because the small value of its solubility product is soon exceeded. The maximum concentration of CrO_4^{-2} that may be present in a $0.1M$ Ba^{+2} solution is 1.8×10^{-9}. (Check these calculations yourself.) As more chromate ion is added, $BaCrO_4$ precipitates alone until the chromate ion concentration reaches 3.6×10^{-4} (neglecting the dilution effect due to the water in which the K_2CrO_4 is dissolved). After this, $SrCrO_4$ begins to precipitate along with the

$BaCrO_4$. At this point, the Ba^{+2} concentration is reduced to 5×10^{-7} molar, so substantially all of the barium is removed. The K_{sp} of $CaCrO_4$ is not exceeded until after the CrO_4^{-2} concentration is greater than 7.1×10^{-3}. (This particular separation may appear to be more difficult than it is. It is not necessary to add K_2CrO_4 solution with special care for fear the chromate ion concentration will exceed 3.6×10^{-4}. We have an easier way of controlling $[CrO_4^{-2}]$. Since chromate ion is a fairly strong base, the equilibrium

$$CrO_4^{-2} + H_3O^+ \rightleftharpoons HCrO_4^- + H_2O$$

is largely displaced to the right in acetic acid solution. By adjusting the acidity of the solution, we can control the concentration of CrO_4^{-2} ion closely enough to precipitate most of the barium ion with very little trouble from strontium or calcium.)

Fractional precipitation is not always so easy or successful as with the chromates of the alkaline earth metal ions. In many cases, especially in precipitating metal sulfides and hydroxides, we have difficulties due to *coprecipitation*. For example, in the precipitations of the ions of Group 2 of the qualitative scheme as sulfides, zinc sulfide may be dragged down with the Group 2 sulfides although it would not precipitate if zinc ion alone were present. Coprecipitation is often due to the adsorption of an ion on a precipitate, while with bulky gelatinous precipitates like $Fe(OH)_3$, mere physical trapping may be involved.

To achieve sharp separations in qualitative analysis, we try to adjust the conditions so that coprecipitation is minimized. A finely divided precipitate with large surface area has a tendency to adsorb foreign ions, besides being slow to settle and difficult to centrifuge. In general, precipitation from hot dilute solutions, followed by a period of *digestion*, that is, of heating the solution and precipitate together before centrifuging, favors the growth of large crystals with a minimum of adsorbed ions.

8.5 / LIMITATIONS OF THE SOLUBILITY PRODUCT PRINCIPLE

The solubility product principle can be most usefully applied to the separations of qualitative analysis if we keep in mind some of its limitations:

1. The effect of interionic attraction is ordinarily neglected in K_{sp} calculations. In a saturated solution of a slightly soluble salt with no other ions present, interionic attraction is insignificant. However, in moderate concentrations of an electrolyte that has no common ion with the precipitate, *salt effects* appear. These are explained as being due to interionic attraction and to the tying up of water molecules as water of hydration of the ions.

2. The solubility product principle cannot be applied to moderately soluble or very soluble substances. At present it is not possible to calculate the necessary corrections for interionic attraction and hydration of ions.

3. The values of solubility products are difficult to measure and are known only approximately. Those for metallic sulfides are not at all precise. Answers to K_{sp} problems should never be expressed to more than two significant figures.

4. Hydrolysis, or acid-base reaction of an ion with water, may occur. For example, since S^{-2} reacts with water

$$S^{-2} + H_2O \rightleftharpoons HS^- + OH^-$$

it is often necessary to consider simultaneously the solution equilibrium of a metal sulfide and the hydrolysis of sulfide ion.

5. A quite similar situation may arise if one of the ions is involved in complex ion formation.

6. Since solubilities often change decidedly with temperature, the K_{sp} value may not mean very much unless we know the temperature at which it was determined. The values listed in tables are usually those for the temperature range 18° to 25°C.

Questions and problems

1. What would be the effect of the addition of each of the following substances on a saturated solution of $BaSO_4$ in equilibrium with some of the undissolved salt? Explain your answer in each case.

   a. H_2SO_4 d. Na_2SO_4
   b. $BaCl_2$ e. Alcohol
   c. KCl f. Additional solid $BaSO_4$

2. Write the solubility product expressions for the following slightly soluble salts:

  a. $PbCl_2$ e. $Fe(OH)_3$
  b. $MgNH_4PO_4$ f. $K_2Na[Co(NO_2)_6]$
  c. $Cu_2[Fe(CN)_6]$ g. Bi_2S_3
  d. Ag_3PO_4 h. Hg_2Cl_2

3. $PbCl_2$ is slightly soluble in pure water, less soluble in $0.1M$ HCl solution, but very soluble in $6M$ HCl solution. Can you explain this?

4. The solubility of silver iodide is 2.8×10^{-7} g/100 ml of H_2O. Calculate its K_{sp}.

> *Answer* 1.4×10^{-16}

5. The solubility of strontium oxalate, SrC_2O_4, is 42 mg/l. What is its K_{sp}?

6. The solubility of CaF_2 is 2.9×10^{-4} mole/l. What is its K_{sp}?

> *Answer* 9.7×10^{-11}

7. The K_{sp} of AgBr is 4.8×10^{-13}.
  a. Calculate the molar solubility of Ag^+ in a saturated solution of AgBr.

> *Answer* 7.0×10^{-7} mole/l

  b. Calculate the molar solubility of Ag^+ in a $0.05M$ solution of HBr.

> *Answer* 9.6×10^{-12} mole/l

8. The K_{sp} of Ag_2CrO_4 is 2.2×10^{-12}, that of $BaCrO_4$ 1.8×10^{-10}.
  a. Which of these substances is more soluble? Calculate the solubilities for each in terms of grams per liter.
  b. Which can give a higher concentration of metal ion in a $0.02M$ K_2CrO_4 solution, Ag^+ or Ba^{+2}? Calculate the maximum amount of each ion in mg/ml which may be present in such a solution.
  c. Does a smaller K_{sp} value always indicate a lower solubility? For substances of the same formula type, for example M_2X, would you expect that the smaller the K_{sp} value, the lower the solubility?

9. What is the solubility of $Cu(IO_3)_2$ in milligrams per milliliter?

10. The K_{sp} of $CaSO_4$ is 2.4×10^{-5}, that of CaC_2O_4 is 2.0×10^{-9}.

  a. Calculate the maximum amount of $C_2O_4^{-2}$ in moles per liter that can be added to a saturated solution of $CaSO_4$ before precipitation of CaC_2O_4 takes place.

  Answer 4.1×10^{-7} mole

  b. How much SO_4^{-2}, in moles per liter, must be added to a saturated solution of CaC_2O_4 before $CaSO_4$ starts to precipitate?

  Answer 5.3×10^{-1} mole

11. Calculate the number of grams of SrF_2 that could be dissolved in 500 ml of each of the following:

  a. Pure water

  b. $0.01M$ $Sr(NO_3)_2$ solution

  c. $0.05M$ KF solution

  Answer c 2.0×10^{-5} g

12. The K_{sp} of $Mg(OH)_2$ is 1.2×10^{-11} and the K_b of NH_3 solution is 1.8×10^{-5}. How much Mg^{+2}, in moles per liter, will remain unprecipitated in a $0.2M$ NH_3 solution? If the $0.2M$ NH_3 was also 0.2 molar with respect to NH_4Cl, how much Mg^{+2} would remain?

13. 100 ml water contains 1 mg Ca^{+2}, 10 mg Sr^{+2}, and 100 mg Ba^{+2}. If $(NH_4)_2C_2O_4$ solution is added drop by drop, which ion will precipitate first?

14. If 500 ml of $0.1M$ HCl is added to 500 ml of $0.01M$ $Hg_2(NO_3)_2$, how many grams of Hg_2Cl_2 will be precipitated and how many moles of Hg_2^{+2} will remain in solution? (Remember that the total volume becomes 1 liter and the molar concentrations are halved.)

15. The solubility of Li_3PO_4 is 0.004 g/100 ml.

  a. What is its solubility in $0.1M$ $LiNO_3$ solution?

  b. What is its solubility in $0.1M$ Na_3PO_4 solution?

16. The solubility product constants of AgCl, $BaSO_4$, and CaF_2 are all about the same: K_{sp} of AgCl $= 1.2 \times 10^{-10}$; K_{sp} of $BaSO_4 = 1.1 \times 10^{-10}$; and K_{sp} of $CaF_2 = 9.6 \times 10^{-11}$. What is the solubility of each of these substances in grams per liter

a. in water, and

b. in $0.1M$ $BaCl_2$ solution?

17. 100 ml of solution contains 0.005 mole of $FeCl_2$ and 0.005 mole of $FeCl_3$. What is the maximum concentration of OH^- that may be present without any precipitation of Fe^{+3}? What is the maximum amount that may be present without precipitation of any of the Fe^{+2}?

Water as an Acid and as a Base

9

9.1 / REACTIONS OF WATER OF INTEREST IN QUALITATIVE ANALYSIS

While we think of water primarily as a solvent in qualitative analysis, we must observe that it is not just an inert medium but is itself involved in reactions of several kinds. If we decide to list the types of reactions of water that are useful or significant in analytical chemistry, we might come up with a classification like this:

1. *Hydration of ions.* Without reactions of this type, electro-valent substances could not be dissolved. Hydrated ions will be referred to again in the next chapter.
2. *Reaction of water with acids.* Water as our common solvent reacts as a base in the practically complete ionization of strong acids like HCl or in the limited ionization of weak acids like HCN or H_2S.
3. *Reaction of water with bases.* The familiar example is that in the ammonia-water equilibrium.
4. *Hydrolysis.* This name is given to the reaction of water with an anion base or a cation acid of a dissolved salt. In hydrolysis, water may function either as an acid or as a base.
5. *Ionization of water.* In the ionization reaction, one molecule of water functions as an acid, the other as a base.

It is the last two types of reactions with which we are most concerned in this chapter.

9.2 / THE ION PRODUCT CONSTANT OF WATER

The equation for the electrolytic dissociation of water into its ions is familiar:

$$H_2O + H_2O \rightleftharpoons H_3O^+ + OH^-$$

The equilibrium constant expression for this reaction is

$$K = \frac{[H_3O^+][OH^-]}{[H_2O][H_2O]}$$

In pure water or in any dilute aqueous solution, the concentration of H_2O molecules remains virtually constant at about 55 moles per liter. Therefore,

$$K = \frac{[H_3O^+][OH^-]}{(55)^2}$$

Collecting our constant terms, we get

$$(55)^2 K = [H_3O^+][OH^-]$$

or

$$K_w = [H_3O^+][OH^-]$$

The constant, K_w, which is the product of the molar concentration of the ions, is called the *ion product constant* of water. Its value at 25°C is 1.0×10^{-14}. The ionization of water increases as the temperature rises; K_w is about 0.11×10^{-14} at 0°C and 9.6×10^{-14} at 60°C. Room temperature in American laboratories is seldom far from 25°C; so 1×10^{-14} is the accepted value of K_w.

The ionization of water produces hydronium and hydroxide ions in equal numbers; therefore, in pure water

$$[H_3O^+] = [OH^-] = 1 \times 10^{-7}$$

If some substance that provides hydronium or hydroxide ions is added to the water, the ionization equilibrium shifts; but, except in very concentrated solutions, the ion product is substantially unchanged. This is illustrated in Table 9.1. The hydronium ion concentration of $0.001M$ HCl solution is 0.001 or 10^{-3}. The hydroxide ion concentration is, then, the number that multiplied by 10^{-3} gives 10^{-14}; that is, 10^{-11}.

TABLE 9.1 / RELATIONSHIP OF HYDRONIUM ION CONCENTRATION
TO HYDROXIDE ION CONCENTRATION

Solution	$[H_3O^+]$	$[OH^-]$	K_w
0.02M NaOH	$10^{-12.3}$	$10^{-1.7}$	10^{-14}
0.01M NaOH	10^{-12}	10^{-2}	10^{-14}
Pure water	10^{-7}	10^{-7}	10^{-14}
0.001M HCl	10^{-3}	10^{-11}	10^{-14}
0.1M HC$_2$H$_3$O$_2$	$10^{-2.9}$	$10^{-11.1}$	10^{-14}

Therefore, if either the hydronium ion or hydroxide ion concentration of a solution is known, the other can be obtained from the relationship

$$[H_3O^+] \times [OH^-] = 1 \times 10^{-14}$$

The acidity or alkalinity of a solution is often expressed in terms of the hydronium ion concentration: a value of 10^{-7} indicates a neutral solution; larger values (with smaller negative exponents) indicate acid solutions; smaller values indicate basic solutions.

In dilute solutions especially, the expression of acidity in terms of hydronium ion concentrations is cumbersome whether decimal or exponential numbers are used. Instead of saying, "The hydronium ion concentration of water is 10^{-7}," we find it more convenient to say, "The pH of water is 7," using the exponent of 10 of the hydronium ion concentration, with its sign reversed. Since the common logarithm of a number is the power to which 10 must be raised to equal the number, we have the relationship

$$pH = -\log[H_3O^+] = \log \frac{1}{[H_3O^+]}$$

The pH of an acid solution is less than 7; that of an alkaline solution, greater. Values of pH usually range between 0 and 14. The pH system is especially useful in describing the acidity or alkalinity of solutions that are not far from neutral, such as those met with in physiological chemistry.

Table 9.2 shows the relationship of pH to hydronium ion concentration for the solutions listed in Table 9.1.

TABLE 9.2 / RELATIONSHIP OF pH AND pOH TO HYDRONIUM
AND HYDROXIDE ION CONCENTRATION

Solution	$[H_3O^+]$	$[OH^-]$	pH	pOH
0.02M NaOH	$10^{-12.3}$	$10^{-1.7}$	12.3	1.7
0.01M NaOH	10^{-12}	10^{-2}	12	1
Pure water	10^{-7}	10^{-7}	7	7
0.001M HCl	10^{-3}	10^{-11}	3	11
0.1M HC$_2$H$_3$O$_2$	$10^{-2.9}$	$10^{-11.1}$	2.9	11.1

The pOH bears the same relationship to the hydroxide ion concentration; it is occasionally found useful. Naturally, at 25°C,

$$pH + pOH = 14$$

Examples

1. What is the pH of a 0.01M NaOH solution?

   Solution: Each mole of NaOH gives 1 mole of OH^- ion, so 0.01M NaOH solution contains 0.01 or 10^{-2} moles of OH^- ion/liter.

   We know that

   $$[H_3O^+] \cdot [OH^-] = 10^{-14}$$

   Therefore

   $$[H_3O^+] \times 10^{-2} = 10^{-14}$$

   $$[H_3O^+] = 10^{-12}$$

   and, by definition,

   $$pH = 12$$

2. What is the pH of a 0.02M NaOH solution?

   Solution: The OH^- ion concentration of this solution is 0.02 or 2×10^{-2}.

   Since

   $$[H_3O^+] \cdot [OH^-] = 1 \times 10^{-14}$$

   $$[H_3O^+] \times (2 \times 10^{-2}) = 1 \times 10^{-14}$$

   Solving for $[H_3O^+]$,

   $$[H_3O^+] = \frac{1 \times 10^{-14}}{2 \times 10^{-2}} = \tfrac{1}{2} \times 10^{-12}$$

The pH is obtained from the $[H_3O^+]$:

$pH = -\log [H_3O^+]$
$pH = -\log (\frac{1}{2} \times 10^{-12})$
$pH = -\log \frac{1}{2} - \log 10^{-12}$
$pH = \log 2 + \log 10^{12}$
$pH = 0.3 + 12 = 12.3$ *Answer*

3. What is the pH of a $0.1M$ solution of acetic acid?
   Solution: The $[H_3O^+]$ of the solution must first be calculated, so we write out the chemical equation and the K_a expression:

$$HC_2H_3O_2 + H_2O \rightleftharpoons H_3O^+ + C_2H_3O_2^-$$

$$K_a = \frac{[H_3O^+][C_2H_3O_2^-]}{[HC_2H_3O_2]}$$

Let $[H_3O^+] = x$

Then $[C_2H_3O_2^-] = x$

and $[HC_2H_3O_2] = 0.1 - x \simeq 0.1$

Substituting in the K_a expression these terms and the K_a value from the table,

$$1.8 \times 10^{-5} = \frac{x \cdot x}{0.1}$$

Solving for x,

$x^2 = 1.8 \times 10^{-6}$
$x = \sqrt{1.8 \times 10^{-6}} = 1.3 \times 10^{-3}$
                    molar concentration of H_3O^+

The pH is obtained from the $[H_3O^+]$ in the usual way:

$pH = -\log [H_3O^+]$
$pH = -\log (1.3 \times 10^{-3})$
$pH = -\log 1.3 - \log 10^{-3}$
$pH = -0.1 + 3$
$pH = 2.9$ *Answer*

Notice that pH calculations, like those for K_a and K_{sp}, are not ordinarily carried out beyond two significant figures. Although some pH *measurements* may be made with greater precision, calculations that involve K_a are not valid for more significant figures than the K_a values.

9.3 / INDICATORS

The measurement of pH may be done either electrometrically or colorimetrically. Electrometrically, by means of various electronic devices, called pH meters, the measurements may be accurate to 0.01 pH unit or less. Colorimetric measurements made by means of *indicators* are less precise but are satisfactory for many purposes, such as ordinary acid-base titrations.

Acid-base indicators are substances that exhibit different colors in solutions of different pH values. They are usually weak organic acids or bases. A typical weak acid indicator exists in water solution in the equilibrium

$$\underset{\text{color } A}{\text{HIn}} + H_2O \rightleftharpoons H_3O^+ + \underset{\text{color } B}{\text{In}^-}$$

with the molecular acid, HIn, having a distinctly different color from that of its conjugate base, In^-. The addition of hydronium ions displaces the equilibrium to the left, increasing the proportion of the molecular form with color A; the addition of hydroxide ions has the opposite effect. The ionization constant for the equilibrium system is called the *indicator constant*, with the expression

$$K_{in} = \frac{[H_3O^+][In^-]}{[HIn]}$$

If we rearrange this,

$$[H_3O^+] = K_{in}\frac{[HIn]}{[In^-]}$$

it becomes apparent that at the point at which the concentrations of ionic and molecular forms are equal, the H_3O^+ concentration is equal to the indicator constant. At a greater H_3O^+ concentration, the acid color predominates; at a smaller H_3O^+ concentration, the alkaline color. Since many indicator substances with different ionization constants are available, one can always be found that changes color in the vicinity of any desired pH value. Table 9.3 lists some indicators favored for use over various pH ranges. A solution of pH 5.2 is alkaline to methyl orange, slightly acid to litmus, and acid to phenolphthalein.

TABLE 9.3 / ACID-BASE INDICATORS

Indicator	Acid color	Alkaline color	pH range
Methyl orange	red	yellow	3.1–4.4
Congo red	blue	red	3.0–5.0
Methyl red	red	yellow	4.4–6.2
Litmus	red	blue	4.6–8.3
Phenolphthalein	colorless	red	8.3–10.0
Alizarin yellow	yellow	violet	10.1–12.1

If an indicator is to be useful, the colors of its acid and alkaline forms should be easily distinguishable by the average eye, its color change should take place over a narrow pH range, and it should not react with any substance present except H_3O^+ or OH^- ion. Litmus is not suited for titration because its color change is not sharp, the change from red to blue occurring gradually over the pH range of 4.6 to 8.3. However, this gradual change makes litmus useful for rough estimations of acidity near the neutral point. Better estimations can be made with special "pH papers," impregnated with several different indicators.

9.4 / BUFFER SOLUTIONS

A solution that contains a weak acid and its conjugate base in approximately equal proportions is called a *buffer solution* because of its ability to resist changes in pH. A solution containing equimolar quantities of acetic acid and sodium acetate typifies the functioning of a buffer system:

$$HC_2H_3O_2 + H_2O \rightleftharpoons H_3O^+ + C_2H_3O_2^-$$

$$K_a = \frac{[H_3O^+][C_2H_3O_2^-]}{[HC_2H_3O_2]}$$

Rearranging,

$$[H_3O^+] = \frac{[HC_2H_3O_2]}{[C_2H_3O_2^-]} \cdot K_a$$

If $HC_2H_3O_2$ and $C_2H_3O_2^-$ are present in equal concentrations,

$$[H_3O^+] = K_a = 1.8 \times 10^{-5}$$

If a small amount of OH^- ion is added to this solution it is considered as reacting with the $HC_2H_3O_2$:

$$HC_2H_3O_2 + OH^- \rightleftharpoons C_2H_3O_2^- + H_2O$$

Assume that the concentrations of $HC_2H_3O_2$ and $C_2H_3O_2^-$ are each 0.1 molar, and that we add 1.85×10^{-5} mole of NaOH per liter, the amount needed to make an unbuffered solution of this acidity exactly neutral. The effect of this addition on the acidity of the buffer solution is negligible:

$$[H_3O^+] = \frac{0.1 - 0.0000185}{0.1 + 0.0000185} \times 1.8 \times 10^{-5} \simeq 1.8 \times 10^{-5}$$

Similarly, a small addition of acid is considered as reacting with the acetate ion:

$$C_2H_3O_2^- + H_3O^+ \rightleftharpoons HC_2H_3O_2 + H_2O$$

Notice that it is the ratio of $[C_2H_3O_2]^-$ to $[HC_2H_3O_2]$, not the actual concentrations, that determines the hydronium ion concentration of the buffer solutions.

Buffer solutions are useful wherever it is desirable to maintain a solution at constant pH. The $NH_4^+ - NH_3$ system is often used in qualitative analysis. The blood is maintained at a pH of 7.4 principally by the $H_2CO_3 - HCO_3^-$ system, and the other body fluids are kept at their proper pH by other buffers.

Example

0.001 mole of HCl was added to a liter of a solution buffered at $[H_3O^+] = 1.8 \times 10^{-5}$ by 0.1 mole of acetic acid and 0.1 mole of sodium acetate. What was the H_3O^+ concentration in the resulting solution?

Solution: The added 0.001 mole of H_3O^+ reacts with acetate ion

$$C_2H_3O_2^- + H_3O^+ \rightleftharpoons HC_2H_3O_2 + H_2O$$

giving

$$(0.1 - 0.001) = 0.099 \text{ mole of } C_2H_3O_2^-$$

and

$$(0.1 + 0.001) = 0.101 \text{ mole of } HC_2H_3O_2$$

Substituting these values in the formula

$$[H_3O^+] = \frac{[HC_2H_3O_2]}{[C_2H_3O_2^-]} \cdot K_a$$

$$[H_3O^+] = \frac{0.101}{0.099} \times 1.8 \times 10^{-5}$$

$$= 1.84 \times 10^{-5} \quad \text{—a negligible increase.} \quad \textit{Answer}$$

9.5 / HYDROLYSIS

The name *hydrolysis* is given to an acid-base reaction between water and an ion of a dissolved salt. There are, of course, two types of hydrolysis reactions:

1. *Reaction of water with an anion base.* Any anion that is the conjugate base of a weak acid acts as a base in water solution.
2. *Reaction of water with a cation acid.* Hydrated ions like $Cu(H_2O)_4^{+2}$ can serve as proton donors, as may some unhydrated cations that contain hydrogen, for example NH_4^+.

9.6 / SALTS WITH BASIC ANIONS

Sodium acetate is a typical salt whose cation is not an acid, but whose anion is a base. The hydrated sodium ion does not react noticeably with water, while the acetate ion reacts to a considerable extent:

$$C_2H_3O_2^- + H_2O \rightleftharpoons HC_2H_3O_2 + OH^-$$

As a result of the hydrolysis of acetate ion, a solution of sodium acetate would be expected to be distinctly alkaline to litmus.

Example

What is the pH of a 0.1 molar solution of sodium acetate? *Solution:* No reaction of sodium ion with water is considered to take place, but the $C_2H_3O_2^-$ ion reacts quite strongly:

$$C_2H_3O_2^- + H_2O \rightleftharpoons HC_2H_3O_2 + OH^-$$

We shall assume (subject to later checking) that the extent of hydrolysis is not great enough to change the concentration of $C_2H_3O_2^-$ appreciably, or

$$[C_2H_3O_2^-] \simeq 0.1$$

Moreover, we shall assume that hydrolysis produces a much greater concentration of OH^- ion than the 10^{-7} present in pure water. That is, practically all of the OH^- ion present is that produced by the hydrolysis reaction. Therefore,

$$[HC_2H_3O_2] = [OH^-]$$

Of course, as $[OH^-]$ increases, $[H_3O^+]$ decreases, since the K_w relationship must be satisfied:

$$[H_3O^+][OH^-] = 10^{-14}$$

Now consider the ionization constant of acetic acid:

$$HC_2H_3O_2 + H_2O \rightleftharpoons H_3O^+ + C_2H_3O_2^-$$

$$K_a = \frac{[H_3O^+][C_2H_3O_2^-]}{[HC_2H_3O_2]} = 1.8 \times 10^{-5}$$

Substituting 0.1 for $[C_2H_3O_2^-]$ and $[OH^-]$ for $[HC_2H_3O_2]$ in the K_a expression,

$$\frac{[H_3O^+]0.1}{[OH^-]} = 1.8 \times 10^{-5}$$

or

$$[H_3O^+] = 1.8 \times 10^{-4} \cdot [OH^-]$$

and, substituting for $[OH^-]$ the value known from the water constant expression,

$$[H_3O^+] = 1.8 \times 10^{-4} \times \frac{10^{-14}}{[H_3O^+]}$$

$$[H_3O^+]^2 = 1.8 \times 10^{-18}$$

$$[H_3O^+] = 1.3 \times 10^{-9}$$

$$pH = -\log (1.3 \times 10^{-9}) = 8.9 \qquad \textit{Answer}$$

When we check our assumptions we find that the concentration of OH^- ion is $1 \times 10^{-14} \div 1.3 \times 10^{-9} = 7.7 \times 10^{-4}$; thus practically all of the OH^- present was that produced in the reaction. The same value, 7.7×10^{-4} also represents the approximate reduction in $[C_2H_3O_2^-]$, so we were justified in considering that the concentration remained almost unchanged at 0.1.

For the general reaction for the hydrolysis of an anion

$$A^- + H_2O \rightleftharpoons HA + OH^-$$

the *hydrolysis constant*, K_h, may be used:

$$K_h = \frac{[HA][OH^-]}{[A^-]}$$

Hydrolysis constant tables are not given separately, since

$$K_h = \frac{K_w}{K_a}$$

Substitute the K_w and K_a expressions

$$K_w = [H_3O^+][OH^-] \quad \text{and} \quad K_a = \frac{[H_3O^+][A^-]}{[HA]}$$

to satisfy yourself that this relationship is correct.

The hydrolysis of a diprotic anion takes place in steps, with the first step being much more complete than the second. For example, for a solution of sodium sulfide, Step 1 is

$$S^{-2} + H_2O \rightleftharpoons HS^- + OH^-$$

$$K_h = \frac{[HS^-][OH^-]}{[S^{-2}]}$$

$$K_h = \frac{K_w}{K_2 \text{ (for } H_2S)} = \frac{1 \times 10^{-14}}{1.2 \times 10^{-15}} = 8.3$$

and Step 2 is

$$HS^- + H_2O \rightleftharpoons H_2S + OH^-$$

$$K_h = \frac{[H_2S][OH^-]}{[HS^-]}$$

$$K_h = \frac{K_w}{K_1 \text{ (for } H_2S)} = \frac{1 \times 10^{-14}}{1.0 \times 10^{-7}} = 1 \times 10^{-7}$$

The decidedly different values of K_h for the two steps are quite typical of the hydrolysis of diprotic anions.

9.7 / SALTS WITH ACIDIC CATIONS

There are two familiar classes of cation acids.

1. Ammonium ion and some substituted ammonium ions like methyl ammonium, $CH_3NH_3^+$, give up a proton to water:

$$NH_4^+ + H_2O \rightleftharpoons H_3O^+ + NH_3$$

2. Many metal ions also react with water. As was pointed out in Section 5.5, dissolved ions are hydrated, the oxygen ends of the water molecules being attracted to the cations. Small ions with high positive charge are especially effective in attracting the oxygen atoms. In so doing they weaken the oxygen-hydrogen bond permitting a proton to be released. Taking the hydrated copper ion as an example,

$$Cu(H_2O)_4^{+2} + H_2O \rightleftharpoons Cu(H_2O)_3(OH)^+ + H_3O^+$$

A second hydrolysis reaction takes place to a much smaller extent:

$$Cu(H_2O)_3(OH)^+ + H_2O \rightleftharpoons Cu(H_2O)_2(OH)_2 + H_3O^+$$

Actually, the number of water molecules attracted to a Cu^{+2} ion in solution is unknown. In crystalline hydrates, each Cu^{+2} is surrounded by 4 water molecules, and the same number is assumed in solution for convenience in equation writing.

Calculations for hydrolysis of cation acids are similar to those for anion bases.

Example

What is the percentage hydrolysis of a $0.2M$ NH_4NO_3 solution? What is the pH of this solution?

Solution: Since nitric acid is a strong acid, nitrate ion is too weak a base to react noticeably. NH_4^+ ion hydrolyzes according to the equation

$$NH_4^+ + H_2O \rightleftharpoons NH_3 + H_3O^+$$

$$K_h = \frac{[NH_3][H_3O^+]}{[NH_4^+]}$$

$$K_h = \frac{K_w}{K_b \text{ (for } NH_3)*}$$

If we let x equal the concentration of hydronium ion produced by the hydrolysis, and assume that it is substantially greater than $[H_3O^+]$ of pure water, then the concentration of NH_3 is also equal to x, and the concentration of NH_4^+ is $(0.2-x)$.

---

*Is this true? Make the necessary substitutions for K_w and K_b and see if it reduces to the K_h expression.

If we also assume that x is small compared to 0.2, then $[NH_4^+] = 0.2$, and we have

$$K_h = \frac{x^2}{0.2}$$

Substituting the known values of K_w and K_b,

$$\frac{x^2}{0.2} = \frac{1 \times 10^{-14}}{1.8 \times 10^{-5}}$$

$$x^2 = 1.1 \times 10^{-10}$$

$$x = 1.0 \times 10^{-5}$$

$$(H_3O^+) = 1.0 \times 10^{-5} \text{ and pH} = 5 \qquad \textit{Answer}$$

The degree of hydrolysis is the fraction of ammonium ion that is hydrolyzed, or

$$\frac{[NH_3]}{[NH_4^+]} = \frac{1.0 \times 10^{-5}}{0.2} = 5 \times 10^{-5}$$

The degree of hydrolysis is usually expressed as percentage; therefore,

$$\text{per cent hydrolysis} = 5 \times 10^{-5} \times 100 = 0.005 \text{ per cent}$$
$$\textit{Answer}$$

If we have in solution a salt of a cation acid and an anion base, both ions undergo hydrolysis, and calculations become somewhat more involved.

The hydrolysis of an ion in equilibrium with a precipitate produces another complex equilibrium system common in qualitative analysis.

Example

Calculate the solubility of CuS in water at 25°C.

Solution: We have here two equilibria to consider simultaneously:

$$CuS \rightleftharpoons Cu^{+2} + S^{-2}$$

$$K_{sp} = [Cu^{+2}][S^{-2}] = 8.7 \times 10^{-36}$$

$$S^{-2} + H_2O \rightleftharpoons HS^- + OH^-$$

$$K_h = \frac{[HS^-][OH^-]}{[S^{-2}]} = 8.3$$

Since we know that the solubility of CuS is slight, we can assume that the amount of hydroxide ion produced by the hydrolysis of S^{-2} is very small compared to the 1×10^{-7} present in pure water.

Therefore,

$$8.3 = \frac{[HS^-](1 \times 10^{-7})}{[S^{-2}]}$$

Solving for $[S^{-2}]$,

$$[S^{-2}] = \frac{[HS^-]}{8.3 \times 10^7}$$

This shows that the hydrolysis of S^{-2} is almost complete; practically all of the S^{-2} ion going into solution from

$$CuS \rightleftharpoons Cu^{+2} + S^{-2}$$

is now in the form of HS^-. The $[Cu^{+2}]$ equals $[S^{-2}]$ plus $[HS^-]$, or for practical purposes

$$[Cu^{+2}] = [HS^-]$$

Now, if we substitute

$$[S^{-2}] = \frac{[HS^-]}{8.3 \times 10^7}$$

for the $[S^{-2}]$ in the solubility product expression

$$K_{sp} = [Cu^{+2}][S^{-2}]$$

$$8.7 \times 10^{-36} = [Cu^{+2}]\frac{[HS^-]}{8.3 \times 10^7}$$

But, since $[Cu^{+2}]$ is practically equal to $[HS^-]$,

$$8.7 \times 10^{-36} = \frac{[Cu^{+2}]^2}{8.3 \times 10^7}$$

$$[Cu^{+2}]^2 = 7.2 \times 10^{-28}$$

$$[Cu^{+2}] = 2.7 \times 10^{-14} \text{ molar solubility of CuS } Answer$$

Notice that if the hydrolysis of S^{-2} were not considered, the calculated molar solubility would be 2.9×10^{-18}. We have shown that the solubility is about ten thousand times greater than this. Actually, our calculated value is still somewhat below the true value, since we neglected to consider the hydrolysis of the hydrated copper cation.

Questions and problems

1. Can you see any advantages to using the ion product constant rather than the equilibrium constant in problems involving the ionization equilibrium of water?

2. Complete the following table for water at 25°C.

$[H_3O^+]$	$[OH^-]$	pH	pOH
10^{-7}			
2×10^{-3}			
	10^{-1}		
2.5			
		2.5	
		8.93	
			10.4

3. Are the following terms synonymous: neutral, neutral to litmus, neutral to phenolphthalein? Explain your answer.

4. Calculate the pH of the following solutions:
   a. $0.01M$ KOH
   b. $0.01M$ HCN
   c. $0.03M$ $HC_2H_3O_2$
   d. $0.2M$ NH_3

5. Since electrometric measurements of pH are easily a hundred times more sensitive than litmus paper, would you suggest throwing all of our litmus into the waste jar?

6. Buffer systems are important in foods, medicines, laboratory reagents, and other materials. Give some *specific* examples.

7. What is the pH of a buffer containing 0.1 mole of formic acid, $HCHO_2$, and 0.2 mole of $NaCHO_2$ per liter? What is the pH of a buffer containing 0.15 mole of $HCHO_2$ and 0.3 mole of $NaCHO_2$ per liter?

8. What is the pH of a system buffered with benzoic acid, $HC_7H_5O_2$, and sodium benzoate in a 2 to 1 ratio?

9. How much $NaC_2H_3O_2$ must be added to a $0.1M$ solution of $HC_2H_3O_2$ to give a buffer solution of pH 5?

Answer   0.18 mole/l

10. What ratio of KCNO and HCNO would be required for a buffer solution of pH 4.2?

11. What ratio of NH_3 and NH_4Cl would you use to get a buffer system of pH 8.5?

Answer   1 to 5.6

12. If 100 ml of $0.1M$ HCN is added to 100 ml of $0.1M$ NaOH, will the resulting solution be neutral? What will its pH be?

13. Calculate the percentage hydrolysis of a $0.1M$ solution of $KCHO_2$.

14. Calculate the value of K_h for:
    a. KBrO   *Answer a* 5×10^{-6}
    b. CH_3NH_3Cl
    c. NaHS
    d. K_2CO_3 *Answer d* 2.1×10^{-4}

15. What is the pH of a $0.05M$ solution of KBrO?

Answer   10.7

16. What is the percentage hydrolysis of $0.1M$ sodium formate solution?

Answer   0.0022

17. What is the pH of a $0.1M$ solution of $NaCHO_2$?

18. What is the solubility of CdS in water, taking into account the hydrolysis of the S^{-2} produced?

19. What is the solubility of $BaCO_3$ in water
    a. Neglecting hydrolysis of the CO_3^- ion?

Answer a 7.1×10^{-5} mole/l

    b. Considering the effect of hydrolysis on the solubility?

Answer b 3.2×10^{-3} mole/l

Complex Ions

10

10.1 / COORDINATION COMPOUNDS

The name *complex ion* is commonly restricted to ions composed of a central metal ion combined with a certain number of *coordinated groups*. These coordinated groups, also called *ligands*, may be either ions or polar molecules. Familiar examples of complex ions include the ferrocyanide ion, $Fe(CN)_6^{-4}$; the deep blue copper ammonia ion, $Cu(NH_3)_4^{+2}$; and the many hydrated ions. It has been pointed out that there is probably no such thing as a simple ion in solution; the dissolving of a salt depends on the hydration of the ions to separate them from one another.

Of course, any ion composed of more than one atom is a complex ion. Because of their small size and their stability, the common oxygen-containing anions like NO_3^- and SO_4^{-2} behave like simple anions, but they are truly complex ions, as are CN^-, S_2^{-2} and even OH^-. The formation of the H_3O^+ ion in water solution has been referred to repeatedly. Although it has been only in recent years that direct evidence has been obtained of the presence of this ion in solutions of acids, its existence has long been assumed. The ionization of an acid like HCl in water can best be understood as a reaction in which the polar water molecule becomes attached to the proton by a coordinate covalent bond.

Some ions composed of more than one atom are too small and too stable to warrant study as complex ions. Some others we cannot profitably study because their composition is too uncertain; for example, in solution the alkali metal ions and most anions are loosely hydrated, with a large and variable number of water molecules. We shall not concern ourselves in this chapter with either these very stable or very unstable combinations. The complex ions we are interested in are groups of atoms having characteristic properties and definite composition, stable enough to go unchanged from solid to solution, yet unstable enough that their dissociation equilibria are of interest.

10.2 / ATTRACTIVE FORCES IN COMPLEX IONS

The forces that hold the particles of complex ions together are of various types. The atoms of the CN^- and OH^- ions are linked by ordinary covalent bonds. Complex ions in which the central ion is a metal ion having only eight electrons in its outer level (the inert gas configuration) are especially likely to be held together by electrostatic forces. Depending on the nature of the ligand, the attraction may be of the ion-ion or ion-dipole type. The hydrates of the alkali metal ions seem to be held together only by the attraction of the positively charged cation for the negative end of the water molecule. Some complexes containing the fluoride ion, for example FeF_6^{-3}, appear to depend mainly on the attraction between the oppositely charged ions. Electrostatic forces are greatest, of course, for a small central cation having a high charge. Thus, the hydrate of Al^{+3} is quite stable, that of Na^+ is much less stable, and Cs^+ is very loosely hydrated.

The complex ions of greatest interest to us, those of intermediate stability, are mostly of the type held together by coordinate covalent bonds. Thus, we have such ions as

$$\left[\begin{array}{ccc} & H & \quad H \\ H\!:\!N\!:\!Ag\!:\!N\!:\!H \\ & H & \quad H \end{array}\right]^{+} \quad \left[\begin{array}{c} H \\ :O: \\ H\!:\!O\!:\!Zn\!:\!O\!:\!H \\ :O: \\ H \end{array}\right]^{-2} \quad \left[\begin{array}{ccc} & :Cl: & \\ :Cl: & & :Cl: \\ & Sn & \\ :Cl: & & :Cl: \\ & :Cl: & \end{array}\right]^{-2}$$

In these cases, each ligand has provided both electrons of the pair bonding it to the central atom. This corresponds to our definition of a *coordinate covalent bond*, page 12. The name of this type of bond, in fact, derives from its occurrence in these coordination compounds. You should notice, also, that the formation of a complex ion of this sort involves an acid-base reaction of the Lewis type. In the reaction

$$Ag^+ + 2: \overset{\displaystyle H}{\underset{\displaystyle H}{N}} : H \rightarrow \left[\overset{\displaystyle H}{\underset{\displaystyle H}{H : N}} : Ag : \overset{\displaystyle H}{\underset{\displaystyle H}{N : H}} \right]^+$$

Ag^+ is an electron pair acceptor or acid, and NH_3 is an electron pair donor, or base.

If the sum of the number of electrons in the central ion and the number of electrons coordinated to it happens to equal a stable electron configuration, we may expect an unusually stable complex ion to result. So cobalt, with the electron configuration 2, 8, 15, 2, forms two ions, $Co^{+2} - 2, 8, 15$ and $Co^{+3} - 2, 8, 14$. Of the two, Co^{+2} is more stable in simple salts. In complex ions, however, Co^{+3} is more stable. The electron configuration resulting from the addition of 12 electrons, from 6 coordinated groups, to Co^{+3} shows 36 electrons, the same number as in the next inert gas, krypton. However, Co^{+2} complexes have 37 electrons; that is, one more than the inert gas configuration.

The number of coordinated groups attached to the central atom is called the *coordination number*. In $Ag(NH_3)_2^+$, this number is 2; in $Cd(CN)_4^{-2}$, it is 4; in $Co(NO_2)_6^{-3}$, it is 6. As these examples show, the coordination number is sometimes twice the valence. Sometimes the coordination number is determined by the number of electrons needed to reach an inert gas structure, as in $Co(NO_2)_6^{-3}$. In general, large ions have higher coordination numbers than small ones. The coordination numbers of an ion may also vary with the concentration or with the nature of the coordinating group. The most common coordination number is 6; the next most common is 4.

The charge on a complex ion is, of course, the algebraic sum of the ionic charges of all its components.

10.3 / NOMENCLATURE

The system of naming coordination compounds is an extension of that described in Chapter 3 for simpler inorganic compounds. A summary of the rules follows:

1. The cation is named first, followed by the anion; this is true both for complex ions and for simple ions.

2. The names of all negative groups coordinated to the central atom end in "-o." Names of neutral groups have no characteristic ending except for water which is called "aquo." Positive coordinated groups, which are very rare, have the ending "-ium."
3. Coordinated groups are listed in this order:
   a. Negative groups, in alphabetical order; for example, "bromo-" before "chloro-."
   b. Neutral groups, with "aquo" preceding other neutral groups.
   c. Positive groups.
4. After the coordinated groups, the central metallic element is named. If the complex is a positive ion or a neutral molecule, the name of the metal is given in its usual form. For a complex anion the ending "-ate" is given to the metal, as in "chromate" or "ferrate." The name of the complex is always followed immediately by the Roman numeral signifying the oxidation number of the central metallic element.
5. In writing formulas, the reverse order is used for the symbols: central element first, then the coordinated groups, with negative groups last. Brackets are usually placed around the formula of the complex ion.

Some of the common coordinating groups and their names are:

aquo	H_2O	hydroxo	OH^-
ammine	NH_3	iodo	I^-
bromo	Br^-	nitro	$NO_2{}^-$
carbonato	$CO_3{}^{-2}$	peroxo	$O_2{}^{-2}$
chloro	Cl^-	oxalato	$C_2O_4{}^{-2}$
cyanato	$-OCN^-$	thio	S^{-2}
cyano	$-CN^-$	thiocyanato	$-SCN^-$
fluoro	F^-	thiosulfato	$S_2O_3{}^{-2}$

A few examples will show how these rules are applied. Notice that the name of a complex ion is written as a single word.

$Na_3[Co(NO_2)_6]$	Sodium hexanitrocobaltate(III)
$[Cr(NH_3)_4Cl_2]Cl$	Dichlorotetraamminechromium(III) chloride
$[Sn(C_2O_4)_3]^{-2}$	Trioxalatostannate(IV) ion
$[Fe(H_2O)_5CNS]^{+2}$	Thiocyanatopentaaquoiron(III) ion
$[Cr(NH_3)_3Cl_3]$	Trichlorotriamminechromium(III)

10.4 / GEOMETRY OF COMPLEX IONS

Complex ions in which the coordination number is 2 might conceivably have the two ligands arranged on opposite sides of the central ion with all three units in a straight line; or there might be an angular arrangement. Apparently, both types do exist.

With coordination number of 4, we might reasonably consider two conformations as most likely: the four ligands could be arranged in a square around the central ion with all in one plane, or they might be positioned at the corners of a regular tetrahedron, or triangular pyramid, with the central ion in the center. Actually, planar complexes are rather more common, but tetrahedral complexes are found with zinc, mercury (II), and some other metal ions.

Complexes having coordination number of 6 invariably have a configuration in which the ligands might be described as being at the corners of a regular octahedron with the metal ion at its center, as illustrated in Figure 10.1.

FIGURE 10.1 / THE HEXACYANOFERRATE(II)
ION, A TYPICAL OCTAHEDRAL COMPLEX

The geometry of complex ions has been one of their most fascinating aspects to chemists. Although many tools, such as x-ray diffraction studies, are now available to help determine the spatial arrangement of complexes, these methods have usually substantiated the conformations suggested several decades earlier. The original investigators used chemical methods alone to deduce the possible geometric structure from the number of different complex ions that could be produced having the same constituents arranged in various positions. A Swiss chemist, Alfred Werner, was outstanding in this field, so complex ions are often called *Werner complexes*.

Some larger molecules or ions are able to coordinate in more than one position on the central ion. For example, ethylene diamine, $H_2NCH_2CH_2NH_2$, can take the place of two ordinary-sized ligands such as NH_3. Such multiple coordinating groups are called *chelating groups* and the ring structure that results is called a *chelate*. (The words are derived from the Greek word *chela*, meaning the claw of a lobster or crab. Like a crab, a chelating group can attach itself with two claws.) Chelation, especially when it produces a five- or six-membered ring, results in a very stable complex. Some complex ions involving chelation are used in analytical work to keep metal ions in solution. Ethylenediaminetetraacetic acid is an especially effective complexing agent because it possesses as many as six coordination sites. When chelation produces a neutral complex rather than an ion, a very insoluble substance may result. An example is nickel dimethylglyoximate used as the confirmatory precipitate for nickel:

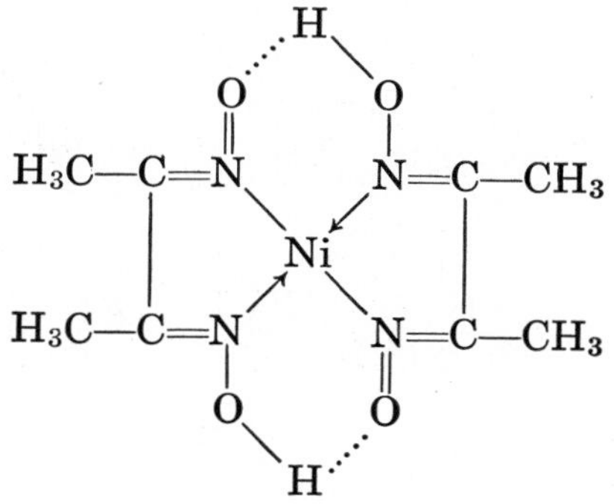

The size and electron configuration of the Ni^{+2} cation appear to be just right to fit in this complex. A few other cations also form complexes with dimethylglyoxime but they are not nearly so stable or so insoluble.

Many chelated complexes are important in biochemistry. For example, chlorophyll contains a chelated Mg^{+2} ion, and hemoglobin a chelated Fe^{+3} ion.

10.5 / INSTABILITY CONSTANTS

The equilibrium reactions involving formation and dissociation of complex ions are usually written with the complex ion on the left and its dissociation products on the right. For a typical example,

$$Cu(NH_3)_4^{+2} \rightleftharpoons Cu^{+2} + 4NH_3$$

the equilibrium constant, called in this case the *instability constant*, has the usual form

$$K_{inst} = \frac{[Cu^{+2}][NH_3]^4}{[Cu(NH_3)_4^{+2}]}$$

However, this is an oversimplification. The formation and dissociation of complex ions is ordinarily a stepwise process:

$$CuNH_3^{+2} \rightleftharpoons Cu^{+2} + NH_3$$

$$K_1 = \frac{[Cu^{+2}][NH_3]}{[CuNH_3^{+2}]} = 7.9 \times 10^{-5}$$

$$Cu(NH_3)_2^{+2} \rightleftharpoons CuNH_3^{+2} + NH_3$$

$$K_2 = \frac{[CuNH_3^{+2}][NH_3]}{[Cu(NH_3)_2^{+2}]} = 3.2 \times 10^{-4}$$

$$Cu(NH_3)_3^{+2} \rightleftharpoons Cu(NH_3)_2^{+2} + NH_3$$

$$K_3 = \frac{[Cu(NH_3)_2^{+2}][NH_3]}{[Cu(NH_3)_3^{+2}]} = 1.3 \times 10^{-3}$$

$$Cu(NH_3)_4^{+2} \rightleftharpoons Cu(NH_3)_3^{+2} + NH_3$$

$$K_4 = \frac{[Cu(NH_3)_3^{+2}][NH_3]}{[Cu(NH_3)_4^{+2}]} = 7.9 \times 10^{-3}$$

The instability constant for $Cu(NH_3)_4^{+2}$ is the product of the equilibrium constants for the individual steps, or

$$K_{inst} = K_1 \times K_2 \times K_3 \times K_4 = 2.6 \times 10^{-13}$$

When we add ammonia to a solution containing Cu^{+2} ion, we may have present, then, not only the simple ion and the tetra-amminecopper ion, but all the intermediate forms.

Calculations based on K_{inst} are limited by the fact that constants for the separate steps are not known for many complex ions. Even where these constants are available, calculations based on them are too complicated for our purposes. However, some useful calculations are possible, because in qualitative analysis we generally use a considerable excess of complexing agent. As a result, most of our metal ion is in the form of the final complex and we can ignore the amount that is present in the intermediate forms.

Examples

1. Calculate the concentration of free Cu^{+2} ion in a solution made by dissolving 0.02 mole of a copper(II) salt in one liter of $3M$ NH_3 solution.

   Solution: Write the chemical equation and the expression for the appropriate constant as usual:

   $$Cu(NH_3)_4^{+2} \rightleftharpoons Cu^{+2} + 4NH_3$$

   $$K_{inst} = \frac{[Cu^{+2}][NH_3]^4}{[Cu(NH_3)_4^{+2}]}$$

   In this strongly ammoniacal solution, practically all of the copper will be tied up in the tetraammine complex; therefore,

   $$[Cu(NH_3)_4^{+2}] \simeq 0.02$$

   Also, most of the ammonia will be present as free NH_3; therefore,

   $$[NH_3] \simeq 3$$

   Nearly 0.08 mole of NH_3 will be present in the form of $Cu(NH_3)_4^{+2}$, about 0.007 mole as NH_4^+, and smaller amounts in intermediate complexes such as $Cu(NH_3)_3^{+2}$. However, the approximation as stated is still satisfactory. Substituting known values in the K_{inst} expression,

   $$2.6 \times 10^{-13} = \frac{[Cu^{+2}](3)^4}{0.02}$$

   $$[Cu^{+2}] = 6 \times 10^{-17} \text{ moles} \qquad\qquad Answer$$

   The results of K_{inst} calculations are not usually trustworthy beyond one significant figure.

2. In a $0.1M$ solution of $Ag(S_2O_3)_2^{-3}$, the concentration of uncomplexed Ag^+ is 1×10^{-5} molar. What is the K_{inst} of this complex?

Solution: The dissociation of the complex ion proceeds according to the equation

$$\mathrm{Ag(S_2O_3)_2^{-3} \rightleftharpoons Ag^+ + 2S_2O_3^{-2}}$$

Then,

$$K_\mathrm{inst} = \frac{[\mathrm{Ag^+}][\mathrm{S_2O_3^{-2}}]^2}{[\mathrm{Ag(S_2O_3)_2^{-3}}]}$$

Very little of the $\mathrm{Ag(S_2O_3)_2^{-3}}$ is dissociated; therefore,

$$[\mathrm{Ag(S_2O_3)_2^{-3}}] \simeq 0.1$$

We are given

$$[\mathrm{Ag^+}] = 1 \times 10^{-5}$$

Also, for each mole of silver ion produced by dissociation of the complex ion, two moles of thiosulfate ion are produced:

$$[\mathrm{S_2O_3^{-2}}] = 2 \times 10^{-5}$$

Substituting these values in the K_inst expression, we get

$$K_\mathrm{inst} = \frac{(1 \times 10^{-5})(2 \times 10^{-5})^2}{0.1}$$

$$K_\mathrm{inst} = 4 \times 10^{-14} \qquad\qquad\qquad \textit{Answer}$$

3. The accepted value of K_inst of the dithiosulfatoargentate(I) ion at 25°C is 6×10^{-14}. If a liter of $\mathrm{Na_2S_2O_3}$ solution is required to dissolve 0.01 mole of AgI, what must be the molarity of the $\mathrm{Na_2S_2O_3}$ solution?

   Solution: When 0.01 mole of AgI is dissolved, 0.01 mole of $\mathrm{I^-}$ goes into solution. The same total amount of silver will also be in solution, but most of it *is* tied up in the complex ion. The maximum amount of free silver ion that may be present is determined by the K_sp of AgI, which has the value 1.4×10^{-16}:

$$[\mathrm{I^-}] = 0.01$$

$$[\mathrm{Ag^+}] = 1.4 \times 10^{-14}$$

   Therefore,

$$[\mathrm{Ag(S_2O_3)_2^{-3}}] = 0.01 - 1.4 \times 10^{-14}$$

$$[\mathrm{Ag(S_2O_3)_2^{-3}}] \simeq 0.01$$

The complex ion equilibrium equation is

$$Ag(S_2O_3)_2^{-3} \rightleftharpoons Ag^+ + 2S_2O_3^{-2}$$

$$K_{inst} = \frac{[Ag^+][S_2O_3^{-2}]^2}{[Ag(S_2O_3)_2^{-3}]}$$

Substituting known values in the K_{inst} expression, we get

$$6 \times 10^{-14} = \frac{(1.4 \times 10^{-14})[S_2O_3^{-2}]^2}{0.01}$$

Rearranging,

$$[S_2O_3^{-2}]^2 = \frac{6 \times 10^{-16}}{1.4 \times 10^{-14}}$$

$$[S_2O_3^{-2}] = 2 \times 10^{-1} \text{ or } 0.2$$

In addition to the 0.2 mole of free $S_2O_3^{-2}$ in solution, some $S_2O_3^{-2}$ is present in the complex ion. Since there are two moles of $S_2O_3^{-2}$ in each mole of complex ion, the total amount of $S_2O_3^{-2}$ which must be present is $0.2 + 0.02$ or 0.22 mole of $S_2O_3^{-2}$.

The $Na_2S_2O_3$ solution must therefore be 0.22 molar. *Answer*

10.6 / COMPLEX IONS OF SPECIAL IMPORTANCE

Many complex ions are important in analytical work. We shall consider a few, classifying them on the basis of the ligands involved.

Ammines. Some of the easiest and most clean-cut separations used in qualitative analysis are based on the fact that some metal ions form soluble ammine complexes while others do not. An example is the separation of copper and cadmium from bismuth in Group 2. Bismuth shows no tendency to form an ammine complex, and bismuth hydroxide is very insoluble. The addition of ammonia to a solution containing bismuth ion gives a precipitate because of the increased hydroxide ion concentration from the reaction

$$NH_3 + H_2O \rightleftharpoons NH_4^+ + OH^-$$

Copper and cadmium hydroxides are also quite insoluble, and the addition of a limited amount of ammonia precipitates them:

$$Cu^{+2} + 2OH^- \rightarrow Cu(OH)_2$$

A larger amount of ammonia, however, gives the ammine complexes:

$$Cu^{+2} + 4NH_3 \rightarrow Cu(NH_3)_4^{+2}$$

Notice that, stoichiometrically, four moles of ammonia are required to complex one mole of copper ion, but only two moles are required to precipitate it. In the presence of a considerable excess of ammonia, the concentration of uncomplexed Cu^{+2} is so low that $Cu(OH)_2$ does not precipitate. Other ammine complexes we work with are those of silver, zinc, nickel, and cobalt.

Cyano complexes. The CN^- group forms some very stable complexes. $Au(CN)_2^-$ and $Ag(CN)_2^-$ are useful in metallurgy. Because the metal ion is tied up so effectively, gold and silver can be oxidized by atmospheric oxygen in the presence of cyanide solutions. The equilibrium

$$4Au + O_2 + 2H_2O \rightleftharpoons 4Au^+ + 4OH^-$$

is certainly displaced very far to the left under ordinary conditions. But the equilibrium

$$Au(CN)_2^- \rightleftharpoons Au^+ + 2CN^-$$

produces even fewer Au^+ ions. The net reaction for the cyanide process is obtained by transposing the second equation, multiplying it by 4, and adding it to the first:

$$4Au + O_2 + 2H_2O + 8CN^- \rightarrow 4Au(CN)_2^- + 4OH^-$$

One analytical separation of copper from cadmium is based on the greater stability of $Cu(CN)_3^{-2}$ over $Cd(CN)_4^{-2}$. Sulfide ion precipitates CdS from a solution containing the two ions, but $Cu(CN)_3^{-2}$ is so stable that no Cu_2S is precipitated.

Many cyano complexes are so stable that they are considered non-poisonous.

Halogen complexes. The chloride ion which is present during many of the procedures of metal analysis is often more than a casual spectator of the reactions of the metals. Tin(IV) in solution is ordinarily in the form of the $SnCl_6^{-2}$ ion. The solubilities of other metals are enhanced by the stabilities of their chloro complexes; $HgCl_4^{-2}$ and $CdCl_4^{-2}$ are examples. Sometimes this is a nuisance; a careless analyst can be embarrassed by losing silver as $AgCl_2^-$.

The effectiveness of aqua regia as a solvent is due to the complexing action of the chloride ion. Nitric acid alone is not able to oxidize Au to Au^{+3}, but if the Au^{+3} is tied up as $AuCl_4^-$ as fast as it is formed, the reaction proceeds to completion.

The usual order of stability of halogen complexes is F > Cl > Br > I. We have some very stable fluoro complexes, such as FeF_6^{-3} and AlF_6^{-3}, both of which find use in analytical work. That the order of stability is not invariable is shown by the easily formed and stable PbI_4^{-2} and HgI_4^{-2} ions.

Aquo complexes and amphoterism. The importance of the hydration of ions in the dissolving of salts is obvious. However, in some ways our knowledge of aquo complexes is less than our knowledge of other complex ions. As has been mentioned, some ions are loosely hydrated. Other ions may have both definitely coordinated water molecules and water molecules gathered around by electrostatic attraction. Unfortunately, it is difficult for us to determine how much water is actually coordinated to a particular ion. Because it is inconvenient to balance an equation containing a formula like $Cu(H_2O)_x^{+2}$, we may prefer to write $Cu(H_2O)_4^{+2}$. We can argue that this is reasonable because copper(II) shows a coordination number of 4 in other complexes and because there are 4 molecules of water grouped around the metal ion in crystalline hydrates. We should not, however, take such a formula too literally.

Because of our uncertainty of the formulas of hydrated ions and because the extra water does not usually help us understand the course of a reaction, we generally omit the water of hydration. Hydrolysis reactions constitute an exception; the hydrolysis of Al^{+3} is understandable in terms of the hydrated ion $Al(H_2O)_6^{+3}$. We write the steps of the hydrolysis as follows:

$$Al(H_2O)_6^{+3} + H_2O \rightleftharpoons Al(H_2O)_5(OH)^{+2} + H_3O^+$$

$$Al(H_2O)_5(OH)^{+2} + H_2O \rightleftharpoons Al(H_2O)_4(OH)_2^+ + H_3O^+$$

$$Al(H_2O)_4(OH)_2^+ + H_2O \rightleftharpoons \underline{Al(H_2O)_3(OH)_3} + H_3O^+$$

The underlined product of the last equation, $Al(H_2O)_3(OH)_3$ or $Al(OH)_3$, hydrated aluminum hydroxide, is *amphoteric*; that is, it dissolves in either an acid or a base. In an acid, it dissolves by the reverse of the reactions above. In a strong base, it dissolves by the following reaction:

$$Al(H_2O)_3(OH)_3 + OH^- \rightarrow Al(H_2O)_2(OH)_4^- + H_2O$$

There are many amphoteric hydroxides—$Cr(H_2O)_3(OH)_3$, $Zn(H_2O)_2(OH)_2$, and $Sn(H_2O)_2(OH)_2$, for example. The reactions for $Zn(H_2O)_2(OH)_2$ with acid and base may be written

$$Zn(H_2O)_2(OH)_2 + 2H_3O^+ \rightarrow Zn(H_2O)_4^{+2} + 2H_2O$$
$$Zn(H_2O)_2(OH)_2 + 2OH^- \rightarrow Zn(OH)_4^{-2} + 2H_2O$$

Although writing the reactions of an amphoteric hydroxide in this way emphasizes that it is a Brönsted acid and base, and points up the relationship of the reaction to hydrolysis, the water of hydration may be omitted. We write, then,

$$Zn(OH)_2 + 2H_3O^+ \rightarrow Zn^{+2} + 4H_2O$$
$$Zn(OH)_2 + 2OH^- \rightarrow Zn(OH)_4^{-2}$$

Questions and problems

1. Look up the following words or terms in an up-to-date desk dictionary such as *Webster's New World Dictionary, College Edition*. If no definition applicable to our course is listed, compose one yourself which you think would be suitable for inclusion in such a book: a. ligand; b. chelate; c. ammine; d. octahedron; e. amphoteric.

2. Write formulas of the following substances, inclosing any complex ions in brackets:
    a. Tetraamminecadmium ion
    b. Dipotassium sodium hexanitrocobaltate(III)
    c. Trithiostannate(IV) ion
    d. Tricyanocuprate(I) ion
    e. Potassium hexacyanoferrate(II)
    f. Chloropentaamminecobalt(III) chloride

3. Give systematic names for the following substances:
    a. $[Ni(NH_3)_6]^{+2}$ d. $K_2[HgI_4]$
    b. $[Ni(NH_3)_4]^{+2}$ e. $Na_2[PtCl_2(OH)_4]$
    c. $[Co(SCN)_4]^{-2}$ f. $[Fe(H_2O)_6](NO_3)_3$

4. What is the coordination number of the central ion of each of the complexes listed in Question 2? In Question 3?

5. Two different forms of the coordination compound, di-chlorodiammine platinum(II), $[Pt(NH_3)_2Cl_2]$, exist. Can you explain this if you assume a planar configuration for the complex? Would two forms of the complex be possible if it had a tetrahedral configuration?

6. Calculate the concentration of free (hydrated) Zn^{+2} ion in a $0.1M$ solution of $Zn(NH_3)_4^{+2}$.

    Answer 3×10^{-3} molar

7. Calculate the concentration of Zn^{+2} in a solution containing 0.1 mole of $Zn(NH_3)_4^{+2}$ and 0.07 mole of NH_3 per liter.

    Answer 1×10^{-6} molar

8. How many micrograms (10^{-6} gram) of Au^+ are there in a liter of 1 per cent $NaAu(CN)_2$ solution? How many gold(I) ions are present in a drop (0.05 ml) of this solution?

9. A solution containing 0.1 mole of $HgCl_4^{-2}$ and 0.2 mole of excess Cl^- per liter has been shown to have a concentration of 5×10^{-14} mole of Hg^{+2}. Calculate the K_{inst} of $HgCl_4^{-2}$.

    Answer 8.0×10^{-16}

10. A solution which is 0.5 molar with respect to $Hg(NH_3)_4^{+2}$ has been found to be 2.5×10^{-5} molar with respect to Hg^{+2}. What is its K_{inst}? Assume $[NH_3]$ is four times $[Hg^{+2}]$.

11. a. How many grams of AgCl can be dissolved by 100 ml of $3M$ NH_3 solution?   *Answer*   1.8 g
    b. How many grams of AgBr can be dissolved by 100 ml of $3M$ NH_3 solution?
    c. How many grams of AgI can be dissolved by 100 ml of $3M$ NH_3 solution? In which, if any, of these cases would you consider $3M$ NH_3 a satisfactory solvent.

12. To a solution which is $0.1M$ with respect to both Cu^{+2} and Cd^{+2}, enough KCN is added to form cyano complexes with most of the metal ions present and in addition make the solution 0.15 molar with excess CN^-. Cadmium forms the complex $Cd(CN)_4^{-2}$; copper is reduced by the cyanide to copper(I) so that the $Cu(CN)_3^{-2}$ complex is formed.
    a. What is the concentration of uncomplexed Cd^{+2} remaining in the solution?

b. What concentration of sulfide ion would be required to precipitate CdS from this solution?

c. What concentration of uncomplexed Cu^+ would be present in the solution?

d. What concentration of sulfide ion would be required to precipitate Cu_2S?

e. Aside from the well-known poisonous nature of the cyanide ion, would this be a satisfactory method of separating copper from cadmium in analysis?

part **TWO**

THE METALS

Metals and Metallurgy

11

The periodic table is largely populated with metals. There are a score or so of *non-metals* found in the upper right of the usual form of the table, and a few borderline cases called *metalloids*. The rest of the elements—65 of the 88 that occur in nature and all but one of the 14 elements so far announced as artificially made—are *metals*. The metals are so important to man that use of them is considered the most obvious mark distinguishing civilized man from savages. The steps of civilization have progressed (upward, we like to think) through the Bronze Age and the Iron Age to our modern technological culture based on the use of many metals and alloys.

11.1 / THE NATURE OF METALS

If you were to inspect samples of various chemical elements, such as aluminum, sulfur, oxygen, arsenic, and chromium, you would in most cases have no difficulty in classifying them as metallic or non-metallic. The most characteristic properties of metals are well known: They are excellent conductors of heat and electricity. They are malleable and ductile; most are heavy, have high melting points, and are hard and strong. They have a characteristic metallic luster; that is, they look like metals. Chemically, metals react by giving up electrons; therefore, they are reducing agents.

The accepted picture of the metallic crystal shown in Figure 11.1 explains these various metallic traits. The crystal is held

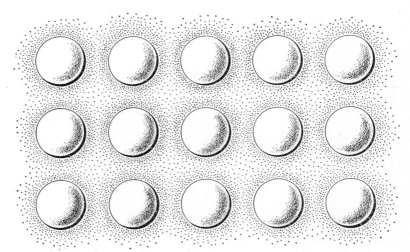

FIGURE 11.1 / REPRESENTATION OF A METALLIC CRYSTAL
A framework of positive ions pervaded by valence electrons.

together by attraction between the positive ions of the metal and
the valence electrons. Comparison of the metallic crystal and
the crystal of a salt (Figure 2.5, page 10) is instructive. The
salt crystal is also made up of positive and negative particles,
the ions, giving a rigid, stable structure. In the metallic crystal
the negative ions are replaced by electrons, which are much more
mobile. In fact, the electrons are thought to pervade the framework of positive ions much like a gas. When a potential difference is applied to a metal crystal the electrons flow easily to
the positive pole. At higher temperatures, the thermal agitation
of the positive ions impedes their flow, accounting for the greater
electrical resistance of metals at high temperatures. At temperatures near absolute zero, the movement of the metal ions
is so slight that corridors are left open for the electrons to flow
along. This fact explains the phenomenon of *superconductivity*
or almost complete lack of electrical resistance exhibited by some
metals at very low temperature. When external forces deform
the crystals, the electrons adjust easily to the new positions of
the ions. This accounts for the malleability and ductility of
metals. Their luster and opacity can be explained by the assump-
tion that the energy needed to disturb the valence electrons is
about the same as the energy of visible light.

We expect metals to react by giving up their valence electrons to non-metals, producing positive and negative ions; for example,

$$Ca: + Cl_2 \rightarrow Ca^{+2} + 2Cl^-$$

As has been mentioned, however, some compounds between metals and non-metals, such as $HgCl_2$ and $AlCl_3$, are essentially covalent. In general, electrons are given up most readily by those metals having large atoms with few valence electrons. For metals with slight attraction for electrons, compounds of the type M—O—H ionize to M^+ and OH^- rather than give up a proton; therefore hydroxides of the more active metals react as bases and not as acids.

11.2 / EXTRACTIVE METALLURGY

Any naturally occurring substance of reasonably definite chemical composition is called a *mineral*. An *ore* is a mineral from which a metal can be profitably extracted. Whether a particular mineral deposit can be a profitable source of a metal depends, of course, on many variables: the nature of the mineral, its richness in the desired metal, the ease with which the metal may be obtained from it, the size and location of the deposit, the availability of the metal from other sources, the price of the metal and the demand for it. An iron mineral would not be considered an ore unless there was a large supply of it, accessible, and rich in iron, while a low-grade ore of gold or uranium is eagerly sought in the arctic wasteland or deepest jungle.

The metal of an ore may be in various chemical combinations. The least active metals usually occur in the native state. Some of the most useful metals occur as oxides, while sulfide ores are the principal sources of a great many metals. A listing of the ways in which metals occur follows, with the most important ore of each metal in italics.

Native: *Gold, platinum*, silver, copper, bismuth, mercury
Oxide: *Iron, aluminum, manganese, chromium, tin, titanium,* copper
Carbonate: *Calcium, strontium,* magnesium, lead, zinc, iron, copper

Sulfide: *Copper, lead, zinc, nickel, cobalt, mercury, bismuth, antimony, cadmium, silver,* iron

Halide: *Sodium, potassium, magnesium, aluminum,* silver, copper

Silicate: *Beryllium, lithium,* zinc, nickel, copper

Sulfate: *Barium,* lead, copper

Misc. $AuTe_2$, $CaWO_4$, $NaNO_3$, $KUO_2VO_4 \cdot H_2O$, $NiSb$, etc.

Most deposits of high-grade ores have long since been mined, and each year the metal industries must rely more and more on low-grade ores which are mixed with relatively large amounts of impurities. At the same time, modern technological advances call for metals in purer and purer form. As a result, most metallurgical processes show three distinct steps: concentration of the ore, reduction, and refining.

Concentration to separate the valuable ore from the *gangue*, as the earthy impurities are called, may be done by a variety of methods, such as washing, sink-and-float, magnetic separation, flotation, and chemical solution.

Washing depends on the fact that most ores are heavier than ordinary dirt and rocks, so that the gangue can be washed away by a current of water while the ore settles out. The principle is the same as that used by the oldtime prospector in panning for gold. In the *sink-and-float* method the separation is accom-

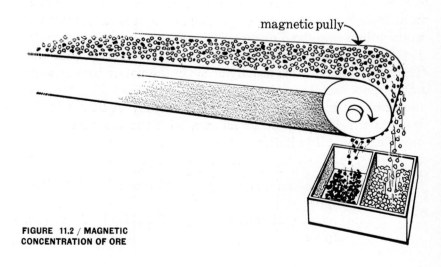

magnetic pully

FIGURE 11.2 / MAGNETIC CONCENTRATION OF ORE

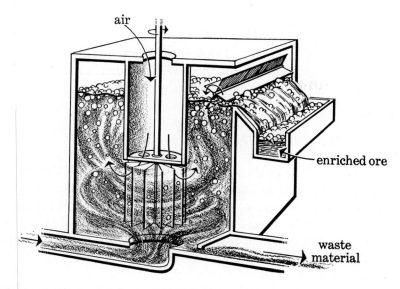

air

enriched ore

waste
material

FIGURE 11.3 / CONCENTRATION OF A LOW-GRADE ORE BY FLOTATION

plished by a liquid intermediate in density between ore and gangue.

Flotation is the most widely used of all concentration processes. The finely ground crude ore is dumped into a tank of water along with a suitable oil which wets the ore but not its gangue. When the mixture is stirred thoroughly and air is forced through it, the air bubbles adhere to the oil, and the oil in turn, adheres to the ore particles. The bubbles carry oil and ore to the surface, leaving the dirt behind. By use of appropriate combinations of flotation agents, it is even possible to separate two or more valuable minerals one at a time from a complex ore by differential flotation. The flotation process is particularly successful in concentrating low-grade sulfide ores.

Concentration is usually accompanied by physical methods of "ore dressing," such as crushing, grinding, or briquetting.

Reduction is necessary for all except native metal ores. Commonly used reducing agents include coke, hydrogen, and active metals like sodium, aluminum, and magnesium. Electrolytic reduction may be used on a molten salt or on a salt dissolved in water or other solvent. The oxide-sulfide type of reaction exemplified in the reduction of copper, page 155, is also important.

Refining is done by many methods, three of which are more widely used than others: electrorefining, oxidation of active impurities by air, and chemical solution of impurities. Examples of these and other methods will be given in the discussions of metals in the following chapters.

11.3 / ADAPTIVE METALLURGY

The science that deals with the problems of converting metals into useful forms is called *adaptive metallurgy*. In the main, adaptive metallurgy is concerned with the physical properties of metals; extractive metallurgy, with their chemical properties.

One problem of adaptive metallurgy is that of forming metals into useful shapes. Some of the methods used are forging, rolling into sheets, drawing into wires, extruding, welding, electrodepositing, casting, and machining. Although it is not within the province of this book to discuss these or other methods of shaping metals, the subject is interesting and important. Better students might profitably pursue it further in textbooks or in an encyclopedia.

A most important aspect of adaptive metallurgy is the production and study of *alloys*. Metals in very pure form have only a few uses, mainly electrical. In most of their familiar applications, we are really dealing with alloys—combinations of two or more metals. Alloys may sometimes show properties intermediate between those of their components, but often they exhibit some completely different properties, and a slight change in the composition of an alloy may decidedly alter its nature. For example, one per cent of beryllium makes copper as strong and hard as steel, while one per cent of antimony makes it a poor conductor of electricity. A little copper in aluminum increases its strength but also makes it more easily corroded. A mere fraction of a per cent of niobium added to some nickel-chromium stainless steels permits them to be welded without losing their rust resistance.

Alloys are of different types: mixtures, solutions, and compounds. Cadmium and bismuth are insoluble in one another in the solid states, and an alloy formed of them is only a mixture of crystals. Many metals are completely soluble in one another either as liquid or solid; this is true of gold-silver alloys and of copper-manganese alloys. Other alloys are true compounds, though with unusual formulas like Cu_3Sn, $Cu_{31}Sn_8$, and Cu_5Sn. Many alloys, of course, are combinations of these types. One common bronze is a mixture of two phases: one of them is a saturated solution of the compound Cu_3Sn in copper, and the other is excess Cu_3Sn.

Heat treatment of metals and alloys is important. The metal is heated to a certain temperature and then cooled slowly—*annealed*—or cooled quickly—*quenched*. Heat treatment governs the size of the crystals in a metal. It is also used to preserve at room temperature some allotropic form of a metal or some intermetallic compound ordinarily stable only at high temperature.

Surface treatment limits modifications of a metal to a thin surface layer. An alloy may be made by heating the metal in contact with the alloying element which diffuses only a short distance into the metal. Probably the earliest method of making steel was by heating iron in contact with charcoal, and similar methods of case-hardening iron with carbon and other alloying elements are much used today. Heat treatment may also be restricted to a surface layer. For example, gear teeth may be hardened by quickly heating and chilling them while the body of the gear is protected from heat to keep it soft and tough.

Questions and problems

1. Classify the following elements as metal, non-metal, or metalloid: Al, As, At, Bi, Fr, Ga, Kr, Pb, Te, U. Then look up their positions in the periodic table. Finally, look up their electrical conductivities in a handbook.

2. Define the following terms in your own words:
   a. Ore
   b. Mineral
   c. Superconductivity
   d. Gangue
   e. Quenching

3. How do you account for the fact that silver is so malleable while sulfur and sodium chloride are brittle?

4. List three different methods used to concentrate ores and explain how one of them works.

5. What method of reduction would you recommend for each of the following ores: $NaCl$, SnO_2, Au, PbS?

6. Name an alloy that is a solid solution of two metals; one that is a mixture of two metals insoluble in one another; one that is an intermetallic compound.

The Metals of Group 1 of the Qualitative Scheme: Silver, Mercury, and Lead

12

The metals considered in this chapter have little in common except that they have insoluble chloride salts: $AgCl$, Hg_2Cl_2, and $PbCl_2$. Two of these metals are also found in Group 2: mercury because its other chloride, $HgCl_2$, does not precipitate at this point, and lead because $PbCl_2$ is incompletely precipitated in Group 1.

12.1 / SILVER

Silver is found in Group Ib of the periodic table along with copper and gold. As a group, these metals are often called the coinage metals. Although none of them is very abundant in the earth's crust, they were the first metals used by man. We can attribute their early use to their striking appearance, their simple metallurgies, and their occurrence in concentrated deposits.

Metallurgy. Besides native silver, other important ores are argentite, Ag_2S, and horn silver, $AgCl$. It is an oddity that most silver does not come from silver mines but from mines for other metals. In the United States in recent years about 70 per cent of the silver has been obtained from the refining of other metals, mainly Cu, Pb, and Zn. The silver is obtained as a by-product in electrorefining, and, in the case of lead, also by the Parkes process. The latter is an extraction process. Molten lead and molten zinc are practically insoluble in one another; and, at temperatures slightly above the melting point of these metals, silver is about 3000 times as soluble in zinc as in lead. Hence, when a small amount of zinc is stirred into a vat of molten lead and allowed to come to the top, it brings nearly all the silver with it. The silver is easily recovered by burning and volatilizing the zinc.

Low-grade silver ores are sometimes mined and concentrated by a cyanide process like that used in gold mining. It is described in Chapter 18, on page 204.

Production. In 1957, a typical year, the production of silver in the United States was over 38 million troy ounces, while the world production was about 230 million ounces, or 7850 tons.* Mexico is the largest producer, the United States second, and Canada third. Besides its own production, the United States consumes about 60 million ounces of imported silver each year.

Properties. Silver is a soft metal of brilliant white luster. It is the best conductor of heat and electricity known and, next to gold, the most malleable and ductile metal. The most familiar chemical reactions of silver are its solution in nitric acid and its tarnishing by hydrogen sulfide.

Uses of the metal. For coinage and jewelry, silver is hardened by alloying with copper. U.S. coinage contains 90 per cent Ag and 10 per cent Cu. Traditionally, sterling is 7.5 per cent copper but most present-day "sterling" ware is a more durable and cheaper material, containing up to 20 per cent copper. Much silver is also used in electrical applications and in mirrors.

Compounds. $AgNO_3$ is an important reagent in chemistry and is useful in medicine as a germicide and caustic. Most photographic processes depend on the light sensitivity of the silver halides, particularly AgBr.

---

*Production figures in this book are generally based on the best available estimates for 1959 and 1960, except for those metals for which production in those years was not typical and those for which recent statistics have not been released.

Reactions of Ag. There are only a few soluble simple compounds of silver, notably the fluoride and nitrate, but the soluble complexes with NH_3, CN^-, and $S_2O_3^{-2}$ are also important. The confirmatory test for silver depends on dissolving AgCl in ammonia solution and reprecipitating the AgCl when the ammonia complex is destroyed by nitric acid:

$$AgCl + 2NH_3 \rightarrow Ag(NH_3)_2^+ + Cl^-$$
$$Ag(NH_3)_2^+ + 2H_3O^+ + Cl^- \rightarrow \underline{AgCl} + 2NH_4^+ + 2H_2O$$

The complexing reaction with $S_2O_3^{-2}$ is used in photographic "fixing" to remove AgBr from those portions of the film that were not affected by light:

$$AgBr + 2S_2O_3^{-2} \rightarrow Ag(S_2O_3)_2^{-3} + Br^-$$

The third important complex, $Ag(CN)_2^-$, is used in silver-plating baths and in the cyanide mining process.

12.2 / MERCURY

Mercury is found in Group IIb of the periodic table, along with zinc and cadmium. Mercury is quite different from the other two, most obviously in three respects: it is a liquid at ordinary temperature; it is quite inert chemically; and it has an oxidation state of 1 as well as the expected state of 2.

The electron configuration of mercury is 2, 8, 18, 32, 18, 2. In forming the mercury(II) ion, mercury gives up the two electrons of the outer shell:

$$Hg: \rightarrow Hg^{+2} + 2e^-$$

The mercury(I) ion is diatomic with the two atoms held together by an electron pair:

$$2Hg: \rightarrow [Hg:Hg]^{+2} + 2e^-$$

Production and metallurgy. The only important ore of mercury is cinnabar, HgS. The metallurgy is basically simple: the ore is decomposed by roasting and the mercury distilled off.

$$HgS + O_2 \xrightarrow{\Delta} Hg\uparrow + SO_2\uparrow$$

The world production of mercury is close to 9000 tons yearly. Italy and Spain are the principal producers of mercury, with the

United States usually in third place. California is the chief mercury-producing state.

Properties. Mercury, with a melting point of −38.9°C and a boiling point of 356.9°C is a liquid at all ordinary temperatures. Its coefficient of expansion is quite constant throughout its liquid range. It is the heaviest liquid, having a density of 13.546 g/cm³, and, as liquids go, it is non-volatile and an excellent conductor of electricity. It dissolves most metals, but not iron, platinum, and a few others. Mercury is not very reactive chemically, but can be dissolved in oxidizing acids like nitric and hot concentrated sulfuric.

Uses. Mercury has many uses, most of which require only small amounts of the metal. It is used for electric switches, thermometers, barometers, ultraviolet and fluorescent lamps, vacuum pumps, and many other devices. Alloys of mercury are called *amalgams.* Dental amalgam contains silver with small amounts of other metals. Sodium amalgam is produced in one type of cell for electrolysis of NaCl solution, using mercury as the cathode. It may be decomposed with water to give NaOH and H₂, or it may be used as a reducing agent, more convenient to handle and more moderate in its reactions than sodium alone.

Compounds. The most familiar compounds are white insoluble Hg_2Cl_2, called calomel, and soluble, covalent $HgCl_2$, called bichloride of mercury or corrosive sublimate. The latter name derives from its preparation by sublimation from a heated mixture of mercury(II) sulfate and sodium chloride:

$$HgSO_4 + 2NaCl \rightarrow HgCl_2 \uparrow + Na_2SO_4$$

A dilute solution of $HgCl_2$ is a powerful germicide. Other compounds of mercury are used as fungicides and weed-killers. Mercury compounds were formerly much used in medicine. Calomel, particularly, was administered in doses that horrify modern physicians. Since mercury is a cumulative poison, its use is dangerous. Even metallic mercury should be handled only in a well-ventilated room.

Reactions, mercury(I). There are only a few soluble compounds of Hg_2^{+2}, the nitrate being most common. Hg_2^{+2} does not appear to form any complex ions. The confirmatory test for mercury in Group 1 is a disproportionation or auto-oxidation-reduction reaction:

$$Hg_2Cl_2 + 2NH_3 \rightarrow \underline{Hg} + \underline{HgNH_2Cl} + NH_4^+ + Cl^-$$

The black precipitate is a mixture of black, finely divided mercury and white mercury(II) amidochloride.

Reactions, mercury(II). Mercury(II) forms complex ions with many different complexing groups. Aqua regia is an especially good solvent for mercury metal because the Hg^{+2} ion produced is tied up in the $HgCl_4^{-2}$ complex:

$$3Hg + 8H_3O^+ + 2NO_3^- + 12Cl^- \rightarrow 3HgCl_4^{-2} + 12H_2O + 2NO$$

HgS dissolves partially in $6M$ KOH solution if S^{-2} is available, so some mercury goes into Subgroup 2B:

$$HgS + S^{-2} \rightarrow HgS_2^{-2}$$

Also, insoluble mercury(II) iodide dissolves in a solution containing excess iodide ions:

$$HgI_2 + 2I^- \rightarrow HgI_4^{-2}$$

The HgI_4^{-2} ion is present in Nessler's reagent, used as an extremely sensitive test for ammonia.

The confirmatory test for mercury(II) depends on the reduction of $HgCl_2$ by tin(II) ion, giving white, insoluble Hg_2Cl_2. If excess tin(II) is present, the reduction proceeds further to black Hg:

$$2HgCl_2 + Sn^{+2} + 4Cl^- \rightarrow \underline{Hg_2Cl_2} + SnCl_6^{-2}$$
$$Hg_2Cl_2 + Sn^{+2} + 4Cl^- \rightarrow \underline{2Hg} + SnCl_6^{-2}$$

This reaction is so characteristic that it is also used as the confirmatory test for tin.

12.3 / LEAD

Lead, the heaviest and most metallic element of Group IVa of the periodic table, has the electron configuration 2, 8, 18, 32, 18, 4. It forms two principal series of compounds: those with oxidation state +2 which are largely ionic, and those with oxidation state +4 which are covalent.

Occurrence. Although lead is not one of the most plentiful elements in nature, concentrated ore deposits are found in many parts of the world, and the metallurgy is not difficult. It was one of the metals known in ancient times; the Romans, especially, were highly skilled lead workers. Our word "plumber," from the Latin *plumbum* for lead, tells us one of their uses for the metal.

Galena, PbS, is the most important ore of lead. Most present-day ores are so lean they must be concentrated by flotation. Some deposits also contain ZnS, and it is possible to separate the two ores by use of suitable flotation agents. The concentrated galena is roasted:

$$2PbS + 3O_2 \xrightarrow{\Delta} 2PbO + 2SO_2$$

The lead oxide is mixed with coke and more galena and smelted in a blast furnace. Two types of reduction reaction probably occur: carbon reduction and oxide-sulfide reduction:

$$PbO + C \rightarrow Pb + CO \uparrow$$
$$2PbO + PbS \rightarrow 3Pb + SO_2 \uparrow$$

The lead may be refined either electrolytically or by the Parkes process. It should be noted that lead-refining is a money-making operation, since the by-products, such as silver, are valuable. The United States produces about 350,000 of the world's total of 2,500,000 tons each year, besides importing another half million tons. The U.S.S.R., Mexico, and Canada are other large producers.

Properties. The soft, gray sheen of freshly cut lead is familiar; so is the darker color of the tarnished metal. It is low-melting (327°C), very soft, malleable, but not very ductile since it has little tensile strength. Its density of 11.3 g/cm^3 makes it the heaviest cheap substance. Chemically, lead is regarded as an inert metal, though it is above hydrogen in activity. The inertness is partly due to the insolubility of many of its compounds. In sulfuric acid, for example, it is covered with a protective coating of PbSO$_4$; when it is dipped in HCl solution, insoluble

$PbCl_2$ protects it from deep attack. Nitric and acetic acids dissolve it because their lead salts are soluble. The anions present in most natural waters combine with lead to form an insoluble protective coating. In soft-water areas of the country, however, cases of chronic lead poisoning have been caused by the use of lead plumbing.

Uses of the metal. The largest use of lead is for storage battery plates. It is also used for cable sheathing, lead shot, and many other purposes that depend on its chemical inertness, heaviness, and ease of fabrication. For most uses it must be hardened by alloying it with another metal—usually antimony. Some well-known lead alloys are solder, type metal, and Babbitt metal.

Compounds. Three of the oxides of lead are useful articles of commerce. Litharge, PbO, is used in optical glass and in glazes for pottery, in rubber goods, and in paints. Red lead, Pb_3O_4, is a mixed oxide. Its formula might be written $2PbO \cdot PbO_2$. It is used especially in rust-preventing paints for priming structural steel. Lead dioxide, PbO_2, is an excellent oxidizing agent. Its greatest use is in storage batteries.

Several lead compounds are valuable ingredients of paints. White lead is the basic carbonate, approximately $(PbCO_3)_2 \cdot Pb(OH)_2$. It is used as a paint body; that is, it supplies opacity or covering power. Lead chromate, which we use as the confirmatory precipitate for lead, is also used as a pigment under the name chrome yellow.

Lead tetraethyl, an anti-knock additive for gasoline, is made by the action of a lead-sodium alloy on ethyl chloride:

$$Pb \cdot 4Na + 4C_2H_5Cl \rightarrow Pb(C_2H_5)_4 + 4NaCl$$

Reactions of Pb. The insoluble lead compounds of interest in qualitative analysis are the chloride, sulfide, sulfate, and chromate. The chloride is soluble in hot water or in excess Cl^-:

$$PbCl_2 + 2Cl^- \rightarrow PbCl_4^{-2}$$

Lead acetate is soluble but does not give many lead ions in solution. The lead is present in species like $Pb(C_2H_3O_2)_2$, $PbC_2H_3O_2^+$, and $Pb(C_2H_3O_2)_3^-$. The use of lead acetate in the confirmatory test for lead is discussed in the note after Procedure 2.4, page 241.

Questions and problems

1. Write the equation for the dissolving of native silver in a solution of sodium cyanide. Oxygen from the air also enters the reaction.

2. If you are given a piece of a chain and asked to determine whether it is sterling silver or an imitation, how would you determine qualitatively that it was sterling? If you had access to the ordinary reagents of qualitative analysis and an analytical balance, could you determine its composition quantitatively?

3. In photography, what is meant by the terms "exposure," "negative," and "fixing."

4. Uncle Oscar, a survivor of the Alaska gold rush, likes to tell about the winters when the mercury went to 60° below. Do you have any remarks to make about Uncle Oscar's veracity?

5. Write net ionic equations for the following reactions:
   a. The dissolving of mercury metal in nitric acid
   b. The dissolving of mercury metal in aqua regia
   c. The precipitation of mercury metal from a solution of mercury(II) nitrate by metallic copper
   d. The roasting of cinnabar in a current of air
   e. The roasting of galena in a current of air
   f. The precipitation of lead acetate solution by potassium chromate solution.

6. Give systematic names for the following substances:
   a. $HgCl_4^{-2}$
   b. $Pb(C_2H_3O_2)_3^-$
   c. AgF_2
   d. $HgNH_2Br$
   e. Pb_2O_3 (consider it to be $PbO \cdot PbO_2$)

7. Define:
   a. Dental amalgam
   b. Sterling
   c. White lead
   d. Calomel

8. How many pounds of white lead can be made from a ton of lead?

The Metals of Subgroup 2B:
Tin, Arsenic, and Antimony

13

Subgroup 2B contains the amphoteric elements of Group 2: arsenic, antimony, tin and mercury(II). Mercury was discussed in the preceding chapter since the mercury(I) ion was precipitated in Group 1; the remaining elements of the subgroup are considered in this chapter.

13.1 / TIN

Tin, with electron configuration 2, 8, 18, 18, 4, is immediately above lead in the periodic table. Tin is less metallic than lead; its covalent oxidation state 4 is about as important as its divalent state, while with lead the largely ionic +2 state is much more important and more common. The greater amphoterism of tin is another noteworthy difference between the two metals.

Occurrence. There is only one important tin ore, SnO_2, cassiterite. Only low-grade ores are available, chiefly in the countries of southeast Asia and the East Indies: Malaya, Indonesia, Thailand, etc. Bolivia is also an important producer. In ancient times, the peninsula of Cornwall in Great Britain provided tin. Daring Phoenician and Greek sailors ventured out into the Atlantic to the "Tin Isles," as Britain was called, to bring back the tin needed to convert soft copper to sturdy bronze. Cornish tin is only of historical interest, however. The mines are virtually exhausted, and production there was never on the scale needed for our modern tin-can economy. The United States, using about a third of the world's tin, produces none, though we have a few ore deposits, principally in Alaska. The total production of tin, including estimates for Russia and China, is a little under 200,000 tons annually.

Metallurgy. Since cassiterite is heavy, with a specific gravity about 7, the ore is easily concentrated by washing. It is then reduced with carbon:

$$SnO_2 + 2C \rightarrow Sn + 2CO$$

Electrolytic refining may be employed. Some very old methods of refining are also successfully used: air oxidation of impurities, and *liquation*, or heating the crude metal on an inclined hearth so the low-melting tin flows away from the impurities.

Properties. Tin is familiar as a very soft, malleable, silvery white metal. Ordinary tin is only one of several allotropic forms of the solid:

$$\underset{\text{(gray tin)}}{Sn_\alpha} \overset{13.2°}{\rightleftharpoons} \underset{\substack{\text{(white or}\\\text{ordinary tin)}}}{Sn_\beta} \overset{161°}{\rightleftharpoons} \underset{\text{(brittle tin)}}{Sn_\gamma} \overset{231.8}{\rightleftharpoons} \text{liquid Sn}$$

The temperatures 13.2° and 161° are called *transition temperatures*. Gray tin is a powder which has a diamond-type rather than a metallic crystal. It is formed very slowly at the transition temperature, but at temperatures as low as −50°C, tin objects are transformed into a crumbly powder in a few days. This phenomenon is often called *tin disease*.

Chemically, tin is particularly resistant to atmospheric oxidation. It dissolves slowly in acids like HCl; because of its amphoteric nature, it also dissolves in strong alkalies like NaOH. Some strong oxidizing agents give tin(IV) compounds. Typical reactions of the metal are

(With hydrochloric acid solution)
$$Sn + 2H_3O^+ \rightarrow Sn^{+2} + H_2 + 2H_2O$$

(With sodium hydroxide solution)
$$Sn + OH^- + 2H_2O \rightarrow Sn(OH)_3^- + H_2$$

(With concentrated nitric acid)
$$3Sn + 4H_3O^+ + 4NO_3^- \rightarrow 3SnO_2 + 6H_2O + 4NO$$

(With chlorine)
$$Sn + 2Cl_2 \rightarrow SnCl_4$$

Uses of the metal. About 60 per cent of the tin used in the United States is for tin-plated steel, mostly for food containers— tin cans. The tin coating is usually applied by electrolytic methods, but some hot-dip plate is still used. The so-called tin roofing material is *terne plate*, sheet steel coated with a lead-tin alloy. Terne plate is also used for gasoline tanks, ventilating ducts in chemistry laboratories, and the like. Representative compositions of some tin alloys are given in Table 13.1. Babbitt is typical of those bearing metals in which the principal metal is tin. Britannia metal is a modern pewter; some old-time pewters contained lead, and their use as food containers must have caused many cases of lead poisoning.

TABLE 13.1 / ALLOYS OF TIN

Babbitt	Sn 89, Sb 7.3, Cu 3.7
Britannia metal	Sn 93, Sb 6, Cu 1
Bell metal bronze	Cu 78, Sn 22
Solder	Sn 50, Pb 50
Christmas tinsel	Sn 60, Pb 40

Solder is a low-melting alloy used for joining metal parts; ordinary solders are lead-tin alloys. Figure 13.1 is a melting point diagram for lead-tin compositions. Lead with a little dissolved tin has a lower melting point than pure lead, and tin with a little dissolved lead has a lower melting point than pure tin. The lowest melting composition, containing 63 per cent tin and 37 per cent lead is called the *eutectic composition*; its melting point of 181° is called the *eutectic point*. If molten lead or molten tin is cooled, it freezes sharply at the freezing point of the metal. Likewise, if an alloy of the eutectic composition is heated till it is liquid (point A on the diagram) and then cooled, it remains liquid until the temperature drops to 181°. Then it freezes sharply to homogeneous crystals of the eutectic composition. An 80 tin-20 lead alloy behaves differently. If it is cooled from point C on the diagram, solidification begins when point D is reached, but tin alone freezes out. The remaining liquid is richer in lead. As tin crystallizes out, the composition of the remaining liquid at any temperature is represented by the curve BD. When the temperature is reduced to the eutectic point, the composition of the liquid corresponds to the eutectic composition, so the rest of the liquid freezes sharply at this point. Depending on the requirements of a particular solder, many compositions may be used. Plumber's solder is 67 Pb and 37 Sn; it sets gradually, permitting the plumber to "wipe" the joint. Half-and-half solder sets quickly; it is used in automatic soldering devices; the extra tin also makes it adhere well to many metals. Other metals may be added, silver for instance, to increase the hardness and electrical conductivity, or bismuth, to lower the melting point.

A diagram similar to that in Figure 13.1 could be drawn to represent the melting points of many other solutions, nonmetallic as well as metallic.

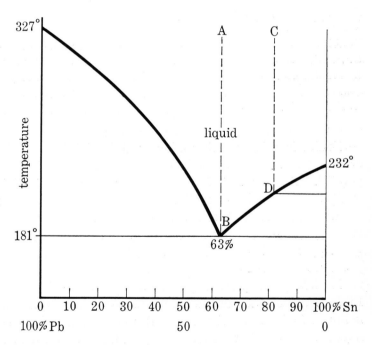

FIGURE 13.1 / MELTING POINTS OF LEAD-TIN COMPOSITIONS

Compounds. The most important tin(II) compound is the chloride which is familiar as the dihydrate, $SnCl_2 \cdot 2H_2O$, known in industry as "tin crystals." It is a valuable reducing agent, not only in qualitative analysis but in other phases of chemistry, both inorganic and organic. It is also used in the dyeing industry as a *mordant* to fasten a dye to cloth. The cloth is soaked in a solution of the salt which is then hydrolyzed, precipitating $Sn(OH)_2$ in the fibers. Many dyes which do not adhere well to cloth alone can be adsorbed and made fast by the hydroxide. Mordants are less used than formerly, since chemists have developed many fine dyes that do not require them.

$SnCl_4$ is probably the best known tin(IV) compound. It is a covalent liquid that hydrolyzes in water to precipitate the hydrated oxide

$$SnCl_4 + 2H_2O \rightarrow 4HCl + SnO_2 \text{ (hydrated)}$$

but in hydrochloric acid solutions, it dissolves as the hexachlorostannate ion $SnCl_6^{-2}$. The salt, $(NH_4)_2SnCl_6$, was formerly called *pink salt* because it was used as a mordant for alizarin, a red dye.

Hydrated SnO_2, which is produced in various reactions, is soluble in acids and bases, but when dehydrated by heat it becomes very inert. The anhydrous form imparts whiteness to glass and ceramic ware. SnS_2 is a yellow pigment called mosaic gold.

Organic tin compounds are the subject of much current research activity. Some of them are valuable catalysts; others can be used to make rubber-like plastics.

Reactions. The tin(II) state is the more stable in acid solutions, as shown by the equation

$$Sn + SnCl_6^{-2} \rightarrow 2Sn^{+2} + 6Cl^-$$

On the other hand, in basic solutions tin(IV) is more stable, so stannite solutions disproportionate:

$$2Sn(OH)_3^- \rightarrow Sn + Sn(OH)_6^{-2}$$

SnS_2 precipitates more readily in Group 2 than does SnS, and dissolves more completely in $3M$ KOH solution in the subgroup separation. For this reason, tin is oxidized to the higher state by H_2O_2 before beginning Group 2 analysis.

SnS_2 is not easily precipitated from solutions containing considerable amounts of oxalate ion because of the stability of the $Sn(C_2O_4)_3^{-2}$ complex ion.

The confirmatory test depends on the reducing action of Sn^{+2} ion. Tin is first reduced to the divalent state with iron or other active metal; the Sn^{+2} solution is then used to reduce

$HgCl_2$, giving a characteristic opalescent, white precipitate of Hg_2Cl_2. If sufficient tin is present, this is further reduced to black metallic mercury. The same reactions are used as the confirmatory test for mercury in Group 2 (see page 133).

13.2 / ARSENIC

Group V of the periodic table gives an especially good illustration of some tendencies that are observed also in neighboring groups: the first two elements, nitrogen and phosphorus, are non-metals; the next, arsenic, is also mainly non-metallic, although it shows enough metallic properties that we find it convenient to include it in cation analysis; antimony is a metalloid, perhaps more metallic than not; and bismuth is a fairly typical metal. Nitrogen exhibits oxidation states ranging from -3 to $+5$, with $+5$ being the most important positive oxidation state; as we go down in the group, we find increasing importance and stability of the $+3$ state until for bismuth it is the only important state. As we should expect, the hydroxides also become less acidic, and bismuth shows scarcely any amphoteric tendencies; so far as we can see, Bi_2S_3 does not dissolve at all in the approximately $2M$ KOH solution used to separate Group 2 into its subgroups in our analytical scheme.

Table 13.2 summarizes some of the similarities and differences of arsenic, antimony, and bismuth.

TABLE 13.2 / SOME PROPERTIES OF ARSENIC, ANTIMONY, AND BISMUTH

	Arsenic	Antimony	Bismuth
Electron configuration	2,8,18,5	2,8,18,18,5	2,8,18,32,18,5
Atomic weight	74.91	121.76	209.00
Density, g/cm^3	3.9 (y)	5.3 (y)	
	5.72 (m)	6.58 (m)	9.8
Melting point	814° (36 atm)	630°	271°
Boiling point	615° (sublimes)	1380°	1560°
Electrical conductivity (Ag = 100)	4 (m)	4 (m)	1.4
Melting point of MCl_3	$-13°$	73°	230°

(y) refers to the yellow allotropic form of arsenic or antimony
(m) refers to the metallic allotrope

Both arsenic and antimony, you will notice, besides their metallic allotropes, have allotropic modifications corresponding to white phosphorus, which do not display the metallic properties of luster, electrical conductivity, and so on. Bismuth exists only in a metallic variety. The behavior of the trichlorides is significant. $AsCl_3$ is typically covalent: it is low-melting, a non-conductor of electricity, and its water solution contains no arsenic cation. $BiCl_3$ is comparatively salt-like: in the molten state it is a good conductor of electricity; its water solution contains bismuth cations, etc. $SbCl_3$ is, of course, intermediate.

Occurrence of arsenic. Arsenic is found in many forms in nature. The red mineral As_4S_4, called realgar, and the yellow As_4S_6, called orpiment (from the Latin *aurum pigmentum* or golden pigment), have been used as pigments for thousands of years, though they are less popular now than formerly. There are many naturally occurring arsenides and mixed arsenides and sulfides; for example, arsenopyrite, $FeAsS$. Arsenic is seldom mined for itself, as embarrassingly large quantities are available from the treatment of copper and lead ores. (A single copper-silver-gold mine in Sweden could supply all the world's arsenic, but other nations have their own problems of excess production. Confronted with huge quantities of this poisonous by-product, the Swedes have even encased their surplus arsenic in cement and dumped it in the ocean, and have stored hundreds of thousands of tons in concrete bins.)

Elementary arsenic. By-product arsenic is recovered as As_4O_6, which sublimes off during roasting operations. Carbon reduction gives the free element:

$$As_4O_6 + 6C \rightarrow As_4 \uparrow + 6CO \uparrow$$

The metallic allotrope is the familiar, stable form. In appearance and properties it is quite metallic—silvery gray, brittle, rather heavy, not very hard, and a fair conductor of electricity. The total American consumption of the free element seldom exceeds 100 tons a year as it is used only in small amounts in a few alloys. Lead shot is made with about 0.2 per cent arsenic, which helps the molten lead assume a spherical shape and hardens the finished shot. A little arsenic added to copper alloys makes them easier to cast.

Compounds. By far the most important compound is "white arsenic," As_4O_6, often called arsenic trioxide from its empirical formula of As_2O_3. Because of its low sublimation point of 193°C, it is easily recovered from ores that contain arsenic and is easily purified by redistillation. All other arsenic compounds are prepared from it. It is slightly soluble in water but much more soluble in alkaline solutions as it is an acid anhydride. In minute doses it has been used in medicine as a stimulant. Because it can be prepared in a state of high purity, it is used in quantitative analysis as a primary standard for oxidation-reduction reactions. A carefully weighed sample of As_4O_6 is used to make up a solution that standardizes an iodine solution:

$$I_2 + HAsO_2 + 3OH^- \rightarrow H_2AsO_4^- + H_2O + 2I^-$$

The relationship of the As_4 molecule found in gaseous arsenic, As_4O_6, As_4S_6, and As_4S_4 is shown in the sketches of Figure 13.2. In the laboratory section, we follow the common practice of using the empirical formula As_2S_3 rather than the molecular formula As_4S_6 for arsenic(III) sulfide.

The arsenic compounds of greatest direct use are $Pb_3(AsO_4)_2$, used as a spray for fruits, and $Ca_3(AsO_4)_2$, used to protect cotton against the boll weevil. Large amounts of organic arsenic compounds are also used as weed killers, insecticides, and fungicides.

Tests for arsenic. Arsenic in solution may be present as arsenite or arsenate anion. Both As_2S_3 and As_2S_5 are very insoluble, but by our method of precipitating Group 2, we obtain only As_2S_3 because of reduction of $As(V)$:

$$H_3AsO_4 + H_2S \rightarrow HAsO_2 + 2H_2O + S$$

Since arsenic is a non-metal, the sulfide is, of course, soluble in KOH solution and arsenic goes into Subgroup 2B. Its separations from the other 2B elements also depend on its essentially non-metallic character, and it is usually found as an anion in confirmatory tests. Besides the yellow ammonium molybdoarsenate, $(NH_4)_3AsMo_{12}O_{40}$, which we use, other common confirmatory precipitates include brick-red silver arsenate, Ag_3AsO_4, and white magnesium ammonium arsenate, $MgNH_4AsO_4 \cdot 6H_2O$. Similar insoluble compounds of phosphorus, but not of antimony, are easily obtained.

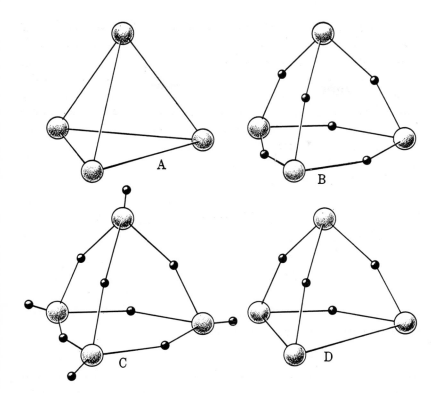

FIGURE 13.2 / REPRESENTATIONS OF
A: *The As$_4$ molecule*
B: *As$_4$O$_6$ (or As$_4$S$_6$)*
C: *As$_4$O$_{10}$*
D: *As$_4$S$_4$*

Because of the popularity of arsenic compounds as poisons with those homicidally inclined, delicate tests for arsenic are necessary in forensic chemistry (that branch of chemistry practiced to obtain legal evidence). The most important of these tests is the Marsh test (Figure 13.3) which depends on the reduction of arsenic to arsine, the arsenic analog of ammonia:

$$HAsO_2 + 3Zn + 6H_3O^+ \rightarrow AsH_3 \uparrow + 3Zn^{+2} + 8H_2O$$

The arsine passes off with the hydrogen also produced. If the hydrogen is burned, the arsine gives a blue color to the flame, or if the gases are passed through a heated glass tube, arsine decomposes to give a mirror-like deposit of elementary arsenic:

$$2AsH_3 \rightarrow 2As + 3H_2$$

Antimony also responds to the Marsh test, but the antimony mirror is insoluble in hypochlorite solution (household bleach), which readily dissolves arsenic.

There are many modifications of Marsh's test. The Gutzeit test, using silver nitrate to detect the arsine, is adaptable to the semimicro scale, as shown in Figure 13.4. Because arsine is ex-

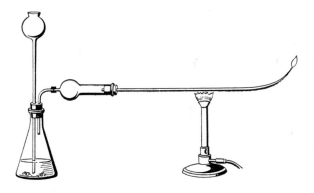

FIGURE 13.3 / THE MARSH TEST

tremely poisonous, these tests are not recommended for student use. The effectiveness of these tests for detecting and measuring even small amounts of material is so well known that arsenic is now regarded as "the amateur's poison."

13.3 / ANTIMONY

Occurrence and metallurgy. The common ore of antimony is stibnite, Sb_2S_3. China is the principal producer of antimony and has much more than half of the world's known reserves, but has not supplied the United States with any appreciable amount since before World War II. Most American antimony is smelted at Laredo, Texas, from Mexican ores. The metallurgy is not difficult; at Laredo the sulfide is converted to the oxide

$$2Sb_2S_3 + 9O_2 \rightarrow 2Sb_2O_3 + 6SO_2 \uparrow$$

then reduced by carbon:

$$Sb_2O_3 + 3C \rightarrow 2Sb + 3CO \uparrow$$

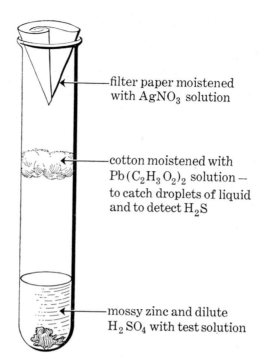

filter paper moistened
with $AgNO_3$ solution

cotton moistened with
$Pb(C_2H_3O_2)_2$ solution —
to catch droplets of liquid
and to detect H_2S

FIGURE 13.4 / THE GUTZEIT TEST

mossy zinc and dilute
H_2SO_4 with test solution

The United States uses about a third of the world's annual production of 50,000 tons.

Properties and uses. Antimony is too brittle to be useful by itself, but in small amounts it hardens tin and lead. Its use in pewter, babbitt, and antimonial lead has been referred to. Antimony is one of the few substances that expand when they freeze, and alloys having considerable amounts of antimony share this property. *Type metals* used in printing are lead-tin-antimony alloys with enough antimony so that they shrink very little when they are cast and reproduce accurately the type face from the mold. Type metal must also be low-melting and hard.

Compounds of antimony. Antimony trioxide, like its arsenic and phosphorus analogs, is really Sb_4O_6. It is truly amphoteric, dissolving about equally well in HCl and NaOH solutions. It is used in the ceramic industry in white glazes.

$SbCl_3$ can be prepared by burning powdered antimony in chlorine. As mentioned earlier, it is not very salt-like; it is soft, low-melting, and soluble in organic solvents. In water it hydrolyzes to precipitate SbOCl (antimony oxychloride or antimonyl chloride) except in strongly acid solutions:

$$Sb^{+3} + 3H_2O + Cl^- \rightleftharpoons \underline{SbOCl} + 2H_3O^+$$

Another halide, SbF_3, is important in organic chemistry as a "fluorine carrier." It reacts with fluorine to produce SbF_5 which in turn fluorinates the organic compound; this method is safer and more convenient than direct fluorination. SbF_5 may also be made by reacting $SbCl_5$ with HF.

Sb_2S_3 is obtained as the orange-red confirmatory precipitate for antimony in qualitative analysis. Heating transforms it into a black variety identical to the mineral stibnite. The first use of antimony we know of was the application of stibnite as a mascara to darken the eyes of women of long ago. In modern times it is used as an easily combustible material on the heads of safety matches and as a filler for rubber goods.

Some antimony compounds have found use in medicine. The most important is potassium antimonyl tartrate, $KSbOC_4H_4O_6$, called tartar emetic.

Reactions. Antimony compounds respond to the Marsh arsenic test. They may be distinguished by using Al with NaOH as the reducing agent, rather than Zn with H_2SO_4. The alkaline reducing agent reduces arsenic but not antimony. Also, if zinc and acid are used, the antimony mirror is different in appearance and is insoluble in sodium hypochlorite solution. The equation for the preparation of stibine (SbH_3) is similar to that for the preparation of arsine:

$$SbO^+ + 3Zn + 5H_3O^+ \rightarrow SbH_3 \uparrow + 3Zn^{+2} + 6H_2O$$

You will observe that antimony in this equation is represented as the *antimonyl* ion, SbO^+, sometimes written as $Sb(OH)_2^+$. Antimony in solution probably exists as this partially hydrolyzed form, except in high concentration of acid:

$$Sb^{+3} + 3H_2O \rightleftharpoons SbO^+ + 2H_3O^+$$

If much chloride ion is present, a chloro complex, $SbCl_4^-$ or $SbCl_6^{-3}$, forms.

The reduction of a soluble antimony ion, Sb^{+3}, SbO^+, or $SbCl_6^{-3}$ to the free element is easy. This fact may be used as the basis of the silver coin test for antimony. A drop of the test solution is placed on a clean silver coin, and a bit of mossy tin is dropped in it. Tin displaces the antimony from solution

$$3Sn + 2Sb^{+3} \rightarrow 3Sn^{+2} + \underline{2Sb}$$

and the antimony deposits as a black stain on the coin. Other metals between tin and silver in activity will do likewise, of course. Hydrogen sulfide must be boiled off completely before making this test, as it, too, would stain the silver.

Antimony(V) solutions contain the antimonate ion $Sb(OH)_6^-$, one of the best precipitants for sodium ion:

$$Na^+ + Sb(OH)_6^- \rightarrow \underline{NaSb(OH)_6}$$

Questions and problems

1. Tin is one of the more expensive metals, usually costing over a dollar a pound. Recovery of tin from scrap metal is therefore important. If you had available chlorine, sodium hydroxide, and hydrochloric acid, which would you select for recovering tin in each of the following cases? Write equations for all reactions that occur.
   a. Used tin cans
   b. Scrap bearing-metal (89 per cent Sn with Sb and Cu)
   c. Plumber's solder
   d. Bronze of composition 82 Cu, 16 Sn, 2 Zn
   e. Type metal

2. Besides chemical separation and recovery of tin from scrap, there are other possibilities: the scrap metal might be made an anode for electrolytic separation; it might simply be melted up and reused; it might be added to a molten metal to provide certain alloying metals. Can you suggest cases where each of these might be a suitable method?

3. A radiator antifreeze solution containing 32.5 per cent ethylene glycol remains liquid to 0°F. Describe what happens if a car protected by such a solution is left out for a long period at −10°F. Would you expect the engine block to be cracked by the expansion of freezing liquid? The eutectic combination of ethylene glycol and water contains 58.5 per cent glycol and freezes at −57°F.

4. Give one reason why each of the following substances would
   not be suitable for the use indicated:
   a. Orpiment as a pigment in a paint for infants' toys
   b. Tin-soldered gasoline cans for a South Polar expedition
      (they were used by the ill-fated Scott expedition of 1912)
   c. Terne plate for food containers
   d. Black Sb_2S_3 for cosmetics to be used around the eyes
   e. Antimony resistance wires for electric toasters

5. Write equations for the following reactions:
   a. Combustion of arsine in air
   b. Dissolving of antimony metal in aqua regia
   c. Dissolving of antimony(III) oxide in sodium hydroxide
   d. Hydrolysis of tin(IV) chloride
   e. The dissolving of $MgNH_4AsO_4 \cdot 6H_2O$ in hydrochloric acid
      solution (remembering that orthoarsenic acid is a weak acid)

6. Write correct formulas of the following substances:
   a. Arsenic(V) oxide
   b. Dihydrogen orthoarsenate ion
   c. Hexachloroantimonate(III) ion
   d. Hexafluoroantimonate(V) ion
   e. Metathioarsenite ion
   f. "Butter of antimony" (library: what does the name sug-
      gest about its properties?)
   g. Sodium hexahydroxoantimonate(V)
   h. Tin(II) chloride dihydrate
   i. Potassium hexafluorostannate
   j. Cassiterite

7. Which of the following substances do you think are gases at
   25°C, which liquid, and which solid? Answer on the basis of
   molecular weight, polarity, and ionic character. Then look
   them up in a handbook or reference book and see if you were
   correct in all cases.

AsF_3	$SnCl_4$
As_2H_4	SnF_4
$SbCl_5$	$SnBr_4$
$SbBr_3$	SnH_4
SbF_3	SbH_3
SbF_5	$SbOCl$
BiF_3	H_3AsO_4

The Metals of Subgroup 2A: Bismuth, Copper, and Cadmium

14

Subgroup 2A contains lead, bismuth, copper, and cadmium. Of these, lead was already discussed with the Group 1 metals in Chapter 12. Bismuth and cadmium are useful but minor metals, only about as plentiful as silver; that is, around 10^{-5} per cent of the earth's crust. The remaining one, copper, is man's oldest useful metal, and still, perhaps, second only to iron in importance.

14.1 / BISMUTH

Some of the principal properties of bismuth were summarized in Section 13.2 of the preceding chapter in comparing it with arsenic and antimony.

Occurrence. Although bismuth has a number of ores, notably Bi_2S_3, called bismuthinite or bismuth glance, most bismuth is now obtained as a by-product of lead, copper, and other ores. The use of bismuth has been increasing in recent years because of wider application of its alloys. The world production is now about 2500 tons annually. The United States is the largest producer, although the actual amount produced has not been published for several years, presumably because much of it is going into atomic energy applications. Peru and Mexico are other important producers.

Metallic bismuth. Bismuth is a brittle metal with the low melting point of 271°C and is not a good conductor of heat or electricity. It expands when it freezes, a property shared by alloys that contain more than half bismuth. Those that are less than half bismuth shrink on freezing, and those about half change very little.

The principal use of bismuth metal is for low-melting alloys. Many of these have been developed, offering low melting points combined with such other properties as strength, hardness, and expansion to varying degrees. They are used for fire safety devices, patterns and molds, special solders, and constant temperature baths. Examples are:

Wood's metal: Bi, 50 Pb, 25   Sn, 12.5 Cd, 12.5 M.P. 71°
Rose's metal: Bi, 50 Pb, 27.1 Sn, 22.9   M.P. 93°
Bismuth solder: Bi, 40 Pb, 40   Sn, 20   M.P. 110°

Compounds. In its compounds, bismuth almost invariably shows an oxidation state of +3, the only common +5 compound being sodium bismuthate, $NaBiO_3$. The use of this compound as an oxidizing agent in the confirmatory test for manganese (Procedure 3.3, page 264) shows the tendency of bismuth(V) to revert to the +3 state.

Bismuth(III) compounds, like those of antimony, are hydrolyzed except in quite acid solution:

$$Bi^{+3} + NO_3^- + 3H_2O \rightleftharpoons \underline{BiONO_3} + 2H_3O^+$$

The compound $BiONO_3$, bismuth oxynitrate or bismuthyl nitrate, is often called in commerce bismuth subnitrate. It and similar compounds, especially bismuth subcarbonate, $(BiO)_2CO_3$, are used in medicine for the treatment of gastric disturbances. It is assumed that the compound forms a soothing, insoluble coating over inflamed areas of the stomach and intestines. Because bismuth has a high atomic weight, its compounds are opaque to x-rays and are used for silhouetting the gastrointestinal tract in diagnostic studies.

Bismuthine, BiH_3, is unstable and very difficult to prepare, so bismuth does not give a Marsh test.

Reactions. Bismuth metal differs from antimony in dissolving in concentrated HNO_3, whereas antimony reacts to form an insoluble oxide. The metal also reacts with the halogens to form trihalides and with hot concentrated sulfuric acid to form $Bi_2(SO_4)_3$. In these reactions it is about as active as copper. The reduction of a compound to the metal also takes place about as easily as with copper, and the confirmatory reaction is based on this property, $Sn(OH)_3^-$ ion being the reducing agent:

$$2Bi(OH)_3 + 3Sn(OH)_3^- + 3OH^- \rightarrow \underline{2Bi} + 3Sn(OH)_6^{-2}$$

14.2 / COPPER

Copper with electron configuration 2, 8, 18, 1 is the lightest of the coinage metals. It also can be considered as the final element of the first transition series, as we shall see in Chapter 15. Historically, the use of copper tools and weapons is regarded as one of the marks distinguishing early civilized man from stone-age savages (there are others; a written language and a distaste for human flesh, for example).

Occurrence. Although much more abundant than the other two members of Group Ib of the periodic table, copper is comparatively rare—perhaps 0.007 per cent of the earth's crust. It is found in more different ores than any other metal. On the basis of the metallurgical treatment required, these ores may be divided into three classes:

Native copper	Cu	
Sulfide ores, such as	Cu_2S	chalcocite
	$CuFeS_2$	chalcopyrite
	Cu_5FeS_4	bornite
Oxidized ores, such as	Cu_2O	cuprite
	$Cu_2(OH)_2CO_3$	malachite
	$Cu_3(OH)_2(CO_3)_2$	azurite

Metallurgy. The metallurgy of native ores, mined only in northern Michigan, involves only grinding, washing, and melting the ore with a limestone flux. The "Lake" copper needs no other purification. Oxidized ores are often dissolved in sulfuric acid, and the metal obtained electrolytically.

Most American copper comes from low-grade sulfide ores found in the western states, particularly Arizona, Utah, and

Montana. Some of these ores contain less than 1 per cent copper; only remarkable organization has made possible the preparation of purified copper from them at competitive prices. An interesting illustration of the principles of extractive metallurgy is provided by the steps in this process:

1. Concentration by flotation is necessary on most of these ores. Almost all of the copper is recovered with very little gangue. Sometimes the ore is enriched from less than 1 per cent to as much as 20 per cent copper.

2. The concentrated ore is roasted in a current of hot air as it falls down from hearth to hearth in a tall furnace. The roasting drives off moisture and removes some of the sulfur as SO_2, but its main function is to remove the oxides of arsenic and antimony, which are very harmful impurities.

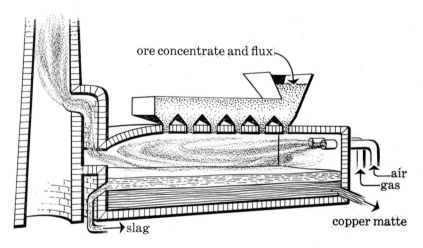

ore concentrate and flux

air
gas

copper matte

slag

FIGURE 14.1 / REVERBERATORY FURNACE

3. The roasted ore is heated in a reverberatory furnace (Figure 14.1) along with some sand as a flux. This procedure removes much of the iron:

$$2FeS + 3O_2 \rightarrow 2FeO + 2SO_2$$

$$FeO + SiO_2 \rightarrow FeSiO_3 \text{(slag)}$$

The slag floats on top of a heavy mixture of molten Cu_2S and the remaining FeS, called *copper matte*.

4. The copper matte is transferred to a copper converter similar in principle to the Bessemer converter used in steel-making. Sufficient air is blown through the molten matte to convert about two-thirds of it to Cu_2O, which reacts with the rest of the Cu_2S in an *oxide-sulfide* reduction:

$$2Cu_2S + 3O_2 \rightarrow 2Cu_2O + 2SO_2$$

$$Cu_2S + 2Cu_2O \rightarrow 6Cu + SO_2$$

Sand is added to remove the remaining iron as slag.

The copper produced in the converter is about 99 per cent pure. While molten, it dissolves a little SO_2 which is given off as it solidifies, giving the surface a blistered appearance; hence its name of *blister copper*.

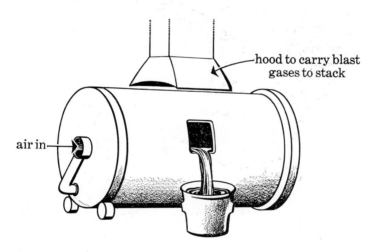

FIGURE 14.2 / COPPER CONVERTER IN POURING POSITION

5. Blister copper is refined by two methods, both of which are usually used. While still molten, the copper is heated further with a flux and is stirred with a pole of freshly cut wood. The wood chars, giving off carbon monoxide and hydrocarbon gases which reduce any extra Cu_2O. After this "poling" process, the copper is cast into thick sheets about a yard square which serve as anodes for the electrolytic refining. A copper sulfate electrolyte is used, and the voltage is regulated so that it is enough to dissolve only copper and more active

metals at the anode. The less active metals that are left behind drop to the bottom as the anode disintegrates, forming *anode sludge*, which is a profitable source of gold, silver, and other metals. The voltage is only sufficient to deposit copper at the cathode. More active metals such as nickel accumulate in the bath.

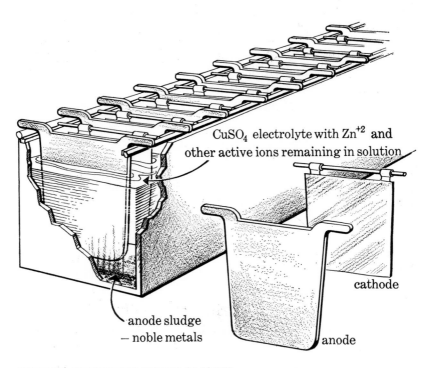

CuSO$_4$ electrolyte with Zn^{+2} and other active ions remaining in solution

cathode

anode sludge — noble metals

anode

FIGURE 14.3 / ELECTROLYTIC REFINING OF COPPER

The United States produces about 30 per cent of the annual total of 4 million tons. Other major producers are Chile, Rhodesia, and the Soviet Union.

Properties. Copper, the red metal, has a density about 8.9 g/cm^3 and melts at 1083°C. It is the most ductile and malleable of all metals except gold and silver, and is exceeded only by silver in electrical conductivity. It resists corrosion, but in different atmospheres takes on a dark tarnish of sulfide or oxide, or a green patina of basic chloride or carbonate. As its oxidation potential indicates (Table III.1, p. 338), copper does not displace hydrogen from acids, but it dissolves readily in nitric acid, evolving NO or NO_2, and in hot concentrated sulfuric acid, evolving SO_2.

Uses. More than half of the copper produced is used for electrical conductors. This use requires relatively pure copper, as small amounts of impurity lower its conductivity markedly. Pure copper is also used for electrotypes from which books are printed, and for some other purposes. Some of the alloys of copper are listed in Table 14.1. Those in which zinc is the principal

TABLE 14.1 / SOME ALLOYS OF COPPER

Alloy	Composition	Typical use
Yellow brass	Cu 65, Zn 35	Auto radiator cores
Red brass	Cu 85, Zn 15	Plumbing
Leaded brass	Cu 62, Zn 36, Pb 2	Watch and clock parts
Nickel silver	Cu 60, Zn 25, Ni 15	Zippers
Bronze	Cu 90, Sn 10	Statues
Phosphor bronze	Cu 91, Sn 8.5, P 0.5	Bearings
Aluminum bronze	Cu 90, Al 10	Ship propellers
Beryllium bronze	Cu 98, Be 2	Springs

alloying metal are called brasses. They are somewhat harder than copper and more easily fabricated. True bronzes have tin as the chief additive; they are hard and corrosion resistant. Copper is also a minor constituent in many alloys of aluminum, iron, magnesium, tin, and other metals.

Compounds. A few copper(I) compounds are important: Cu_2O is used as a coloring for red glass. It is precipitated by reduction of alkaline copper(II) solutions in Fehling's and Benedict's tests for sugars. Copper is electroplated from solutions containing the $Cu(CN)_3^{-2}$ ion.

The most important copper compound is $CuSO_4 \cdot 5H_2O$, *blue vitriol.* It is the common source of copper ion and is the electrolyte in copper refining and in some electric cells. Copper compounds are not particularly poisonous to higher forms of life— in fact, copper is an essential trace element in nutrition—but they are very poisonous to algae and fungi. Hence copper sulfate is used in swimming pools, and *Bordeaux mixture*, a fresh suspension of $Cu(OH)_2$, is used as a plant spray.

CuO is an oxidizing agent in organic chemistry and is also used to color glass green or blue.

Reactions. The stability of the deep blue $Cu(NH_3)_4^{+2}$ ion is utilized in separating Cu^{+2} from Bi^{+3}, since the bismuth precipitates while copper stays in solution:

$$Cu^{+2} + 4NH_3 \rightarrow Cu(NH_3)_4^{+2}$$

However, unless several times as much NH_3 is present as Cu^{+2}, $Cu(OH)_2$ precipitates along with $Bi(OH)_3$:

$$Cu^{+2} + 2NH_3 + 2H_2O \rightarrow \underline{Cu(OH)_2} + 2NH_4^+$$

The chloro complex also forms easily and gives a greenish yellow color to solutions containing copper(II) and chloride ions:

$$Cu^{+2} + 4Cl^- \rightleftharpoons CuCl_4^{-2}$$

The hydroxo complex $Cu(OH)_4^{-2}$ has such slight stability that Cu^{+2} is not very soluble even in strongly alkaline solution.

The equilibrium

$$2Cu^+ \rightleftharpoons Cu + Cu^{+2}$$

is so far displaced to the right that the only stable $Cu(I)$ compounds are those that give little Cu^+ in solution. Cu_2O and $CuCl$ are very insoluble; $Cu(CN)_3^{-2}$ is a very stable complex.

14.3 / CADMIUM

Cadmium is little more than a footnote to zinc. No cadmium mineral occurs in sufficient quantity to be mined for itself, but all zinc ores contain the metal in amounts ranging from traces up to 0.5 per cent. Cadmium is separated by distillation (it boils at about 770° compared to over 900° for zinc) or by displacement from a solution of impure zinc sulfate by zinc dust. Of the world production of 10,000 tons, slightly more than half is contributed by the United States. As the United States produces only about 15 per cent of the world's zinc, we see evidence both that American zinc ores are richer in cadmium than most and that American metal technology is superior to that of much of the world.

Cadmium metal. Cadmium has a low melting point (321°) and is slightly softer, but more ductile and more malleable, than zinc. The principal use of cadmium is as a plating to rust-proof iron. Compared to zinc, cadmium adheres better to iron and plates intricate shapes more evenly. It is also more resistant to corrosion, especially by salt water.

There are a few cadmium alloys of importance, including some low-melting alloys and some bearing metals. About 1 per cent cadmium added to copper doubles the tensile strength without greatly affecting the electrical conductivity.

Because cadmium absorbs neutrons, it is used for control rods for nuclear reactors.

Compounds. Cadmium always shows an oxidation state of $+2$ in its compounds. In general its compounds resemble those of zinc, except that cadmium is not amphoteric. The most important is the sulfate, $3CdSO_4 \cdot 8H_2O$, the electrolyte in the Weston standard cell. This cell is used in electrical instruments because it gives a very exact voltage. The nickel-cadmium storage cell, more used in Europe than in America, has the anode reaction

$$Cd + 2OH^- \rightarrow Cd(OH)_2 + 2e$$

The *cadmium yellow* of commerce is the same yellow CdS that is used as the confirmatory precipitate for the element. It is an excellent though expensive pigment for paints.

Questions and problems

1. Bismuthine can be prepared by the action of a magnesium-bismuth alloy on dilute hydrochloric acid. Write the equations for the reactions.

2. Write the formulas of the following substances:
   Bismuth pentafluoride
   Copper(I) iodide
   Tetracyanocadmate ion
   Copper(II) sulfate pentahydrate
   Tetrachlorocuprate(II) ion
   Tricyanocuprate(I) ion
   Blue vitriol
   Chalcocite

3. Name the following substances:

   $3CdSO_4 \cdot 8H_2O$ $BiOCl$

   $NaBiO_3$ CdS

   Cu_2O Bi_2S_3

   $Cd[CdCl_4]$ $Cu_2Fe(CN)_6$

4. CdS is often used as a yellow pigment for paints that might be exposed to fumes of H_2S. What would you expect to happen to a paint containing the cheaper yellow pigment $PbCrO_4$, in an atmosphere containing H_2S?

5. Bismuth subnitrate was once used in face powders. H_2S is given off in the burning of some grades of coal. Can you imagine what might have happened to some young lady of Victorian times as she sat in romantic tête-à-tête before an open fire?

6. Copper is one of only two colored metals. What is the other one?

7. A low grade bornite ore from Arizona assayed 0.9 per cent copper. Assuming 90 per cent recovery of the copper, how much ore would be mined for each ton of copper produced?

The Metals of Group 3:
Mn, Fe, Co, Ni, Al, Cr, Zn

15

Except for aluminum, the metals of Qualitative Group 3 are all found in the fourth period of the periodic table. The first twelve elements of the fourth period with their electron configurations are:

K	Ca	Sc	Ti	V	Cr	Mn	Fe	Co	Ni	Cu	Zn
2	2	2	2	2	2	2	2	2	2	2	2
8	8	8	8	8	8	8	8	8	8	8	8
8	8	9	10	11	13	13	14	15	16	18	18
1	2	2	2	2	1	2	2	2	2	1	2

Between the elements calcium and zinc, the third electron shell is filled from 8 to its maximum of 18 electrons, giving us the transition metals. We can define a *transition metal* as *any metal that can give up valence electrons from more than one shell.* A second transition series is located directly below these metals in the fifth period, and a third transition series in the sixth period.

Some of the properties of the metals of the first transition series are summarized in Table 15.1. Many properties such as melting point, hardness, and tensile strength seem, in a general way, to increase as we move toward the middle of the series and then fall off toward the end. In their lower valences, the metals of the series resemble one another; in their higher valences, they resemble the elements of the corresponding group. Thus Mn^{+2} is like Fe^{+2} and Ni^{+2} in solubilities and crystal forms of its salts, while MnO_4^- resembles ClO_4^-.

Because of the chemical similarities between these metals, it is not surprising that most of them precipitate together in quali-

TABLE 15.1 / SOME CHARACTERISTICS OF THE METALS OF THE FIRST TRANSITION SERIES

	M.P. (°C)	Density (g/cm^3)	Oxidation states	Abundance in earth's crust (%)
Sc	1550	3.0	3	0.0005
Ti	1700	4.5	2, 3, 4	0.44
V	1900	6.0	2, 3, 4, 5	0.015
Cr	1930	7.1	2, 3, 6	0.02
Mn	1260	7.2	2, 3, 4, 6, 7	0.1
Fe	1540	7.9	2, 3, 6	5.0
Co	1500	8.8	2, 3	0.002
Ni	1450	8.9	2, (4)	0.008
Cu	1083	8.9	1, 2	0.007

tative Group 3. Sc, Ti, and V, though not included in our scheme, also precipitate in this group. The only exception is copper, which precipitates in Group 2 because CuS is somewhat less soluble than the sulfides of the other metals of this series.

15.1 / MANGANESE

As noted in Table 15.1, manganese is rather plentiful; it ranks thirteenth in abundance among the elements and eighth among the metals. It is also a very important element, as much as 5 million tons being used each year, although most of its uses are not apparent to the average consumer.

Production. The chief ore is pyrolusite, MnO_2. The United States has abundant supplies of low-grade ore, but we find it economical to import nearly 90 per cent of our needs, equivalent to about a million tons of the metal, mainly from India, Brazil, and Ghana. The Soviet Union is by far the largest producer of manganese, but supplies none to us.

Manganese metal. Most of the pyrolusite is mixed with a little iron ore and reduced by carbon to *ferromanganese*, about 20 per cent iron and 80 per cent manganese. Ferromanganese is used in the steel industry to make manganese steels, but it is even more important as a *scavenger*, to remove traces of impurity from the finished molten steel. Manganese, more active than iron, combines with oxygen and sulfur, the MnS and MnO combining with the slag and being poured off. It is said that manganese is used in the manufacture of every pound of present-day steel.

For non-ferrous manganese alloys such as manganese bronze and some aluminum alloys, pure manganese may be obtained by electrolytic or aluminum reduction.

Compounds. Simple manganese compounds are known with oxidation states of 2, 3, 4, 6, and 7, and coordination complexes have been prepared in which it has states of 0, 1, and 5. Only a few of the many compounds are important.

Pink manganese(II) ion has a strongly basic oxide. The most used compound of this oxidation state is the sulfate, used as a catalyst to accelerate the drying of paints and varnishes and as an additive to fertilizers for manganese-deficient soils. Manganese is an essential element in plant and animal nutrition; the human requirement is about 4 mg daily.

MnO_2 is the most important compound by far. It is used in the laboratory and commercially as a catalyst and as an oxidizing agent. The best known use is in dry cells.

$KMnO_4$ and $NaMnO_4$ are used as disinfectants, bactericides, and oxidizing agents. In quantitative analysis, MnO_4^- is a good oxidizing agent with an intense purple color which makes it self-indicating.

Reactions. MnO_2 is a favorite laboratory oxidizing agent. In the laboratory preparation of chlorine, it oxidizes Cl^- ion:

$$MnO_2 + 4H_3O^+ + 2Cl^- \rightarrow Mn^{+2} + 6H_2O + Cl_2$$

This was once also a commercial process for making Cl_2. Other reducing agents besides HCl reduce MnO_2 to Mn(II). In qualitative analysis, where we wish to avoid the addition of Cl^-, we use H_2O_2 as the *reducing* agent along with HNO_3 to provide H_3O^+:

$$MnO_2 + 2H_3O^+ + H_2O_2 \rightarrow Mn^{+2} + 4H_2O + O_2$$

Oxidation of the lower valence states of manganese under strongly alkaline conditions gives green manganate ion, MnO_4^{-2}. For example, when MnO_2 is fused with alkalis in the presence of air, the reaction proceeds

$$4NaOH + 2MnO_2 + O_2 \rightarrow 2Na_2MnO_4 + 2H_2O$$

In neutral or acid conditions, oxidation of manganese in its lower oxidation states yields permanganate. Permanganates are manufactured commercially by treating a solution of a manganate, prepared according to the preceding reaction, with chlorine:

$$2MnO_4^{-2} + Cl_2 \rightarrow 2Cl^- + 2MnO_4^-$$

In our confirmatory test we begin with Mn^{+2} and use $NaBiO_3$ as the oxidizing agent. Since the reaction takes place in acid solution, the product is permanganate ion:

$$2Mn^{+2} + 14H_3O^+ + 5BiO_3^- \rightarrow 2MnO_4^- + 5Bi^{+3} + 21H_2O$$

15.2 / IRON

Iron, comprising 5 per cent of the earth's crust, is the fourth most abundant element. In the entire earth, however, it must be the most plentiful element, as it is believed that the earth's core is composed of iron alloyed with a little nickel. This belief is based on the density of the earth, the rate at which earthquake waves travel, and the composition of meteorites. (Some meteorites have compositions resembling igneous rocks of the earth's crust; others are composed of nickel-iron alloys like that postulated for the core.)

Occurrence. The principal ore of iron is hematite, Fe_2O_3. Other ores that are used are magnetite, Fe_3O_4, limonite, $Fe_2O_3 \cdot 2H_2O$, and siderite, $FeCO_3$. By far the most important source of iron ore in the world is the Mesabi Range in northern Minnesota, with its vast open pit mines, which has produced over 60 per cent of all American iron ore since 1890. Michigan and Alabama are other important iron mining states. In recent years, there has been a growing dependence on imported ores, mostly from Canada and Venezuela. Another trend has been toward concentration of low-grade iron ores. Almost half of the ore is now treated by flotation, magnetic separation, or other concentration process.

Metallurgy: Pig iron. Iron ore is first reduced in a blast furnace to an impure form called pig iron. A blast furnace is a steel stack about 100 feet tall, lined with firebrick. A blast of hot air is blown in near the bottom while the solid ingredients of the charge, iron ore, coke, and limestone, are admitted through a valve device at the top. Where the blast enters, some of the coke is burned to CO_2, which, as it passes upward, reacts with more coke to produce CO. The CO reduces the ore, and the limestone flux combines with earthy impurities to make a slag. The molten iron and slag collect in the crucible at the bottom and are drawn off periodically. The CO content of the gas given off at the top is high enough that it can be burned to preheat the air of the blast. Once started, a blast furnace operates continuously, often for several years, until it must be taken out of operation for repairs. An average size blast furnace uses about 2000 tons of iron ore, 1000 tons of coke, 400 tons of limestone, and 4000 tons of air each twenty-four hours. During that time it produces about 1000 tons of pig iron, 600 tons of slag, and 5800 tons of exit gas.

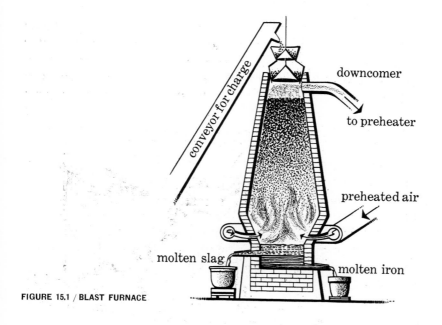

FIGURE 15.1 / BLAST FURNACE

Cast iron. Pig iron is the crudest sort of cast iron, containing upwards of six per cent impurities, mostly carbon. To make a useful cast iron, it is remelted, and most of the impurities are removed with an air blast and a flux. It still contains several per cent of carbon which is present in molten iron as the compound Fe_3C, called cementite. If a casting is cooled quickly, the carbon remains as cementite, giving *white cast iron,* which is hard and brittle. If it is cooled slowly, the iron carbide has a chance to decompose to iron and graphite, giving soft, tough *gray cast iron.* When a casting is held for several days at dull red heat, the graphite flakes migrate together into droplets. The *malleable iron* produced in this way is tough and shock-resistant, suitable for such things as engine-blocks.

Steel. Most pig iron is made into steel—iron alloyed with a small amount of carbon. About 85 per cent of American steel is produced by heating pig iron with pure iron ore or rusty scrap iron in a double reverberatory furnace called an *open-hearth* (Figure 15.2). The iron oxide removes carbon

$$Fe_2O_3 + 3C \rightarrow 2Fe + 3CO$$

and a basic flux of limestone removes oxides of phosphorus, sulfur, and silicon as slag. After about 10 hours, when the carbon content is lowered to the desired amount, scavengers such as ferromanganese and aluminum are added to remove traces of sulfur, oxygen, and the like, and the steel is run off into a ladle.

charging door through which pig iron is added

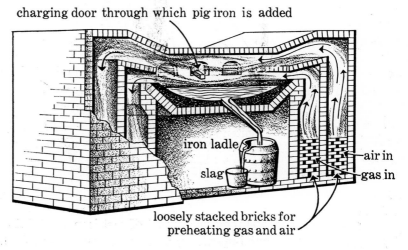

FIGURE 15.2 / MAKING STEEL BY THE OPEN-HEARTH PROCESS

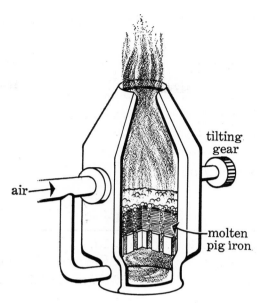

air→

tilting gear

molten pig iron

FIGURE 15.3 / BESSEMER CONVERTER

The *Bessemer process* (Figure 15.3) is cheaper and faster. Air is blown through molten pig iron to oxidize the impurities; the reaction is exothermic until all of the carbon is burned out. An acid flux, SiO_2, is usually used. After the blast has been shut off, the necessary amount of carbon is added, along with scavengers. Bessemer steel is excellent for many purposes, such as nails and wire, but not for more critical uses. In the new *oxygen process*, pure O_2 is blown into the pig iron from above, converting it rapidly into high-grade steel. Alloy steels are made by refining open-hearth steel still further in an electric furnace and adding the necessary alloying metals.

The steelmaking capacity of the United States in 1960 was 150 million tons a year compared to about 400 million for the entire world.

Properties. The properties of iron are greatly dependent on the presence of other elements, especially carbon. The amount of carbon, the rate of cooling, and the extent of subsequent reheating (called tempering) produce variations in the chemical combination between iron and carbon, in the allotropic form of iron present, and in crystal size. Carbon steels are classed as follows:

Mild steel, up to 0.2% carbon, for tin cans, wire
Medium steel, 0.2 to 0.5% carbon, structural steel, rails
High carbon steel, 0.5 to 1.5% carbon, springs, razor blades

The properties and uses of a few typical alloy steels are summarized in Table 15.2.

TABLE 15.2 / ALLOY STEELS

Name	Alloying metals	Characteristics	Typical use
Armor plate	4% Ni, 3% Cr	Hard, tough, heat treatable	Army tanks
High-speed steel	16% W or 8% Mo	Retains temper when heated	Cutting tools, drills
Duriron	12% Si	Acid resistant	Plumbing in chemistry labs
18–8 stainless	18% Cr, 8% Ni	Stainless, hard	Cutlery
Manganese	13% Mn	Tough, work-hardening	Railroad switches, army helmets
Chrome-vanadium	1% Cr, 0.1% V	Strong, vibration-resistant	Axles

Chemically, iron is only a moderately active metal, but it corrodes to a much greater extent than more active metals such as zinc and aluminum because the product of corrosion does not adhere and protect the metal beneath.

Rusting is ordinarily a complicated process involving water, air, and carbon dioxide. The water containing dissolved CO_2 is acid enough to dissolve iron as Fe^{+2} ions; oxygen oxidizes it further to hydrated Fe_2O_3, rust. Some of the methods used to make iron rustproof or rust-resistant are:

1. Alloying it, as with Cr, Ni, or Cu
2. Treating the surface to produce an adherent coating of Fe_3O_4 or $FePO_4$ by "bluing," "Bonderizing," etc.

3. Coating it with another metal, especially a more active one like zinc
4. Coating it with porcelain
5. Painting, especially with a rust-inhibiting paint like red lead
6. Lowering the humidity, as in naval vessels of the reserve fleet which have all openings sealed and dehumidifiers kept operating

Compounds. The common oxides are Fe_2O_3, familiar as hematite ore, as rust, and as the pigment known as Venetian red, and Fe_3O_4, magnetite ore. Fe_3O_4 is a mixed oxide $FeO \cdot Fe_2O_3$. Iron(II) oxide, FeO, is unstable to atmospheric oxidation and unimportant.

$FeSO_4 \cdot 7H_2O$ is used in medicine for iron tonics and is also used as a reducing agent. $FeCl_3$, the common iron(III) compound, is used as a mordant and as an oxidizing agent.

Among the important iron complexes are $FeCNS^{+2}$, thiocyanate iron(III) ion, which is used as a test for iron, and $FeNO^{+2}$, nitrosyl iron(III) ion, used in the brown-ring test for nitrates. The hexacyanoferrates, $Fe(CN)_6^{-4}$ and $Fe(CN)_6^{-3}$, are both important reagents. When Fe^{+3} ions are added to a solution of $K_4Fe(CN)_6$, a blue precipitate called *Prussian blue* is formed. An identical precipitate called, in this case, *Turnbull's blue*, is formed from Fe^{+2} ions and a solution of $K_3Fe(CN)_6$. The composition of both precipitates is approximately $KFeFe(CN)_6 \cdot H_2O$. This precipitate is the coloring material in blueprint paper, and it is also used in laundry bluing and as a paint pigment.

Reactions. From the oxidation potentials

$$Fe \rightarrow Fe^{+2} + 2e \qquad\qquad\qquad E = +0.44$$
$$Fe^{+2} \rightarrow Fe^{+3} + e \qquad\qquad\qquad E = -0.77$$

we see that Fe^{+3} ion is reduced to Fe^{+2} by metallic iron; that is,

$$Fe + 2Fe^{+3} \rightarrow 3Fe^{+2} \qquad\qquad\qquad E = +1.21$$

The voltage is positive as written, so the reaction proceeds spontaneously. Therefore iron(II) ion in solution can be stabilized by the addition of a few nails. In the absence of metallic iron, solutions of iron(II) are oxidized to iron(III) by atmospheric oxygen. In qualitative analysis and elsewhere in chemistry, metallic iron and iron(II) ion are widely used reducing agents, and iron(III) is a common oxidizing agent.

In the systematic analysis of an iron salt, only iron(III) is left after treatment with HCl and H_2O_2 in Procedure 2.1. There may be some reduction to Fe^{+2} by H_2S during the precipitation of Group 2, and more during the precipitation of Group 3; but it does not matter as both iron(II) and iron(III) precipitate together in Group 3 as FeS and $Fe(OH)_3$ respectively, and only iron(III) is left after treatment with strong oxidizing agents in Procedure 3.2. $Fe(OH)_3$ is very insoluble, and its amphoterism is so slight that it has practically no tendency to redissolve in alkaline solutions of the strength used in Group 3. If any Fe^{+3} is found in Subgroup 3B, it may be assumed that $Fe(OH)_3$ was carried over mechanically.

15.3 / COBALT

German miners of the Middle Ages found a mineral that looked like a metallic ore, but when heated it gave off poisonous fumes, but no metal. They called it the "goblin" ore or *kobold*; it is now known as cobaltite, CoAsS. The metal was obtained in 1735 by Brandt, a Swedish chemist.

Production. Most of the world's cobalt has come from the Congo for many years. Whether production of this strategic metal will be maintained at as high a level in the newly independent nation as it was under Belgian control is a very serious question which may not be finally answered for some years. Canada is another important producer, and the United States, which uses more than half the world's cobalt, has increased its production to provide rather more than 20 per cent of its needs. Since cobalt ores always occur mixed with those of other metals, the metallurgy is very complex. After the purified oxide is obtained, it may be reduced by electrolysis or other methods.

Properties and uses. Cobalt is similar to iron except that it is harder and is resistant to corrosion. Its principal uses are in permanent magnet alloys like *Alnico* (Al, Ni, Co, and Fe) and in cobalt-chromium-tungsten-molybdenum-iron alloys, called *stellites*, which maintain their hardness even at red heat. It is also used for alloys like *Carboloy,* composed of particles of extremely hard tungsten carbide, W_2C, cemented together by cobalt metal.

Compounds. Cobalt(II) is found chiefly as simple compounds; in complexes, the cobalt(III) state is stable, as explained in Chapter 10, page 106.

A familiar cobalt(II) compound is the chloride, which is used as a humidity indicator. The anhydrous form, $CoCl_2$, is blue; $CoCl_2 \cdot 6H_2O$ is red. Concentrated solutions are red when cold, blue when hot. To explain this behavior, an equilibrium like the following is postulated:

$$Co(H_2O)_6^{+2} + 4Cl^- \rightleftharpoons CoCl_4^{-2} + 6H_2O$$
$$\text{red} \qquad\qquad\qquad\qquad \text{blue}$$

CoO imparts a deep blue color to ceramic ware. It also is used to improve the adherence of porcelain coatings to steel.

Vitamin B_{12}, needed in the body's manufacture of hemoglobin, is a cobalt compound. Also, ruminant, or cud-chewing, animals require cobalt to help them utilize their food. There are areas in Australia with no cobalt in the soil; sheep in those regions sicken and die unless they are given small amounts of cobalt compounds.

Reactions. Cobalt dissolves slowly in dilute acids to give Co^{+2} ion. In acid, it is difficult to oxidize Co^{+2} to Co^{+3}, but it is quite easy in basic solutions, as shown by the potentials:

Acid	$Co^{+2} \rightarrow Co^{+3} + e$	$E = -1.83$
Base	$Co(OH)_2 + OH^- \rightarrow Co(OH)_3 + e$	$E = 0.17$

In Group 3 analysis, we find that $Co(OH)_3$ is produced by NaOH and H_2O_2 during the separation of Subgroups 3A and 3B, but as soon as the 3A precipitate is dissolved in acid, cobalt reverts to the $+2$ state.

15.4 / NICKEL

The name "nickel" has an origin similar to that of cobalt. A mineral resembling a copper ore but yielding no metal was called *kupfernickel* or "Old Nick's copper." Cronstedt is credited with obtaining the metal in 1751, although for thousands of years the Chinese had used it in alloys resembling nickel silver.

Production. Of an annual world production of over 300,000 tons of nickel, about 60 per cent comes from Canada. The Soviet Union is another important producer. The United States, consuming nearly half the world's nickel, produced none until a few years ago; however, some is now obtained from mines in Oregon.

The Canadian ore is pentlandite, $NiS \cdot 2FeS$, occurring in low-grade deposits which also contain recoverable amounts of copper, cobalt, platinum, gold, silver, selenium, tellurium, and other elements. The metallurgy is therefore complex, final purification being usually done electrolytically or by the Mond process. The latter process, carried on in Great Britain on Canadian ore concentrates, involves the reaction between nickel and carbon monoxide to form nickel carbonyl, $Ni(CO)_4$. This is a low-boiling liquid which is distilled and then decomposed by heat:

$$Ni + 4CO \rightleftharpoons Ni(CO)_4$$

Since no other metal carbonyl is formed so easily or is so volatile, the metal produced in this way is very pure.

Properties and uses. Like cobalt, nickel is a tough, magnetic, corrosion resistant metal. It is softer and more malleable than cobalt and less active chemically. Nickel is unusual in its ability to adsorb hydrogen and to catalyze various reactions of hydrogen. It shares this property with Pd and Pt, the metals directly below it in the periodic table.

Over 3000 alloys of nickel are in use. Some nickel steels have already been referred to. Nickel-iron alloys with over 50 per cent Ni have unusual magnetic properties, while those with about 35 per cent Ni have very low coefficients of expansion and are useful for such things as surveyors' tapes. Nichrome resists oxidation at high temperatures, and is used for electrical heating elements. Among the alloys with copper are nickel silver, 5-cent coinage (75 Cu, 25 Ni), and monel. The latter is about two-thirds nickel and one-third copper. Because of its strength and resistance to corrosion, monel is useful for equipment in chemical plants.

Compounds and reactions. Nickel commonly shows an oxidation state of $+2$ in its compounds. Green $NiSO_4 \cdot 6H_2O$, the most familiar salt of nickel(II), is used in nickel-plating baths.

Nickel(III) and nickel(IV) compounds are unstable and not definitely characterized, but the higher oxide, ordinarily formulated as $NiO_2 \cdot 2H_2O$ is used in the Edison storage battery. The Edison cell uses an electrolyte of KOH solution containing a little LiOH. Its cathode reaction is

$$NiO_2 \cdot 2H_2O + 2e \rightarrow Ni(OH)_2 + 2OH^-$$

and the anode reaction,

$$Fe + 2OH^- \rightarrow Fe(OH)_2 + 2e$$

The cell is rugged and has a very long life. A similar cell using Cd instead of Fe is even more durable but also more expensive.

The oxidation state of nickel in $Ni(CO)_4$ is zero. As in complex ions, the nickel accepts an electron pair from each carbon monoxide molecule, so that its electron configuration is increased from 2, 8, 16, 2 to 2, 8, 18, 8, which is an inert gas structure. The compound is several hundred times as poisonous as hydrogen cyanide and is probably the most poisonous substance used in a regular commercial process.

Nickel does not undergo any oxidation-reduction reaction in qualitative analysis. The insoluble compounds utilized are the sulfide, hydroxide, and dimethylglyoximate. Since the deep blue tetraammine complex is quite stable, nickel hydroxide is not precipitated from strongly ammoniacal solutions.

15.5 / CHROMIUM

The metal that we associate primarily with ornamental trim on automobiles impressed its discoverer, Vauquelin (1798), with the various colors of its compounds; hence its name, from the Greek *chroma*, meaning color.

Production. The only important ore of chromium is chromite, $FeO \cdot Cr_2O_3$. Chromium is a moderately plentiful element. Under ordinary conditions, the rather low-grade ores of Montana and other states are not extensively worked, most of our chromite being imported from such places as Turkey, South Africa, and the Philippines. Russia is also an important producer. The United States consumes about half the world's production, which amounts to about 1,300,000 tons, measured as chromium metal.

Since about two-thirds of the chromium is used in alloy steels, the chromite is usually reduced with carbon in an electric furnace to *ferrochrome* which is added to the steel in the proper amount, imparting hardness, corrosion resistance, and strength at high temperatures. For non-ferrous alloys, the Cr_2O_3 is separated and reduced by silicon.

Properties. Chromium is familiar as a hard, very white metal. Although it dissolves easily in dilute HCl and similar acids, chromium is not noticeably affected by strong oxidizing agents like concentrated nitric acid. In fact, once it has been treated with such an agent, it becomes *passive* and no longer reacts with dilute hydrochloric acid. The passivity may be removed by heat, mechanical shock, or long action of dilute acids.

Compounds. Chromium(II) compounds are so easily oxidized by air that they are important only as powerful reducing agents. Chromium(III) chloride and sulfate are used as mordants for deep colored dyes, and Cr_2O_3 is a fine green pigment for paints. Hexavalent chromium is represented by chromate and dichromate, related as follows:

$$CrO_4^{-2} \underset{H_2O}{\overset{H_3O^+}{\rightleftharpoons}} HCrO_4^- \underset{H_2O}{\overset{H_3O^+}{\rightleftharpoons}} Cr_2O_7^{-2}$$

yellow   orange-red

The chromates and dichromates are valuable oxidizing and precipitating agents in the laboratory, and have similar uses industrially. They are also used for tanning leather. In this process, they partially oxidize the skin of the animal, precipitating $Cr(OH)_3$ in the fibers. CrO_3, the anhydride of chromic acid, is used in chromium-plating baths. Chromium(III) ion forms a large number of stable complexes. The ordinary green solution may contain such an ion as $Cr(H_2O)_5Cl^{+2}$, while $Cr(H_2O)_6^{+3}$ is violet.

Reactions. Chromium(III) ion precipitates in neutral or basic solution

$$Cr^{+3} + 3OH^- \rightarrow Cr(OH)_3$$

but redissolves in excess base:

$$Cr(OH)_3 + OH^- \rightleftharpoons Cr(OH)_4^-$$

Since the latter reaction is not complete, we oxidize the chromium to the +6 state in order to get a sharp separation between Subgroups 3A and 3B:

$$2Cr(OH)_4^- + 3H_2O_2 + 2OH^- \rightarrow 2CrO_4^{-2} + 8H_2O$$

See Procedure 3.8, Notes 2 and 3, (page 270) for a discussion of the confirmatory substance, blue CrO_5.

15.6 / ZINC

Zinc, which is not a transition metal, uses only the two electrons of its outer shell in chemical reactions. Zn^{+2} does resemble the divalent ions of the transition metals, however, and is found in the same qualitative group with most of them. Zinc also shows more resemblance to the metals of periodic Group IIa, especially magnesium, than do the other IIb metals, cadmium and mercury.

Occurrence. Zinc is a moderately abundant metal and its metallurgy is rather easy, so it is, next to iron, the cheapest metal per pound. The most important ore is ZnS, called zinc blende or sphalerite, which usually occurs mixed with ores of other metals, especially lead. After concentration by flotation, the ore may be dissolved in acid and reduced electrolytically, or it may be roasted to the oxide

$$2ZnS + 3O_2 \rightarrow 2ZnO + 2SO_2$$

and reduced with carbon:

$$ZnO + C \rightarrow Zn + CO$$

The United States produces about one-sixth and consumes about one-third of the world's yearly production of over 3,000,000 tons. Canada, the U.S.S.R., and Mexico follow the United States as zinc producers.

Properties and uses. Zinc is rather brittle, low-melting (420°), and quite active. It dissolves readily in acids

$$Zn + 2H_3O^+ \rightarrow Zn^{+2} + 2H_2O + H_2$$

and in strongly basic solutions:

$$Zn + 2OH^- + 2H_2O \rightarrow Zn(OH)_4^{-2} + H_2$$

It resists atmospheric oxidation because of a protective film of basic carbonate.

The largest use of zinc is as a rust-proofing coat for iron. Zinc is more active than iron; therefore, if the coating is scratched through, the zinc corrodes preferentially, giving anodic protection to the iron. Hence, zinc plating is called *galvanizing*. It is applied by dipping the steel into molten zinc, by electroplating, by spraying molten zinc on the iron (*metallizing*), or by tumbling iron objects with zinc dust in a heated drum (*sherardizing*).

A strong second to galvanizing as a use for zinc is die-casting. Zinc is the preferred metal for this cheap, rapid process because it is low-melting, does not shrink much when it freezes, and is reasonably strong.

Sheet zinc is used in flashlight batteries and in other electrochemical cells.

Among the alloys of zinc are the brasses, nickel silver, and some solders and bearing metals.

Compounds. ZnO is the most used compound in industry. It is used as a pigment in white exterior paints and as a filler for rubber goods, as in white sidewall tires. ZnS has similar uses and is often coprecipitated with $BaSO_4$ as *lithopone*, a favorite body and pigment for interior paints:

$$[Zn^{+2} + SO_4^{-2}] + [Ba^{+2} + S^{-2}] \rightarrow \underline{ZnS} + \underline{BaSO_4}$$

The most used soluble compounds are $ZnSO_4 \cdot 7H_2O$ and $ZnCl_2$. The sulfate is the common source of Zn^{+2} ion in solution. The chloride, which is not very ionic, is used as a wood preservative and for making parchment paper.

Reactions. Zinc differs from the other elements of its periodic group in being strongly amphoteric. The hydroxide precipitates in neutral or weakly alkaline solutions but dissolves easily in acid, alkali, or ammonia:

$$Zn(OH)_2 + 2H_3O^+ \rightarrow Zn^{+2} + 4H_2O$$

$$Zn(OH)_2 + 2OH^- \rightarrow Zn(OH)_4^{-2}$$

$$Zn(OH)_2 + 4NH_3 \rightarrow Zn(NH_3)_4^{+2} + 2OH^-$$

Almost all zinc ions and compounds met with in qualitative analysis are white or colorless. An exception is $Zn[Hg(SCN)_4]$

which, though white when pure, forms a bright lavender co-precipitate with $Cu[Hg(SCN)_4]$.

15.7 / ALUMINUM

The remaining metal to be discussed in this chapter is the only one of periodic Group III to merit inclusion in our qualitative scheme. Boron, the first element in the group, is a non-metal. None of the others, either in the IIIa or IIIb subgroup, is found in large scale ore deposits, though most of them are not really rare in the earth's crust. Several of them are commercially available and may some day have more importance than now.

Occurrence. Aluminum, comprising over 8 per cent of the earth's crust, is the most plentiful metal. Among its many minerals are such complex silicates as the feldspars and micas which are common constituents of granite. Pure white clay, *kaolin*, is $(HAlSiO_4)_2 \cdot H_2O$; it is usually colored red by impurities of iron oxide. With the assortment of minerals available, aluminum producers can afford to be choosy. At present, practically the only source of the metal is bauxite, $Al_2O_3 \cdot 2H_2O$. More than half the world's bauxite comes from the Caribbean region—Jamaica, British Guiana, and Surinam (Dutch Guiana). American bauxite is mined in Arkansas. The location of aluminum reduction plants is determined by the availability of electric power rather than by nearness to mines or market.

Metallurgy. The process for obtaining metallic aluminum was invented simultaneously and independently in 1886 by Charles Martin Hall, an American, and Paul Héroult, a Frenchman, both twenty-two years old at the time. The method consists in electrolyzing a solution of aluminum oxide in molten cryolite, Na_3AlF_6.

In modern practice, the bauxite is first purified by dissolving it in hot sodium hydroxide solution, leaving behind such impurities as iron oxide:

$$Al_2O_3 \cdot 2H_2O + 2OH^- + H_2O \rightarrow 2Al(OH)_4^-$$

When the solution is diluted and cooled, aluminum hydroxide is precipitated by hydrolysis:

$$Al(OH)_4^- \rightarrow \underline{Al(OH)_3} + OH^-$$

After heating to drive off water, the precipitate is dissolved in molten cryolite or in a mixture of molten fluorides and electrolyzed in a cell like that in Figure 15.4.

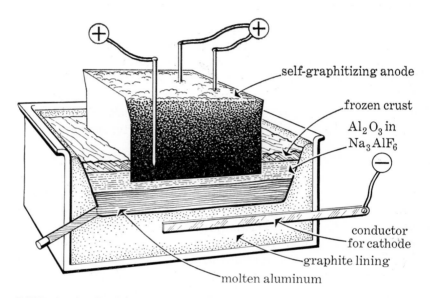

self-graphitizing anode

frozen crust

Al_2O_3 in Na_3AlF_6

conductor for cathode

graphite lining

molten aluminum

FIGURE 15.4 / ONE MODERN FORM OF THE HALL CELL
FOR ELECTROLYTIC REDUCTION OF ALUMINUM

The production of a pound of aluminum requires about 10 kilowatt-hours of electricity. Another major item of expense is the graphite anodes, which are oxidized away at the rate of about 0.8 pound per pound of aluminum.

Of the nearly 4,000,000 tons of aluminum produced annually, the United States produces over 40 per cent and Canada nearly 20 per cent. For the whole world the consumption has not yet overtaken that of copper, but in our country more aluminum has been used than any other metal except iron for some years.

Properties. Aluminum has a melting point of 660° and a density of 2.71 g/cm³. It is not easy to solder, cast, weld, or machine, and it fatigues easily; but alloys or techniques have been devised to overcome all of these shortcomings. Although it is only about 65 per cent as good a conductor of electricity as copper for a wire of the same diameter, it is about twice as good for a wire of the same weight.

Chemically, aluminum is an active metal, but it is ordinarily protected by an adherent film of aluminum oxide. In HCl, aluminum reacts slowly at first till the Al_2O_3 is dissolved, then it dissolves rapidly. It also dissolves in NaOH solution

$$2Al + 2OH^- + 6H_2O \rightarrow 2Al(OH)_4^- + 3H_2$$

but in concentrated HNO_3 the protective oxide coating only becomes heavier. The coating can also be made more dense by making the aluminum the anode in a solution containing sulfate or chromate ion. Since the Al_2O_3 coating can adsorb dyes, anodized aluminum is available in many brilliant colors.

Uses of the metal and its alloys. Many of the uses of aluminum depend on the great affinity it displays for oxygen, once the protective film has been destroyed. Upwards of 30,000 tons a year is used as a scavenger to remove oxygen from steel. Along with an oxidizing agent like ammonium nitrate it is used in explosives. *Thermite* is a mixture of iron oxide and aluminum. The reaction is initiated only at high temperature, but once started is highly exothermic

$$3Fe_3O_4 + 8Al \rightarrow 4Al_2O_3 + 9Fe$$

A temperature in excess of 2500°C is obtained. Thermite mixtures are used in incendiary bombs and in welding. The Goldschmidt process uses aluminum on oxides like Cr_2O_3 or MnO_2, reducing them to their metals.

The resistance of aluminum to oxidation under ordinary conditions is among the properties that make it useful for cooking utensils, wrapping foil, toothpaste tubes, and the like.

Duralumin, Al 94, Cu 4, with small amounts of Mn, Mg, and other elements, is the light, strong alloy used for airplane construction. However, it is subject to corrosion; so, for such uses as boat hulls, it is clad with specially purified aluminum, making *Alclad*. Other important aluminum alloys are those with Mn, with Si, and with Mg.

Compounds. In all its ordinary compounds, aluminum has an oxidation state of +3. The oxide, which in its hydrated form is found as bauxite, also occurs in the anhydrous form, Al_2O_3, corundum, which is the hardest naturally occurring substance, next to diamond. Crude impure corundum is called emery, while nicely crystalline forms colored by traces of impurities are gems such as ruby and sapphire. These may also be made synthetically by melting Al_2O_3 with traces of colored oxides in an oxyhydrogen flame. Another crystalline form of Al_2O_3 obtained at lower temperature is known as activated alumina. It is an effective dehydrating agent and catalyst.

Anhydrous $AlCl_3$ is not ionic. Its formula

$$:\overset{..}{\underset{..}{Cl}}:$$
$$:\overset{..}{\underset{..}{Cl}}:Al$$
$$:\overset{..}{\underset{..}{Cl}}:$$

shows that it is a Lewis acid, explaining its catalytic activity for many reactions. In the vapor state, the formula is Al_2Cl_6, with the apparent structure

The most used salt, $Al_2(SO_4)_3 \cdot 18H_2O$, is called commercial alum because it is used for many of the purposes for which alum, $KAl(SO_4)_2 \cdot 12H_2O$ was once used. Salts similar to alum are known which have other univalent ions substituted for K^+ and other tervalent ions for Al^{+3}; thus $(NH_4)Cr(SO_4)_2 \cdot 12H_2O$ is ammonium chromium alum. The word "alum" in this sense then means any of the isomorphous salts of the general formula $M^IM^{III}(SO_4)_2 \cdot 12H_2O$.

The hydrolysis and amphoterism of the hydrated aluminum ion were discussed on page 115, Chapter 10.

Questions and problems

1. What is the electron configuration of V? of Mn? What are the lowest and the highest oxidation states exhibited in compounds of these metals? Are the oxidation states in harmony with the electron configurations? Can the oxidation states and the electron configuration of Cr be related in any simple way?

2. The atomic number of molybdenum, of the second transition series, is 42. Without consulting a periodic table, write out the electron configuration you think it might have and decide which of the metals of the first series it should resemble. Does a comparison of physical and chemical properties confirm the similarities of the two metals?

3. Define the following terms:
   a. Transition metal
   b. Steel
   c. Pig iron
   d. Scavenger
   e. Malleable cast iron
   f. White cast iron
   g. Sherardizing
   h. Galvanizing

4. Answer by formula:
   a. Cementite
   b. Nickel carbonyl
   c. Aluminate ion
   d. Prussian blue
   e. Chromite ion
   f. Chromium peroxide
   g. Tetraaminenickel(II) ion
   h. Potassium iron alum
   i. White vitriol (library)
   j. Manganate ion

5. Explain the nature of the valence bonding in nickel carbonyl. What would you expect the formula of iron carbonyl to be?

6. Use equations to show the following:
   a. The over-all reaction of the Edison cell (add the cathode and anode reactions)
   b. The roasting of sphalerite
   c. The removal of carbon from pig iron in a Bessemer converter
   d. The removal of carbon from pig iron in an open hearth
   e. The amphoterism of aluminum hydroxide
   f. The amphoterism of zinc hydroxide
   g. The preparation of lithopone
   h. The refining of bauxite
   i. The rusting of iron

7. For each of the following cases, suggest an alloy that will be satisfactory and tell what properties of the alloy led you to select it:
   a. An aluminum alloy for a racing motorboat
   b. An alloy for crucible tongs for repeated use in a bunsen flame
   c. An alloy for clock pendulums

d. An alloy for permanent magnets in radio speakers

e. An alloy for a surgical instrument that can be sterilized in a flame without losing its temper

f. An alloy for burglar-proof safes

8. What weight of ferrochrome (65 per cent Cr) would need to be added to 24 tons of open-hearth steel to make an Enduro S15 stainless steel containing 14.0 per cent chromium? How much chromite ore analyzing 48 per cent Cr would be needed to provide this much ferrochrome?

9. List *all* of the properties of aluminum that are significant in each of the following applications:

a. The mirror for the 200-inch Mt. Palomar telescope

b. Cans to replace tin cans for food containers

c. High voltage electric lines

d. Foil in photographic flash bulbs

e. Brightly colored drinking tumblers

f. Screen doors and windows

The Metals of Group 4:
Calcium, Strontium, Barium

16

Periodic Group IIa, called the *alkaline earth metals*, have the electron configuration

Be	2, 2
Mg	2, 8, 2
Ca	2, 8, 8, 2
Sr	2, 8, 18, 8, 2
Ba	2, 8, 18, 18, 8, 2
Ra	2, 8, 18, 32, 18, 8, 2

As each metal has just two more electrons than the preceding inert gas, they show only the +2 oxidation state in their compounds. Beryllium, because of the very small size of the Be atom and the Be^{+2} ion, does not act much like the other elements of the group; in fact, it resembles aluminum quite closely. $MgCO_3$ is not quite insoluble enough to precipitate in analytical Group 4, so it is considered in the next chapter. Since radium is not included for obvious reasons, we have left only calcium, strontium, and barium to take up in detail. Table 16.1 gives some of the properties of the alkaline earth metals; the similarities of Ca, Sr, and Ba are especially noticeable.

While most of the metals in chapters 12 to 16 have been primarily important as the free metals, the three elements of this chapter are most useful in the combined state. Calcium compounds were used even by ancient peoples; compounds of barium and strontium came into later use. The free metals were obtained by Humphry Davy, who used one of the first electric batteries to prepare calcium, strontium, and barium.

TABLE 16.1 / SOME PROPERTIES OF THE ALKALINE EARTH METALS

	M.P. (°C)	Density (g/cm^3)	$E°$ for M→M^{+2} +2e	K_{sp} of M(OH)$_2$	K_{sp} of MCO$_3$	Abundance in earth's crust (%)
Be	1285	1.85	1.85	1×10^{-13}		0.0006
Mg	650	1.74	2.37	1×10^{-11}	4×10^{-5}	2.1
Ca	850	1.55	2.87	4×10^{-5}	7×10^{-9}	3.6
Sr	800	2.6	2.89	1×10^{-4}	1×10^{-9}	0.03
Ba	850	3.6	2.90	4×10^{-3}	5×10^{-9}	0.025
Ra	(700)	(5)	(2.92)			10^{-10}

16.1 / CALCIUM

Occurrence. As noted in Table 16.1, calcium is one of the most abundant elements. As with strontium and barium, its best known minerals are the carbonate and the sulfate, though other minerals—silicates, phosphates, and so forth—are also common. The carbonate occurs as limestone, as marble (limestone in which the crystals have grown larger by metamorphosis), and as Iceland spar (still larger crystals) and also as coral, pearls, oyster shells, and other forms. The sulfate occurs as anhydrite, $CaSO_4$, and as gypsum, $CaSO_4 \cdot 2H_2O$.

The Metal. Calcium metal is produced by heating lime with aluminum in vacuum retorts:

$$3CaO + 2Al \xrightarrow{\Delta} Al_2O_3 + 3Ca \uparrow$$

The reaction proceeds to the right because the volatile calcium metal is distilled off. Most of the world's production is in Canada, with the United States ordinarily using about 50 tons a year, though consumption has gone as high as 500 tons.

There are many special uses of calcium metal, mostly based on its reactivity. It has been used to reduce uranium, to scavenge certain alloys, to harden lead for battery plates, and for other purposes, none of which require much metal.

Compounds. CaO, lime or quicklime or unslaked lime, is one of the largest tonnage chemicals in industry. It is prepared by heating limestone:

$$CaCO_3 \xrightarrow{\Delta} CaO + CO_2$$

Many different types of kiln are used successfully; they all are devised so that the CO_2 is swept away by a draft of air and burning gases, enabling the reaction to go to completion. Figure 16.1

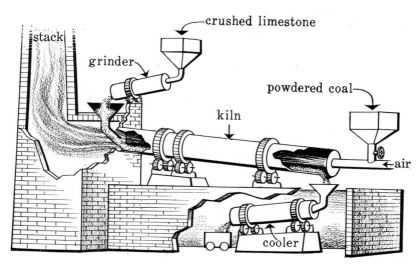

FIGURE 16.1 / ROTARY LIME KILN

shows schematically the type of kiln most used in the United States. The same reaction takes place when limestone is used for fluxing, as in the blast furnace; many millions of tons of CaO produced in metallurgical furnaces are immediately used in slag formation.

Much of the quicklime is slaked by the addition of water:

$$CaO + H_2O \rightarrow Ca(OH)_2$$

Slaked lime is a valuable cheap base; its low solubility may be partially compensated by the use of a saturated solution containing excess $Ca(OH)_2$ in suspension. Lime mortar is a mixture of slaked lime, sand, and water. When the mixture is exposed to air, it quickly sets, then slowly hardens over a period of years by taking up carbon dioxide:

$$Ca(OH)_2 + CO_2 \rightarrow CaCO_3 + H_2O$$

Modern wall plaster is plaster of Paris, which is easier to apply and dries more quickly. Plaster of Paris is prepared by partial dehydration of gypsum:

$$2CaSO_4 \cdot 2H_2O \xrightarrow{200°} (CaSO_4)_2 \cdot H_2O + 3H_2O$$

When plaster of Paris is mixed with water, it recombines:

$$(CaSO_4)_2 \cdot H_2O + 3H_2O \rightarrow 2CaSO_4 \cdot 2H_2O$$

Because plaster of Paris sets quickly, expanding slightly, and is fairly hard and strong when set, it is suited for wall board and rocklath, surgical casts, molds for pottery, metal casting molds, statuary, and many more uses.

$CaCl_2$ is available in large quantities as a by-product of the Solvay process, as we shall see in the next chapter. It is very soluble and has great affinity for water. It is used on roads to settle dust in summer and to melt ice in winter; in the laboratory, it is a convenient drying agent.

When CaO is heated with coke in an electric furnace, calcium carbide is produced:

$$CaO + 3C \xrightarrow{\Delta} CaC_2 + CO$$

Calcium carbide reacts with water to give acetylene, valuable as a fuel and as a substance from which many organic compounds are made

$$CaC_2 + 2H_2O \rightarrow Ca(OH)_2 + C_2H_2$$

and with nitrogen to give calcium cyanamide, used as a fertilizer:

$$CaC_2 + N_2 \rightarrow CaCN_2 + C$$

Because of their cheapness, calcium compounds are often used where the interest is in the anion, the calcium ion being only incidental. Examples are $Ca(ClO)_2$, bleaching powder, $Ca(H_2PO_4)_2$, used as a fertilizer, and $Ca(HSO_3)_2$, used in making paper pulp. The mineral matter of bones is mainly $Ca_3(PO_4)_2$. Although adequate calcium is present in most diets, it cannot be assimilated unless the body also has Vitamin D.

Hard water. The common cause of hardness in water is calcium ion from dissolved gypsum (solubility about 2.5 g/l), or from limestone which is soluble in water containing dissolved carbon dioxide:

$$CaCO_3 + H_2O + CO_2 \rightarrow Ca^{+2} + 2HCO_3^-$$

Bicarbonate hardness is sometimes called temporary hardness because the reaction reverses on heating, precipitating calcium carbonate. $MgCO_3$ and $FeCO_3$ react similarly.

The many manifestations of hard water are well known: the formation of caverns by the dissolving of limestone; the re-precipitation of $CaCO_3$ in caves as stalactites and stalagmites; the deposition of $CaCO_3$ as teakettle lime and boiler scale when hard water is heated; the precipitation of insoluble calcium soaps as hard water scum, bathtub ring, or tattletale gray.

Hardness may be removed by the use of a water softener such as borax, $Na_2B_4O_7$:

$$[Ca^{+2} + 2HCO_3{}^-] + [2Na^+ + B_4O_7{}^{-2}] \rightarrow$$
$$CaB_4O_7 + 2Na^+ + 2HCO_3{}^-$$

On a commercial scale, slaked lime is used:

$$[Ca^{+2} + 2HCO_3{}^-] + [Ca^{+2} + 2OH^-] \rightarrow 2CaCO_3 + 2H_2O$$

If noncarbonate hardness is present, sodium carbonate is added:

$$[Ca^{+2} + SO_4{}^{-2}] + [2Na^+ + CO_3{}^{-2}] \rightarrow$$
$$CaCO_3 + 2Na^+ + SO_4{}^{-2}$$

The small amount of Na^+ ion added to the water is of no sig-nificance for most purposes. Household softeners of the zeolite or *Permutit* type contain a porous sodium aluminum silicate, $NaAlSiO_4$. As the hard water passes through the zeolite, the sodium and calcium ions are exchanged:

$$Ca^{+2} + 2NaAlSiO_4 \rightarrow 2Na^+ + Ca(AlSiO_4)_2$$

When the zeolite is saturated with Ca^{+2} ions, it may be restored by soaking it in strong NaCl solution, reversing the above reac-tion. Synthetic resin ion exchangers are also available which may be regenerated with acid. They replace Ca^{+2} with H_3O^+:

$$Ca^{+2} + 2H(resin) + 2H_2O \rightarrow 2H_3O^+ + Ca(resin)$$

If we combine this with an anion exchange resin which removes the $HCO_3{}^-$ or $SO_4{}^{-2}$, we end up with pure water, equal in quality to distilled water.

16.2 / STRONTIUM

Strontium is of limited importance, as almost anything it does can be done more cheaply by either calcium or barium. The ores are $SrSO_4$, celestite, and $SrCO_3$, strontianite. The metal may be made by aluminum reduction, like calcium, but there is little peacetime demand. In wartime it is used in tracer bullets because it burns with a brilliant red flame. $Sr(NO_3)_2$ is used in red highway flares and in Fourth of July fireworks. In Europe, $Sr(OH)_2$ is used in beet sugar refining, but $Ca(OH)_2$ is preferred for the same purpose here.

In recent years, the radioactive isotope strontium-90, present in fallout from nuclear explosions, has caused much concern. It is concentrated in the bones along with calcium as $Sr_3(PO_4)_2$. No one knows at present how serious the danger really is.

16.3 / BARIUM

Though barium is less plentiful than strontium, it is found more frequently in concentrated deposits. Also, its properties are enough different from those of calcium for it to have many uses for which calcium could not be substituted. Barite, $BaSO_4$, is the most important mineral; a little witherite, $BaCO_3$, is also mined.

Metallic barium is usually made by aluminum reduction. The uses are of a type to require only small amounts of metal— a few tons a year. As a *getter* in vacuum tubes, it reacts with the residual gases, improving the vacuum and increasing the efficiency of the tube:

$$3Ba + N_2 \rightarrow Ba_3N_2$$
$$2Ba + O_2 \rightarrow 2BaO$$

Barium is an effective scavenger for some copper alloys. A few alloys are in use; one of them, Frary metal, is a lead alloy containing barium and calcium. It is made by electrolyzing barium and calcium chlorides, using a molten lead cathode.

Because $BaSO_4$ is so insoluble, it is reduced with carbon to give moderately soluble BaS:

$$BaSO_4 + 4C \xrightarrow{\Delta} BaS + 4CO$$

Other barium compounds can be made from BaS or $BaCO_3$.

Much barite is simply ground up to make drilling muds for oil well drilling, to buoy up the heavy drilling equipment and to prevent gas and oil from blowing out. Precipitated $BaSO_4$ is a finer quality; often it is precipitated together with ZnS (see lithopone, p. 176).

Ba(NO$_3$)$_2$ is used in green flares and fireworks, and barium compounds are added to some optical glasses.

Soluble barium compounds are very poisonous; some of them are used for rat poisons and insecticides. However, BaSO$_4$ is so insoluble that it may safely be taken internally to render the stomach and intestines opaque to x-rays.

Questions and problems

1. Compare the properties of the alkaline earth metals with the metals of periodic Group IIb, considering especially chemical reactivities, melting and boiling points, densities, solubilities of compounds, and formation of complex ions.

2. Make a similar comparison of the alkaline earth and the alkali metals.

3. Write equations for the following reactions:
   a. Reduction of uranium tetrafluoride by calcium
   b. Slaking of lime
   c. Setting of lime mortar
   d. Setting of plaster of Paris
   e. Preparation of calcium carbide
   f. Preparation of calcium cyanamide
   g. Preparation of strontium carbonate by fusing celestite with sodium carbonate

4. What is meant by hard water? How is it formed? For what reasons is it objectionable? In how many different ways might water be softened?

5. By the use of barium as a getter, the gas pressure in a vacuum tube having an internal volume of 23 ml is reduced from 10^{-6} atmospheres to 10^{-7} atmospheres at 21°C. What is the total number of molecules of gas remaining in the tube?

6. (Library.) In addition to the rotary lime kiln shown in Figure 16.1, other types have been used. Sketch one other type of lime kiln and discuss its relative advantages and disadvantages compared to the rotary kiln.

The Metals of Group 5: Magnesium, Sodium, and Potassium, with Ammonium Ion

17

Group 5 contains the alkaline earth metal, magnesium, and the alkali metals, sodium and potassium. The ammonium ion, which is included because of the importance of its salts, resembles in its solubilities the alkali metal ions, particularly the potassium ion.

17.1 / MAGNESIUM

In Chapter 16, magnesium was referred to, and some of its properties were listed in Table 16.1. The element is in analytical Group 5 because the solubilities of its salts differ somewhat from those of the other alkaline earth metals.

Occurrence and metallurgy. Among the very familiar magnesium minerals are magnesite, $MgCO_3$, dolomite, $MgCO_3 \cdot CaCO_3$, and many silicates. Most American magnesium of commerce is obtained from sea water, at a plant at Freeport, Texas. Magnesium is precipitated from sea water as insoluble $Mg(OH)_2$ which is converted to $MgCl_2$ and electrolyzed.

Some magnesium of high purity is produced by reduction of MgO, from magnesite or dolomite, by ferrosilicon. The latter is an alloy of approximate composition Fe 35, Si 65, used primarily to scavenge steel and to add silicon to steels. In this reduction, only the silicon is involved:

$$2MgO + Si \rightarrow SiO_2 + 2Mg$$

The reaction is carried out in a vacuum furnace, the volatile magnesium distilling off.

American production for the past ten years has fluctuated between about 50 and 100 thousand tons; Russia is believed to have built her production to about the same level.

Properties and uses. With a density of 1.74, magnesium is the lightest structural metal. It is the most easily machined metal, and can also be cast, rolled, or extruded. It is ordinarily protected by a film of basic magnesium carbonate, but corrodes rapidly in salt water. If ignited, it burns violently. Strength in metals involves several factors, so comparisons are difficult, but for beams of equal weight, magnesium provides more than twice the stiffness of aluminum and nineteen times that of steel. Common alloys contain about 10 per cent Al or about 5 per cent Zn. Magnesium alloyed with aluminum and thorium is used for rocket hulls.

In wartime, magnesium is used for incendiary bombs. Its action may be combined with that of thermite or jellied gasoline. Once ignited, it burns in water

$$Mg + H_2O \rightarrow MgO + H_2$$

or in carbon dioxide

$$2Mg + CO_2 \rightarrow 2MgO + C$$

or in nitrogen

$$3Mg + N_2 \rightarrow Mg_3N_2$$

Compounds. The familiar salt is $MgSO_4 \cdot 7H_2O$, Epsom salt, which, in contrast to the sulfates of the heavier alkaline earth metals, is very soluble. Besides its use as a purgative, it is used in fireproofing and finishing fabrics.

When magnesium carbonate is heated to about 800°, it decomposes to *light magnesium oxide:*

$$MgCO_3 \rightarrow MgO + CO_2$$

When this oxide is added to water, a suspension of $Mg(OH)_2$, called milk of magnesia, is obtained. MgO and $Mg(OH)_2$ are used in toothpastes and many other preparations.

If MgO is heated above 1400°C, it compacts to *dense magnesium oxide,* a refractory substance melting above 2800°, useful for firebrick.

Insoluble compounds of use in qualitative analysis are $MgNH_4PO_4$ and $Mg(OH)_2$. The latter, a colorless gelatinous precipitate, is more distinctive when it adsorbs the dye para-nitrobenzeneazoresorcinol, to give a blue *lake*.

17.2 / SODIUM

Some properties of the alkali metals are shown in Table 17.1. You will observe that they are low-melting, low-boiling, light, and very active metals. As we would expect, there is a regular progression in the magnitude of most properties. Although the ease with which the valence electron is given up increases regularly from lithium to cesium, the oxidation potential of lithium is surprisingly high. This is because oxidation potentials measure the tendency of a metal to go into aqueous solution, and the value for lithium is enhanced by the high energy of hydration of the lithium ion. Sodium and potassium are about equally plentiful, but the greater solubility of sodium compounds has caused much Na^+ ion to be leached out of igneous rocks. Potassium is consequently more plentiful in primary rocks, while

TABLE 17.1 / PROPERTIES OF THE ALKALI METALS

	M.P. (°C)	B.P. (°C)	Density (g/cm³)	Potential $M \rightarrow M^+ + e$	Abundance (%)
Li	186	1336	0.53	3.02	0.006
Na	97.7	890	0.97	2.71	2.83
K	63.6	775	0.86	2.92	2.59
Rb	39.0	690	1.53	2.92	0.03
Cs	28.5	670	1.90	2.92	0.0007

sodium has been concentrated in the ocean, in salt lakes, and in deposits left behind by the evaporation of salt lakes of past eras.

Minerals and metallurgy. Besides vast deposits of rock salt in many parts of the world (including Michigan, New York, Ohio, Louisiana, and Kansas) other sources that have been exploited are $NaNO_3$ from Chile, $Na_2B_4O_7 \cdot 10H_2O$, borax, from

California, and Na_2CO_3 from alkali lakes in our western states. Of course, the quantity of sodium ion in sea water is tremendous, and even greater amounts are present in the silicate minerals of the earth.

Sodium metal is prepared commercially by electrolysis of molten NaCl in a Downs cell as shown in Figure 17.1, chlorine

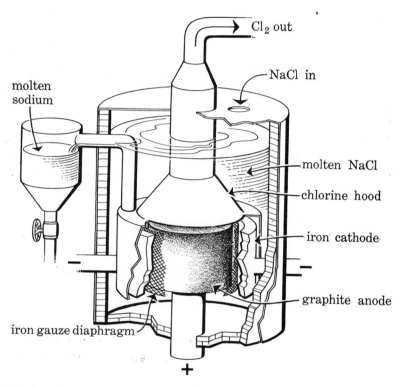

FIGURE 17.1 / DOWNS CELL FOR PRODUCTION OF SODIUM BY ELECTROLYSIS OF MOLTEN SODIUM CHLORIDE

being a valuable by-product. American production and use of nearly 150,000 tons a year makes sodium a larger tonnage metal than nickel, tin, or magnesium. The importance of sodium is not ordinarily appreciated because most of the uses are of a sort not apparent to the consuming public. At the prevailing price of 17 cents a pound, sodium is, next to iron, the cheapest metal per cubic foot.

Most of the uses of sodium depend on its reactivity. The largest single use, the manufacture of lead tetraethyl, has been referred to. It is used in metallurgy in the preparation of Ti, Zr, and other metals thus:

$$TiCl_4 + 4Na \rightarrow Ti + 4NaCl$$

Sodium is a powerful reducing agent in organic chemistry; for this purpose its action is often moderated by alloying it with mercury or lead.

A few uses of the metal depend on its physical properties: sodium vapor lamps give a brilliant yellow light; valves used in large gasoline or diesel engines have a hollow stem filled with sodium metal to conduct heat away from the valve head, and molten sodium metal is used as a heat transfer medium in some nuclear power plants.

Some sodium compounds are most easily prepared from metallic sodium. Sodium burns in air to Na_2O_2; in a limited supply of air, to Na_2O; in hydrogen, to NaH; and in ammonia, to $NaNH_2$.

Compounds. Ordinary salt, $NaCl$, besides being a necessary constituent of our diet, is used to flavor and preserve food. In one way or another, about 20 pounds of salt are used by each of us every year in our foods. However this is only a small percentage of the 25 million tons of salt consumed in the United States annually—a third of the world's consumption. It is used in the production of chlorine, sodium carbonate, and sodium hydroxide, in the removal of ice and snow from highways, in refrigerating brines, in water-softening, and in innumerable other ways.

Na_2CO_3, commonly called soda ash or washing soda, is used in the manufacture of glass, in soap-making, in water-softening, and many other ways—over seven million tons annually. It has a greater variety of uses than any other compound except sulfuric acid. Most of it is made by the Solvay process in which NH_3 and CO_2 are passed into a saturated solution of sodium chloride, giving NH_4^+ and HCO_3^- ions:

$$NH_3 + CO_2 + H_2O \rightarrow NH_4^+ + HCO_3^-$$

With the Na^+ and Cl^- ions already present, this gives a solution containing the ions Na^+, NH_4^+, Cl^-, and HCO_3^-. Although all four possible combinations of these ions are quite soluble, the solution is so concentrated that the least soluble, $NaHCO_3$, precipitates:

$$Na^+ + Cl^- + NH_4^+ + HCO_3^- \rightarrow \underline{NaHCO_3} + NH_4^+ + Cl^-$$

The $NaHCO_3$ is filtered off and heated:

$$2NaHCO_3 \xrightarrow{\Delta} Na_2CO_3 + H_2O + CO_2$$

The relatively expensive ammonia is recovered and reused by treating the ammonium chloride with slaked lime, giving $CaCl_2$ solution as a by-product:

$$2NH_4^+ + 2Cl^- + Ca^{+2} + 2OH^- \rightarrow 2NH_3 + 2H_2O + Ca^{+2} + 2Cl^-$$

The only raw materials needed are limestone, salt, and water. Though most of the $NaHCO_3$ produced in this process is converted to Na_2CO_3 as shown, some of it is used as baking soda.

NaOH. known in commerce as caustic soda or lye, is obtained along with chlorine and hydrogen by the electrolysis of sodium chloride solutions. Some is also made by treating sodium carbonate solutions with slaked lime:

$$2Na^+ + CO_3^{-2} + Ca^{+2} + 2OH^- \rightarrow \underline{CaCO_3} + 2Na^+ + 2OH^-$$

Sodium hydroxide is used in the manufacture of rayon, of soap and of paper, in petroleum refining, and in reclaiming scrap tin.

A sodium compound that has become important recently is NaH, which cleans rust and scale from steel forgings and castings without attacking the metal itself as other methods—acid pickling or sand blasting—do:

$$Fe_2O_3 + 3NaH \rightarrow 2Fe + 3NaOH$$

Many other sodium compounds are important because of their cheapness and their solubility: $Na_2SO_4 \cdot 10H_2O$, NaCN, $Na_2S_2O_3 \cdot 5H_2O$, the various phosphates and silicates, to name only a few.

A few sodium compounds of limited solubility are available for analytical work. Among those that are less soluble than the corresponding potassium compounds are

$NaSb(OH)_6$
$NaZn(UO_2)_3(C_2H_3O_2)_9 \cdot 6H_2O$
$NaMg(UO_2)_3(C_2H_3O_2)_9 \cdot 5H_2O$

None of the precipitation tests is very sensitive. The yellow flame test for sodium must be used cautiously since it responds nicely to the presence of a few sodium ions from dissolved glass or other extraneous source.

17.3 / POTASSIUM

Because potassium rocks have less tendency to dissolve than those of sodium, the oceans average only about 0.035 per cent K, but some salt lakes and some underground salt deposits are much richer in potassium. Especially noteworthy are the deposits of Stassfurt, Germany, of Alsace in France, and of New Mexico. The Stassfurt deposits contain carnallite, $KCl \cdot MgCl_2 \cdot 6H_2O$, and the New Mexico deposits, mainly sylvinite, $KCl \cdot NaCl$.

Potassium metal. At present, the only production of the metal is by the reaction

$$KCl + Na \overset{\Delta}{\rightleftharpoons} NaCl + K$$

The reaction proceeds to the right because of the lower boiling point of potassium. By varying conditions, pure potassium or a potassium-sodium alloy can be obtained. Because there are few uses for which potassium is preferable to the much cheaper sodium, only a few tons are produced annually. An alloy containing two parts potassium to one part sodium remains liquid to $-22°C$, and this alloy is often more convenient to handle than the pure metal. The liquid alloy has also been considered as a heat transfer medium in nuclear reactors. Potassium is used in photoelectric cells more sensitive than those containing sodium. Cesium cells are still more sensitive to light.

Compounds. 95 per cent of all potassium is used for agricultural purposes, since potassium is required by all land plants and is insufficiently supplied by many soils.

Because potassium compounds are generally less soluble than those of sodium, they are more easily purified by crystallization and do not absorb water as readily. Although the cheaper sodium compounds are usually preferred in industry, the potassium compounds may be more suitable for laboratory use. $KClO_3$, $K_2Cr_2O_7$, $KMnO_4$, KNO_3 are common reagents; in large scale applications the sodium compounds would be economical.

Sometimes the properties of the sodium and potassium compounds differ in respects that are essential for a particular use. Potassium soaps are soft and can be squeezed from a tube; potash glass is hard and high-melting.

Compounds of potassium which have limited solubility are: $K_3Co(NO_2)_6$, $K_2NaCo(NO_2)_6$, K_2PtCl_6, K_2SiF_6, and $KClO_4$. Two very insoluble organic compounds of potassium are potassium tetraphenylborate and potassium dipicrylamide. The latter has been suggested for precipitating potassium from sea water on a commercial scale. Potassium gives a characteristic violet flame test.

17.4 / AMMONIUM COMPOUNDS

Ammonium salts resemble potassium salts closely in their solubilities, presumably because the ammonium and potassium ions are about the same size. Before testing for potassium, remove the ammonium ion completely if you wish to avoid errors.

All ammonium salts liberate ammonia when warmed gently with NaOH:

$$NH_4^+ + OH^- \rightarrow NH_3 \uparrow + H_2O$$

The test is sufficiently sensitive to detect ammonium ion easily.

Ammonium salts decompose when heated, usually giving ammonia and an acid:

$$NH_4Cl \underset{\Delta}{\rightleftarrows} NH_3 + HCl$$

However, with some oxidizing anions, the reaction follows a different course:

$$(NH_4)_2Cr_2O_7 \underset{\Delta}{\rightleftarrows} N_2 + Cr_2O_3 + 4H_2O$$
$$NH_4NO_2 \underset{\Delta}{\rightleftarrows} N_2 + 2H_2O$$
$$NH_4NO_3 \underset{\Delta}{\rightleftarrows} N_2O + 2H_2O$$

Several ammonium compounds are used as fertilizers, especially $(NH_4)_2SO_4$, $(NH_4)_2HPO_4$, and NH_4NO_3. NH_4Cl, called *sal ammoniac*, is used in dry cells and also as a soldering flux.

Most of the ammonium compounds of commerce are prepared by neutralizing ammonia, produced by the Haber process, with the proper acid. Ammonium sulfate is also obtained as a by-product of coke manufacture; the evolved gases are passed over sulfuric acid to remove the ammonia. Nearly a million tons of $(NH_4)_2SO_4$ are obtained each year in this way.

Questions and problems

1. Assuming that the density of sea water is 1.025 g/cm^3 or 63.86 pounds per cubic foot, and that its average NaCl content is 2.9 per cent, how much sodium ion is present in each cubic mile of the ocean?

    Answer   Over 52,000,000 tons

2. The magnesium ion content of sea water is about 0.13 per cent. How much magnesium metal could be obtained from a cubic mile of sea water, and how much would it be worth at a price of 36 cents a pound?

3. Write equations for the following reactions:
    a. The burning of sodium in hydrogen
    b. The burning of sodium in excess air
    c. The burning of sodium in a limited supply of air to sodium monoxide
    d. The burning of sodium in ammonia
    e. The reduction of beryllium chloride by sodium metal
    f. The reaction which would result if water were used in an attempt to extinguish a magnesium incendiary bomb
    g. The preparation of magnesium metal by reduction with ferrosilicon
    h. The reduction of KCl by sodium metal
    i. The removal of scale, Fe_3O_4, from iron by NaH

4. K_2CO_3 is prepared by bubbling CO_2 through a solution of KOH prepared electrolytically. Look up the solubilities of KCl, NH_4Cl, NH_4HCO_3, and $KHCO_3$, and explain why a method similar to the Solvay process is not used.

5. Identify by formulas (library, if necessary, for some):
    Caustic soda   Washing soda
    Caustic potash   Saleratus
    Soda ash   Halite
    Sal ammoniac   Potassium superoxide
    Epsom salt   Orthoclase

6. Look up the derivation of the word "potassium."

Other Metals of Interest

18

```
H                                                              He
Li  Be                                          B  C  N  O  F  Ne
Na  Mg                                          Al Si P  S  Cl Ar
K   Ca Sc **Ti** **V**  Cr Mn Fe Co Ni Cu Zn Ga Ge As Se Br Kr
Rb  Sr Y  **Zr** **Cb** **Mo** Tc **Ru** **Rh** **Pd** Ag Cd In Sn Sb Te I  Xe
Cs  Ba La **Hf** **Ta** **W**  Re **Os** **Ir** **Pt** **Au** Hg Tl Pb Bi Po At Rn
Fr  Ra Ac
```

The metals included in our qualitative scheme have been selected on various grounds: their importance, their familiarity, ease of analysis, their value for illustrating typical methods of analysis, and whim. In this chapter we shall consider some of the metals that were omitted.

18.1 / LITHIUM

Some of the properties of lithium were summarized in Table 17.1, page 192. It is not a particularly rare element, but its availability is limited by the fact that it occurs principally in small amounts in silicate ores. It is mined in North Carolina and in the Black Hills of South Dakota. A metal of slight importance ten or fifteen years ago, lithium has many new applications. Foremost is the use of the lithium-6 isotope in thermonuclear bombs (H-bombs). Lithium-6 constitutes about 7.4 per cent of natural lithium. The methods by which this isotope is separated, and, indeed, the production data and much other information about lithium, are secret. Lithium metal from electrolysis of molten LiCl, when added in small amounts to magnesium, aluminum, or beryllium, gives light, strong alloys which are quite resistant to corrosion. LiH and the complex compounds, lithium borohydride and lithium aluminum hydride, $LiBH_4$ and $LiAlH_4$, are valuable reducing agents and light-weight sources of hydrogen. The very soluble, and hence deliquescent, LiCl and LiBr are used in commercial dehumidifying systems, and lithium soaps are used as additives for lubricating greases, in which they are soluble.

The solubilities of lithium compounds resemble those of the alkaline earth metals; Li_3PO_4, Li_2CO_3, and $Li_2C_2O_4$ are insoluble. The lithium flame test is a beautiful carmine red, noticeably different from those of calcium and strontium.

The more active alkali metals, rubidium and cesium, are used in sensitive photoelectric cells.

18.2 / BERYLLIUM

The only beryllium ore is beryl, $Be_3Al_2Si_6O_{18}$ (the rare gem stone, emerald, is a transparent green beryl). Brazil is the largest producer of beryllium ore, and the United States uses two-thirds of the world's yearly production of about a thousand tons of metal. The difficult metallurgy contributes to the high price of over $70 a pound. The metal is very light, strong, hard, fairly high-melting, and is resistant to corrosion; but the scarcity and high price limit its use to specialty items that require only small quantities. The largest use is for fatigue-resistant beryllium-copper, but other alloys, such as light, hard beryllium-aluminum, are also used. Beryllium is important in nuclear research because it emits neutrons when bombarded by alpha particles. It is strange that the element was known for almost a hundred and fifty years before its very poisonous nature was realized during World War II research.

18.3 / TITANIUM, ZIRCONIUM, AND HAFNIUM

These metals are all hard, strong, tough, and, at ordinary temperatures, more resistant to corrosion than stainless steel. In addition, all have special properties that give them exciting potential as engineering metals. Titanium weighs less than 60 per cent as much as steel though it is fully as strong; it is used particularly for jet engine parts and for construction in chemical plants where extremely corrosive conditions are encountered. Since zirconium does not absorb neutrons, it does not become radioactive when it is used for construction of nuclear power plants. Hafnium, on the other hand, is an excellent absorber of neutrons and is therefore used for control rods of nuclear reactors.

Titanium, at 0.44 per cent of the earth's crust, is the tenth most abundant element; the chief ore, ilmenite, $FeTiO_3$, is rather common. Zirconium, at 0.02 per cent, is widely scattered, but enough is concentrated in deposits of baddeleyite, ZrO_2, that scarcity is no problem. Hafnium is less abundant but is present in all zirconium ores to the extent of about two per cent.

Although these metals are ordinarily unreactive, at very high temperatures they combine so vigorously with both oxygen and nitrogen that they can be used as scavengers. The metallurgies are therefore difficult. All three metals are obtained by reduction of the tetrachlorides with magnesium or sodium in an inert atmosphere. In fabrication, they are cast or welded either in vacuum or in an atmosphere of argon or helium. Their high melting points make this still more difficult.

The much different uses of zirconium and hafnium require that they be completely separated from one another. Undoubtedly one of the hardest separations commercially practiced, it can be done by extracting solutions containing their thiocyanate complexes with the organic compound methyl ethyl ketone ("MEK"). Zirconium remains in the water layer, and hafnium goes into the MEK layer.

Of the compounds of this group, the most important is TiO_2, of which a half million tons are used annually for a paint body and for a filler for paper, rubber, linoleum, and the like. The gem zircon is $ZrSiO_4$. The stable oxidation state for all of the group is +4; reduction of solutions containing $TiCl_4$ by zinc gives purple Ti^{+3}, which is a popular reducing agent in the laboratory.

18.4 / VANADIUM, NIOBIUM, AND TANTALUM

About 85 per cent of the world's production of 4000 tons of vanadium is a by-product of uranium mining in the western

United States. Metallic vanadium is used almost entirely in alloy steels. With oxidation states of $+2$, $+3$, $+4$, and $+5$, vanadium undergoes some interesting oxidation-reduction reactions with characteristic color changes. Doubtless you remember the use of V_2O_5 as a catalyst for the contact process of sulfuric acid manufacture.

Niobite, $Fe(NbO_3)_2$, and tantalite, $Fe(TaO_3)_2$ occur as mixed ores in Nigeria, Congo, and elsewhere. Stainless steel containing a very small amount of niobium can be welded without losing its stainless qualities. Tantalum, even more than the other metals of the group, is resistant to corrosion. It is used in the chemical industry for such things as stills, valves, and heat exchangers in nitric acid systems. Tantalum is used in surgical repair work because it does not set up any adverse reactions in the body.

18.5 / MOLYBDENUM AND TUNGSTEN

The chief ore of molybdenum is molybdenite, MoS_2. Most of the world's supply comes from Colorado and Utah. Tungsten occurs mainly in China, but some is also mined in the United States, Portugal, and the Republic of Korea. The American ore is scheelite, $CaWO_4$. Molybdenum and tungsten resemble chromium in many ways, showing even more tendency toward passivity. All of the group are very hard, and each is the highest melting member of its transition series.

Most of the molybdenum and tungsten are used for alloy steels that maintain their hardness and strength at high temperatures. Pure molybdenum has high temperature applications, as in filament supports of light bulbs and parts for jet and rocket engines. Tungsten, the highest melting of all metals, is used for light filaments and welding electrodes. Carboloy, W_2C and Co, was mentioned in Chapter 15.

The $+6$ oxidation state is the important one for both metals. $(NH_4)_2MoO_4$ is a useful analytical reagent.

18.6 / PLATINUM METALS

The two triads below Fe, Co, and Ni in the periodic table are known collectively as the light (Ru, Rh, Pd) and heavy (Os,

Ir, Pt) platinum metals. They are scarce in nature—platinum at 5×10^{-7} per cent of the earth's crust is about the same as gold; palladium is slightly more plentiful; the others, less. Of the million ounces of these metals produced annually, more than half comes from South Africa, and most of the rest from Canada. Russia occasionally dumps enough on the market to upset prices. The United States imports about three-fourths of the world's platinum metals, besides producing a little in Alaska and California. Platinum and palladium are produced in more or less equal amounts; together they comprise well over ninety per cent of the total.

The light platinum metals have densities of about 12 g/cm^3; the heavy ones, about 22; with osmium, at 22.7, considered the heaviest of all metals. Mostly, they are white, lustrous, malleable, ductile, and very inert; and all except palladium and platinum are hard. Platinum and palladium, which adsorb hydrogen and other gases, have catalytic applications in the petroleum industry and elsewhere. Other uses of the metals of the group are for electrical contacts, chemical ware, fountain pen nibs, dental appliances, and the like, where the high cost is offset by their resistance to chemical attack and by other desirable properties. For these purposes, they may be used alone or alloyed with each other or with gold or other metal.

Few platinum-group compounds are important. OsO_4, poisonous and foul-smelling, is used as an oxidizing agent, catalyst, and biological stain. Some platinum complexes are important; K_2PtCl_6 is an insoluble potassium salt.

18.7 / GOLD

Gold, electron configuration 2, 8, 18, 32, 18, 1, is much less active than the other two coinage metals and almost always occurs in the free state, although telluride ores are known. Extraction of gold from its ores is often done simply by washing away the dirt; the heavy gold (density 19.32 g/cm^3) remains behind. Movies and TV have shown us how this is accomplished by the prospector equipped with burro, pickax, whiskers, and tin pan. The same process is accomplished on a large scale in placer mining and dredging. The water, sand, and gravel run down sluices, the gold collecting behind slats. Amalgamated copper plates in the sluice improve the efficiency of the operation. Very low-grade deposits can be worked by the cyanide process:

$$4Au + 8CN^- + 2H_2O + O_2 \rightarrow 4Au(CN)_2^- + 4OH^-$$

The gold can be recovered by electrolysis or by displacement by zinc:

$$2Au(CN)_2^- + Zn \rightarrow Zn(CN)_4^{-2} + 2Au$$

The amalgamation process is often used first to remove larger gold particles, followed by cyaniding.

Each year South Africa produces about half of the world's 40 million troy ounces, and the Soviet Union about half the remainder. Canada, the United States, and Australia are other large producers.

Gold is the most malleable and ductile of all metals and, except for silver and copper, is the best conductor of heat and electricity. It is the lowest metal in the activity series but is dissolved by chlorine water and by aqua regia. The latter reagent is effective because it combines the oxidizing action of nitric acid with the complexing action of the chloride ion:

$$Au + 4H_3O^+ + NO_3^- + 4Cl^- \rightarrow AuCl_4^- + 6H_2O + NO$$

The cyanide process works for a similar reason: the $Au(CN)_2^-$ ion is so extremely stable that even atmospheric oxygen is able to oxidize the metal.

Pure gold is too soft for many uses and is generally alloyed with silver, copper, or other metal. The proportion of metal is usually expressed in *carats*; pure gold is 24 carat, half gold and half alloying metal is 12 carat, and so on. Most newly mined gold goes into monetary reserves. Of that used industrially, most is used for jewelry and other decorative purposes. Dental, chemical, and electrical uses are important.

Except for the dicyanoaurate(I) ion, the only stable oxidation state of gold is +3. Gold(III) chloride and its complex, chlorauric acid, $HAuCl_4$, are the common compounds. Analytically, gold precipitates in Group 2. The usual confirmatory test is *purple of Cassius*, a mixture of colloidal gold and hydrated SnO_2 formed by reducing a neutral or slightly acid solution of Au(III) with $SnCl_2$ solution.

Questions and problems

1. Write equations for the following reactions:
   a. Reduction of $TiCl_4$ by sodium
   b. Reduction of $ZrCl_4$ by magnesium
   c. The solution of platinum in aqua regia, giving $PtCl_6^{-2}$
   d. The dissolving of silver ore by the cyanide process
   e. The formation of purple of Cassius from solutions of $AuCl_3$ and $SnCl_2$

2. What volume of H_2 (measured at STP) can be obtained from each of the following:
   a. 1 g zinc with sulfuric acid
   b. 1 g CaH_2 with water
   c. 1 g sodium with water
   d. 1 g lithium with water
   e. 1 g $LiBH_4$ with water
   f. 1 g $LiAlH_4$ with water   *Answer f* 2.36 liters

3. Transparency to x-rays appears to be inversely proportional to atomic weight. What material, having the necessary structural strength and containing no atoms of high atomic weight, would you recommend for windows in x-ray tubes?

4. (Partly library.) List the platinum metals and give a use for each of them.

5. Can you account for the resemblance of Li to Mg and of Be to Al?

6. At one time, a beryllium compound was used as a fluorescent material in fluorescent lamps. Can you suggest a reason why it is no longer used for this purpose?

7. Which of the metals discussed in this chapter would you use for each of the following:
   a. Aircraft tail assemblies that must withstand considerable stress
   b. Construction material for the reactor of a nuclear-powered submarine
   c. Alloying material to make copper hard and strong
   d. Alloying metal to harden magnesium without increasing its density

e. Catalyst for the oxidation of NH_3 to NO (the Ostwald process)

f. Crucibles that can withstand many reagents even at white heat

g. Dental bridgework

h. Screws and wire for repairing fractured bones

8. The filament of a 60-watt electric lamp weighs 0.020 g. Assuming that this is the average size lamp, how many tons of tungsten are required for the 8 billion lamps made in this country each year?

part THREE

THE LABORATORY

Introduction to the Laboratory

19

Since the system of laboratory and stockroom operation varies somewhat from school to school, and because each instructor develops a preference for certain techniques, some of the directions in this chapter are subject to modification. Needless to say, it is the prerogative of the instructor, not of the student, to make changes. Although there is more than one good way to do many things, it is important that you understand why an operation may be carried out in a certain way. It is the aim in this chapter and in the rest of the laboratory part to describe methods of operation that will give good results and at the same time to suggest why each operation is done as it is. Let us hope that the directions in this book, combined with the advice of the laboratory instructor, will build up in each student that combination of dexterity and understanding which is known as laboratory technique.

19.1 / LABORATORY EQUIPMENT

At the first meeting of your laboratory class you will be assigned a workspace and a locker. Your first task will be to check the apparatus in your locker against the equipment list. (A list of equipment suitable for use with this book is given in the Appendix, page 332.) Examine your apparatus carefully; defective equipment must be reported the first day. If you don't know the name of a piece of apparatus, ask.

Extra equipment. In addition to the regular locker equipment, some items are needed which in most schools the student is expected to make for himself:

Stirring rods (Figure 19.1). Cut off a 15 cm length of 3 mm glass rod and fire polish both ends so completely that the ends

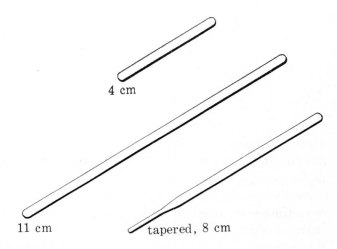

4 cm

11 cm   tapered, 8 cm

FIGURE 19.1 / STIRRING RODS

have a hemispherical shape. *Let it cool,* then cut it into two pieces, 4 and 11 centimeters long, fire polishing the newly cut ends. The 11 cm stirring rod is a convenient length for use in 75 mm test tubes and the 4 cm length can stand in a 5 or 10 ml beaker without tipping it over. Make several stirring rods of each size. If desired, a few tapered stirring rods may be made by heating near the middle of a 15 cm length and drawing down to a diameter of about 2 mm before cutting. The narrow end is useful for dislodging precipitates from the bottom of a 2 ml centrifuge tube. All stirring rods should be *thoroughly* fire polished. A sharp edge on a rod can be as effective as a file for scratching glassware and causing it to break.

Capillary pipettes (Figure 19.2). In addition to the medicine droppers supplied with reagent bottles, each student needs three

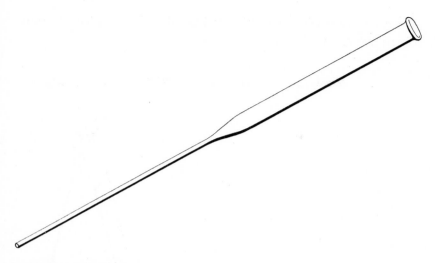

FIGURE 19.2 / CAPILLARY PIPETTE

or more capillary pipettes. These have long narrow tips for withdrawing liquids from test tubes and centrifuge tubes.

To make capillary pipettes, heat a 20 cm length of 7 mm glass tubing at its center, without using a wing top. Rotate the tubing between the fingers and continue heating until it is so hot it sags in the middle. Then remove it from the flame and pull it out to a diameter between 1 and 2 mm. When the glass has cooled, cut it to make two pipettes with capillary sections about 7 or 8 cm long—long enough to reach to the bottom of a 75 mm test tube. In order that the other end of the pipette will hold the rubber bulb firmly, heat it till it is soft, then take it out of the flame and flare it slightly with a battery carbon or the tip of a file. Then heat it again and press it down on a flat porcelain or steel surface.

Calibrate each pipette by counting the drops while it delivers several milliliters into your graduate, and paste a label on it, giving the number of drops per ml. Pipettes delivering at the rate of 40 drops per ml are especially convenient. Since medicine droppers deliver at about 20 drops per ml for most solutions, a "drop" in qualitative analysis is considered to be 0.05 ml. The drops delivered by capillary pipettes are considerably smaller. If your pipettes deliver at about 40 drops per ml, you can use them for measuring reagents by just dispensing twice as many drops as are called for.

FIGURE 19.3 / WASH BOTTLE

Wash bottle (Figure 19.3). This is not a necessity in semi-micro work because a capillary pipette is usually more satisfactory for washing precipitates. However, your instructor may wish you to make a wash bottle for extra convenience in transferring precipitates and rinsing equipment. A 125 ml erlenmeyer fitted with 5 mm glass tubing makes a wash bottle of handy size. With such a small wash bottle, a flexible tip is unnecessary. The tip may be made by drawing out the end of the delivery tube, or a more rugged tip may be made by fire polishing the end until it is almost closed. In either case, the tip should have an inside diameter no greater than 0.5 mm, so that it will deliver a very fine stream. A polyethylene squeeze bottle also makes a good wash bottle, although it cannot be heated.

Reagent bottles (Figure 19.4). In some laboratories, the individual reagent system is used, with each student having almost all reagents in his desk; in other schools, most reagents are kept on reagent shelves supplying an entire section. Each system has advantages. Although the equipment list in Appendix II.1 is intended for the general reagent shelf system, it is easily modified to fit the use of individual reagents.

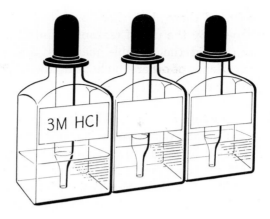

FIGURE 19.4 / DROPPING BOTTLES
All labels neatly lettered,
level, and at same height.

The six dropping bottles included in the equipment list may contain:

    $6M$ acetic acid
    $3M$ hydrochloric acid
    $12M$ hydrochloric acid
    $3M$ sulfuric acid
    $3M$ ammonia ("ammonium hydroxide")
    $15M$ ammonia

At the discretion of the instructor, more reagents, such as $3M$ nitric acid and thioacetamide solution may be added to this list. Some reagents are not suitably kept in ordinary dropping bottles: $16M$ nitric and $18M$ sulfuric acid may be kept in glass stoppered bottles and $6M$ sodium hydroxide in a plastic bottle. In any case, unstable solutions like sodium hexanitrocobaltate (III) should never be kept in individual bottles. Instead, they should be kept on the general reagent shelf and replaced periodically. Label the bottles neatly and protect the labels with cellophane tape.

19.2 / LABORATORY TECHNIQUES

There are many operations that you will perform repeatedly in qualitative analysis. There may not be a single best way to do each of these, but there are always good, poor, and horrible ways. By the use of reasonable intelligence and carefulness you can avoid the horrible methods, and you can benefit by the experience of others in choosing those methods that have proved most satisfactory.

Heating solutions. Heating the small quantities of liquids used in qualitative analysis presents some special problems. If a solution is heated directly over the flame in a 75 mm test tube or 2 ml centrifuge tube, bubbles of escaping steam will throw liquid out of the tube. Test tubes and centrifuge tubes must be heated in a water bath as shown in Figure 19.5. A 150 ml beaker

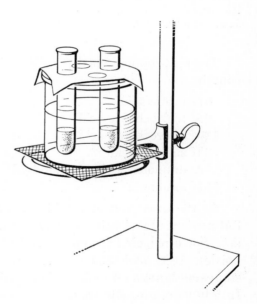

FIGURE 19.5 / WATER BATH

and a sheet of aluminum or lead with several holes make a satisfactory bath. If a rubber band is slipped around the tube near the top, it is easier to remove it from the hot bath.

Evaporating solutions. If solutions are to be boiled down, they should be in a wider container than a test tube—a 5 or 10 ml beaker, a crucible, or a casserole. A microbeaker can be placed on a wire gauze and heated much like an ordinary size beaker, by using a micro burner with a small flame and playing the flame back and forth. Slower heating can be accomplished by heating the wire gauze a short distance away, letting the gauze conduct the heat to the beaker.

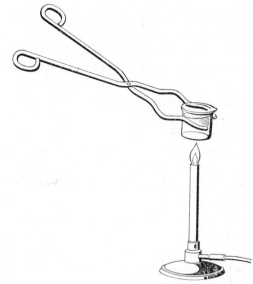

FIGURE 19.6 / HOLDING A BEAKER
WITH A CRUCIBLE TONGS

Another method of heating a beaker is to hold it in a crucible tongs and wave it gently back and forth in the flame. The beaker should be held as shown in Figure 19.6 with both jaws of the tongs *outside* the beaker. To grip the side of the beaker with the tongs so that one of the jaws is inside the beaker, perhaps even dipping into the solution, is one of the worst mistakes in technique that a student can make. Not only does it contaminate the solution, but it hurts the feelings of the laboratory equipment manufacturer who has gone to great pains to design a tongs that can hold several sizes of beakers and crucibles properly.

Smooth evaporation can be accomplished by the use of an air bath made of a 100 ml beaker or iron crucible and a nichrome triangle. Even smoother, but rather slow, evaporation can be obtained with an infrared lamp pointed down on the solution from several inches above. These methods are especially useful for evaporating liquids that contain considerable amounts of suspended solids.

It is often necessary in qualitative analysis to boil a solution down just to dryness without overheating. When you are doing this, remember that the beaker or crucible will retain enough heat to evaporate away the last drop of two of liquid after it has been removed from the flame. To prevent the solid residue from being baked by overheating, always have handy in a pipette a little of the same liquid being evaporated. Then if you seem to have overheated the material, just add a drop or two of liquid.

Separation. Separation of precipitate and solution is accomplished by centrifuging to settle and compact the precipitate and then withdrawing or decanting the solution.

Mixtures should ordinarily be centrifuged in 75 mm test tubes. The use of 2 ml centrifuge tubes should be limited to confirmatory tests to make small amounts of precipitate more visible. The tube with the material to be centrifuged should be balanced by a similar tube containing an equal volume of water placed in the opposite position in the centrifuge. You will soon learn how much time you need to allow for centrifuging. Heavy crystalline precipitates require only a few seconds; sometimes several minutes at top speed may be required for very fine, almost colloidal precipitates. *Never* start the centrifuge and walk away; stay beside it while your material is centrifuging.

After centrifuging, the clear liquid, called the *centrifugate*, may be simply decanted from a dense, tightly packed precipitate such as is obtained on centrifuging AgCl or PbSO$_4$. Lighter precipitates like the sulfides and hydroxides of Groups 2 and 3 must be treated more carefully, removing the liquid with a capillary pipette. In doing this, squeeze the air from the bulb before dipping the pipette in the liquid, and move the tip down in the liquid gradually to avoid stirring up the precipitate. If you observe that the precipitate is being stirred up, recentrifuge. A tiny plug of cotton in the tip of the pipette, as in Figure 19.7, will help prevent a light precipitate from being drawn into the pipette.

Washing. As there will always be some liquid adhering to a precipitate, washing is generally necessary. In fact, subsequent

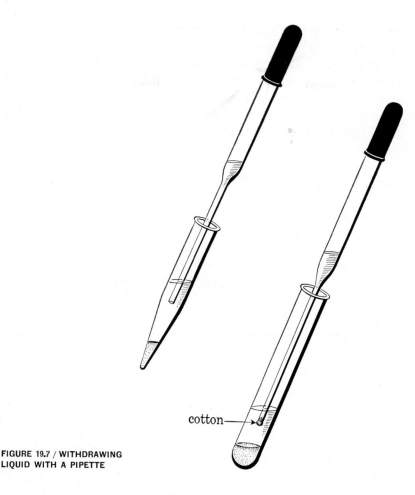

cotton—

**FIGURE 19.7 / WITHDRAWING
LIQUID WITH A PIPETTE**

tests will sometimes not work unless a precipitate is washed free
of adsorbed ions. Add the wash water or other prescribed wash
liquid to the precipitate and stir it up *thoroughly*—the water will
penetrate a compacted precipitate scarcely at all. Then centrifuge and withdraw or decant the wash water. Often the first
wash is added to the separated centrifugate, since it is likely to
contain an appreciable amount of the soluble ions. When washing must be thorough, it is better to use several small portions
of wash water rather than a single large portion.

Transferring of precipitates. You will do well to plan your
work to reduce to a minimum the transfer of precipitates. When

you must remove a precipitate from one container to another, the best way is to loosen it with a stirring rod and wash it with a fine spray of water or other liquid from a capillary pipette. Very small amounts of precipitate may be suspended in water by stirring, and then sucked up into a pipette for transferring. Your nickel microspatula is also useful for transferring precipitates that are not wet with acid.

Mixing. Reaction cannot very well take place between different solutions unless they are mixed, and mixing becomes a problem in semimicro work. Solutions in beakers can be mixed by thorough stirring with a glass rod, but in a test tube, even combining an up-and-down with a rotary motion, stirring is not very efficient. The best way to mix solutions in a test tube is to hold the tube at the top in one hand and snap it near the bottom with the other. Practice with a tube containing water; surprisingly, there will be no splashing unless the tube is nearly full. Liquids in centrifuge tubes can be mixed by drawing a little liquid into a pipette and squirting it back.

Neutralizing. Proper neutralization requires thorough mixing —an obvious point that is often not sufficiently appreciated. Various indicators may be used: inside indicators like phenolphthalein or methyl orange are put into the solution being tested; outside indicators like the various indicator papers are touched by the stirring rod wet with the thoroughly mixed solution. Litmus paper is the only indicator we need. Remember never to dip it into the solution; it will give solutions and precipitates an unwanted color and it is less sensitive as an indicator than when used properly.

Measuring. Liquid reagents are measured in drops or milliliters. It is accurate enough for our purposes to assume that 20 drops from a medicine dropper equal 1 ml. Make the necessary adjustments when using your calibrated pipettes.

A triple-beam balance accurate to 0.01 g gives sufficient accuracy for weighing solids. It is recommended that centrifuge tubes containing the proper amounts of different solids be displayed in the laboratory so that quantities may be estimated by bulk. Commonly used solids are:

NH_4NO_3	0.1 g	Procedure 3.7
$(NH_4)_2SO_4$	0.4 g	Procedure 2.4
$KClO_3$	0.15 g	Procedure 3.3
$NaBiO_3$	0.05 g	Procedure 3.3
$Na_2S_2O_4$	0.04 g	Procedure 2.7
$H_2C_2O_4$	0.5 g	Procedure 2.12

19.3 / GENERAL LABORATORY SUGGESTIONS

Try to be orderly and neat. Organize your work space and return each item to its proper position as soon as you have used it. Pipettes and stirring rods may be kept on a clean towel or a sheet of paper, or in a rack made from a cardboard box, or in a beaker of distilled water. If your space is not near a waste jar, you can save steps if you use a beaker as a private waste jar. Remember, the sink is only for liquids and soluble solids. Broken glass, matches, paper, and such go in the waste jar.

Keep all equipment clean. An instructor quickly forms an opinion of a student who asks for his assistance and can't offer him a clean beaker or test tube to work with. If a liquid dish-washing detergent is not provided, get yourself a small plastic bottle of it. Wash your glassware carefully with a little detergent, rinse it thoroughly with tap water, then rinse again with distilled water. Pipe cleaners make excellent brushes for centrifuge tubes and dropper tubes. Cleanliness pays.

A laboratory class should be prepared for, just like any other class. Study the procedures you expect to cover. Plan your work carefully and do it intelligently. If you are supposed to have a blue precipitate and you get a yellow one, don't plunge blindly ahead. Try to figure out what went wrong and repeat your work but not your mistake. Don't skimp on labels. At the end of each procedure and at the end of each day's work, label everything—your solutions, your precipitates, the girl at the next desk. A good way to affix a label to a test tube is to clip a piece of paper to it with a rubber band.

19.4 / NOTEBOOK

A major part of your laboratory work is the keeping of a neat, honest, up-to-date notebook recording your analyses of both knowns and unknowns. Since most instructors have definite ideas about the type of notebook they prefer, no detailed suggestions will be given.

Cation Analysis

About two dozen cations are usually included in qualitative analysis schemes devised for instructional purposes for freshman chemistry. With the aid of extra separations and tests, such schemes can easily be extended to include rarer metals, but that is in the province of texts intended for advanced courses.

By the use of *group reagents* you will divide the ions into *groups* of convenient size for further manipulation. Ordinarily you will separate an ion from all others before applying a *confirmatory test*, though a few of these tests may be applied in the presence of other ions that do not interfere. The outline of our qualitative scheme as it would be used on a general unknown follows.

Group 1

Group 1 is often called the *Silver Group* for its most important member.

> *Group reagent:* Hydrochloric acid.
> *Precipitate:* $AgCl$, $PbCl_2$, Hg_2Cl_2. (All other ions tested for are soluble in approximately $0.5M$ HCl.)

Since a much more sensitive test for lead is obtained in Group 2, and there are only a few soluble compounds of mercury(I), silver is the only ion here of real importance. In an extended scheme of analysis, thallium(I) chloride would also be precipitated.

Any Group 1 precipitate is removed by centrifuging and decanting the solution, which contains the ions of later groups.

Group 2

Group 2 is often called the *Copper-Arsenic Group.*

> *Group reagent:* H_2S (from thioacetamide) in $0.5M$ HCl.
> *Precipitate:* Group 2A, the Copper Subgroup: PbS, Bi_2S_3, CuS, CdS.
> Group 2B, the Arsenic Subgroup: HgS, As_2S_3, Sb_2S_3, SnS_2.

The subgroups are separated by treatment with KOH solution in which Subgroup 2B is soluble.

The mercury precipitated in this group is Hg(II). Mercury is the only element that has separate tests for its different oxidation states. Other elements are changed in the course of the qualitative procedures to a single oxidation state. This is true of Sn(II) and Sn(IV), of As(III) and As(V), etc. If you desire to know which oxidation state was present to begin with, you must make a suitable distinguishing test on a portion of your original sample.

There is no arsenic cation; it is found in water solution either as arsenite or arsenate. However, since both of these anions give precipitates with H_2S, arsenic is included in the cation analysis for convenience.

Many rarer elements can be precipitated in Group 2. These include molybdenum, selenium, tellurium, gold, and the platinum metals.

After Group 2 has been removed, the solution is tested for Group 3.

Group 3

Group 3 is sometimes called the *Nickel-Aluminum Group.*

> *Group reagent:* $(NH_4)_2S$, NH_3 solution, and NH_4Cl.
> *Precipitate:* Group 3A, the Nickel Subgroup: $Fe(OH)_3$, MnS, CoS, NiS.
> Group 3B, the Aluminum Subgroup: $Al(OH)_3$, $Cr(OH)_3$, ZnS.

The elements of Subgroup 3B are soluble on treatment with NaOH and H_2O_2.

Some elements of considerable practical importance could be added to this group, if desired: uranium, titanium, zirconium, vanadium, beryllium, and the rare earth metals. Some of these, like the fourteen rare earth metals, are extremely difficult to separate from one another.

After removing the Group 3 precipitate, the solution is used for the Group 4 procedures.

Group 4

Group 4 is sometimes called the *Barium Group*.

Group reagent: $(NH_4)_2CO_3$, NH_3 solution, and NH_4Cl.
Precipitate: $BaCO_3$, $SrCO_3$, $CaCO_3$, $MgCO_3$.

Only if a large amount of magnesium is present does any precipitate in this group. The test for it in Group 5 is more significant.

After the Group 4 precipitate has been removed only Group 5 remains in solution.

Group 5

Group 5 is called the *Soluble Group*.

Ions present: Mg^{+2}, Na^+, K^+, NH_4^+.

The other alkali metal ions, Li^+, Rb^+, and Cs^+ would also be found here.

Since it is convenient to add reagents in the form of their ammonium salts and to render solutions alkaline with NH_3 solution throughout the qualitative scheme, NH_4^+ ion must always be tested for on an original sample of substance.

For each one of these groups, you will first be given a *known solution* which contains all of the ions of the group. After you have successfully analyzed the known, you should have acquired sufficient skill in the operations required in the group and sufficient familiarity with the appearance of the confirmatory tests to analyze an *unknown solution* correctly. After you have

Cation analysis, flowsheet form

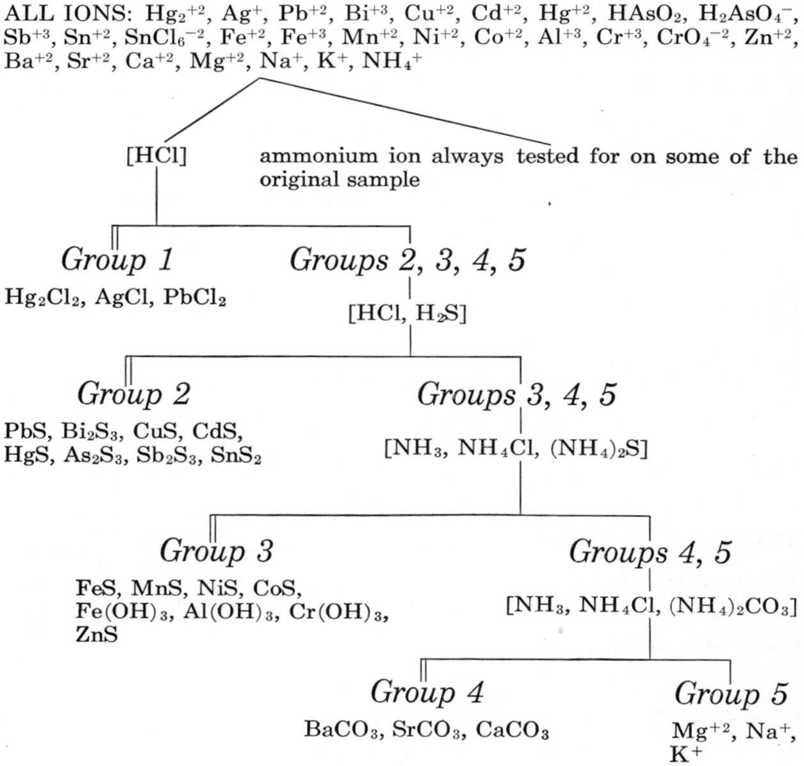

ALL IONS: Hg_2^{+2}, Ag^+, Pb^{+2}, Bi^{+3}, Cu^{+2}, Cd^{+2}, Hg^{+2}, $HAsO_2$, $H_2AsO_4^-$, Sb^{+3}, Sn^{+2}, $SnCl_6^{-2}$, Fe^{+2}, Fe^{+3}, Mn^{+2}, Ni^{+2}, Co^{+2}, Al^{+3}, Cr^{+3}, CrO_4^{-2}, Zn^{+2}, Ba^{+2}, Sr^{+2}, Ca^{+2}, Mg^{+2}, Na^+, K^+, NH_4^+

[HCl]   ammonium ion always tested for on some of the original sample

Group 1
Hg_2Cl_2, AgCl, $PbCl_2$

Groups 2, 3, 4, 5
[HCl, H_2S]

Group 2
PbS, Bi_2S_3, CuS, CdS, HgS, As_2S_3, Sb_2S_3, SnS_2

Groups 3, 4, 5
[NH_3, NH_4Cl, $(NH_4)_2S$]

Group 3
FeS, MnS, NiS, CoS, $Fe(OH)_3$, $Al(OH)_3$, $Cr(OH)_3$, ZnS

Groups 4, 5
[NH_3, NH_4Cl, $(NH_4)_2CO_3$]

Group 4
$BaCO_3$, $SrCO_3$, $CaCO_3$

Group 5
Mg^{+2}, Na^+, K^+

FIGURE 20.1 / THE SEPARATION OF THE GROUPS

done known and unknown solutions for all five groups, you are considered competent to handle *general unknowns*, either alloys, salts, or mixtures of salts. When analyzing a general unknown you must test for the different groups in their proper order, as any group reagent will also precipitate all ions of previous groups.

The conventions that we will use in flowsheets for the analytical schemes for the various groups are illustrated in Figure 20.1. Reagents are written with molecular formulas and enclosed in brackets, [ ]. A horizontal line is used to indicate separation by centrifuging, with the precipitate written at the left below two short vertical lines, and the centrifugate to the right below a single vertical line. Two branching diagonal lines, $\wedge$, indicate separation of the material into two portions.

Procedures for Analysis
of Group 1

21

The only common metal chlorides that are insoluble in a moderately acid solution are those of silver, mercury(I) and lead. This fact is the basis of the separation of Group 1. When chloride ion is added in the form of dilute HCl to a solution containing the ions Ag^+, Hg_2^{+2}, and Pb^{+2}, a precipitate of AgCl, Hg_2Cl_2, and $PbCl_2$ is formed. The acidity produced by adding the chloride ion as HCl rather than as, say, NH_4Cl will prevent the formation of basic chlorides such as SbOCl and BiOCl. The K_{sp} of $PbCl_2$ is large enough, especially if the solution is warm, that its precipitation is by no means as complete as that of Hg_2Cl_2 and AgCl. In fact, there will always be enough Pb^{+2} remaining in solution to give a test in Group 2. Furthermore, if a fairly large excess of HCl is added, the soluble $PbCl_4^{-2}$ ion will be formed and lead will be completely missed in Group 1. Of course, if a general unknown is being analyzed, the lead which escapes precipitation in Group 1 will be detected in Group 2 anyway, but the student missing Pb^{+2} in a Group 1 unknown will get scant comfort from this.

PROCEDURE 1.1 / Precipitation of Group 1

Dilute five drops of a Group 1 known or unknown, in a 75 mm test tube with fifteen standard drops of distilled water to a total volume of 1 ml. To this add two or three drops of $3M$ HCl, stir

Group 1

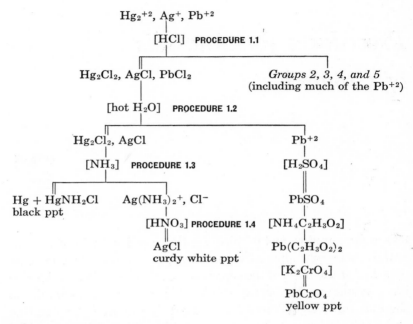

FIGURE 21.1 / THE ANALYSIS OF GROUP 1

and centrifuge. To test for complete precipitation, add another drop of HCl and notice whether a considerable amount of additional precipitate forms (a little cloudiness does not matter). If more precipitation takes place, repeat the stirring, centrifuging, and testing for complete precipitation. Continue according to either paragraph *A* or *B*.

A: If the test solution is either a Group 1 known or a Group 1 unknown. If you are going to analyze the material according to the Procedures of Group 1 only, it is a good idea to cool the mixture by dipping the test tube into cold water and stir, rubbing the side of the test tube with the glass stirring rod. This helps bring down the $PbCl_2$ precipitate. Centrifuge and decant off the solution which may be discarded. The precipitate which will be referred to as *Precipitate 1.1* (Note 1) may contain AgCl, Hg_2Cl_2 and $PbCl_2$ and is to be analyzed according to Procedure 1.2.

B: If the test solution is a general unknown. The solution need not be cooled to insure complete precipitation of $PbCl_2$. After centrifuging, decant off the supernatant liquid to a test tube, stopper it, label it *Solution 1.1* and save it for analysis of later groups. Analyze *Precipitate 1.1* (Note 1) according to Procedure 1.2.

Notes

1. Throughout the Laboratory Procedures, the solution and precipitate obtained in Procedure 1.1 are referred to as *Solution 1.1* and *Precipitate 1.1*; those obtained in Procedure 1.2 are referred to as *Solution 1.2* and *Precipitate 1.2*, and so on.

PROCEDURE 1.2 / Separation and identification of lead

Wash the Precipitate 1.1 from Procedure 1.1 with a mixture of 1 drop of $3M$ HCl and 2 drops of H_2O, stir, and centrifuge. Decant and discard the washings. Add 1 ml of H_2O to the precipitate in the test tube and heat it in the boiling water bath for several minutes, stirring constantly. Centrifuge immediately (Note 1) and decant the hot *Solution 1.2* into a test tube to be tested for lead. Wash the *Precipitate 1.2* with 10 drops of hot water by stirring and heating in the boiling water bath for half a minute. Quickly centrifuge and discard the hot wash water, saving Precipitate 1.2 for Procedure 1.3 (Note 2).

To test for lead on Solution 1.2, add 4 drops of $18M$ H_2SO_4 carefully to the solution. Stir and cool it thoroughly. A fine granular precipitate of $PbSO_4$ slowly forms. Centrifuge, decant off the solution, and add 0.5 ml of $NH_4C_2H_3O_2$ solution. Heat in the water bath and stir for several minutes. The precipitate should dissolve completely leaving a clear solution (if it is not clear, centrifuge to settle the suspended material and transfer the solution to another test tube). Add 1 drop of $6M$ acetic acid and 2 drops of K_2CrO_4 solution. A yellow precipitate of $PbCrO_4$ confirms the presence of Pb^{+2} (Note 3).

Notes

1. The basis of the separation of lead from silver and mercury (I) is the solubility of $PbCl_2$ in hot water. It is necessary to

centrifuge and decant off the solution quickly since $PbCl_2$ reprecipitates as soon as it cools.

2. If $PbCl_2$ is not completely removed from Precipitate 1.2 by washing, it will react with NH_3 in Procedure 1.3, giving a white precipitate of $Pb(OH)_2$ or $Pb(OH)Cl$ which can mask the desired black test for mercury.

3. The quantity of any confirmatory test should always be noted. This is usually best observed after centrifuging. The amount of confirmatory test obtained with an unknown should always be at least equal to that obtained with the known, since the amount of each element given in an unknown is always at least equal to that present in the known. None of our unknowns are supposed to contain elements in trace quantities.

PROCEDURE 1.3 / Separation and detection of mercury(I)

To Precipitate 1.2, add 5 drops of water and 5 drops of $15M$ NH_3 solution, stir thoroughly and centrifuge. Decant the *Solution 1.3* into a 10 ml beaker to test for silver in Procedure 1.4. A black or very dark gray precipitate of $Hg + HgNH_2Cl$ proves the presence of mercury(I) (Notes 1 and 2).

Notes

1. As noted on page 133, the confirmatory reaction involves the auto-oxidation-reduction of mercury(I) to mercury metal and mercury(II) amidochloride.

2. If the precipitate is light gray or white, it may contain $Pb(OH)_2$ or $AgCl$. The first should have been removed by the hot water treatment, the second by NH_3. These treatments may be repeated, or mercury(I) may be further confirmed by dissolving the gray precipitate in 1 drop of $16M$ HNO_3 and 4 drops of $12M$ HCl, heating in the water bath and stirring. Then transfer the solution to a 5 ml beaker, add 2 drops of $12M$ HCl, and boil down almost to dryness to destroy excess aqua regia. Then add 4 drops of water and transfer to a centrifuge tube. Centrifuge if necessary to obtain a clear

solution and add 2 drops of $SnCl_2$ solution. A white, gray, or black precipitate of Hg and Hg_2Cl_2 confirms Hg_2^{+2}.

PROCEDURE 1.4 / Identification of silver

To Solution 1.3 carefully add $3M$ HNO_3 with constant stirring until the mixture is acid. (Do not dip the litmus into the solution. Instead, touch the tip of the stirring rod to a piece of blue litmus on a watch glass.) A white precipitate of AgCl confirms the presence of silver. Be sure you have completely neutralized the solution; stir thoroughly after each addition of acid before testing on the litmus. Often students fail to stir the mixture and have merely acidified the tip of the stirring rod. In this way, they miss silver, the easiest of all elements to detect.

Word equations for the reactions of Group 1

With these to guide you, you should have no trouble working out the formula equations. The equations for confirmatory reactions are marked with an asterisk.

Lead:

1. Lead ion + chloride ion → lead chloride
2. Lead chloride $\xrightarrow{\text{(hot water)}}$ lead ion + chloride ion
3. Lead ion + sulfate ion → lead sulfate
4. Lead sulfate + acetate ion → lead acetate + sulfate ion
5.* Lead acetate + chromate ion → lead chromate + acetate ion

Mercury:

1. Mercury(I) ion + chloride ion → mercury(I) chloride
2.* Mercury(I) chloride + ammonia →
$\qquad$ mercury + mercury(II) amidochloride
$\qquad$ + ammonium ion + chloride ion

Silver:

1. Silver ion + chloride ion → silver chloride
2. Silver chloride + ammonia →
$\qquad$ diamminesilver ion + chloride ion
3.* Diammine silver ion + hydronium ion + chloride ion →
$\qquad$ silver chloride + ammonium ion + water

Questions and problems

1. Instead of using hydrochloric acid to precipitate the Group 1 metals, why not use a solution of NaCl? Would there be any objection to acidifying the Group 1 solution with $3M$ H_2SO_4 and then adding solid NaCl?

2. In precipitating Group 1, you added about 4 drops of $3M$ HCl to 1 ml of material. If the Group 1 solution was neutral to begin with, what is the H_3O^+ concentration of the solution after the addition of the acid?

3. Tell what might be wrong with each of the following techniques:
   a. Use concentrated HCl instead of $3M$ solution to precipitate Group 1.
   b. In separating lead from the other Group 1 metals, after treating Precipitate 1.1 with boiling water for several minutes, chill it in an ice bath before centrifuging.
   c. Do Procedure 1.3 and 1.4 before doing Procedure 1.2.
   d. In Procedure 1.4 use $3M$ HCl rather than HNO_3 to precipitate silver.

4. AgCl dissolves in strong HCl solution as the complex ion $AgCl_2^-$; Hg_2^{+2} has practically no tendency to form complex ions. Could you use this as the basis of an alternate separation of mercury(I) and silver?

5. Would it be possible to substitute HBr for HCl in Group 1 analysis? Would it be desirable? Explain your answers.

6. A Group 1 unknown gave a white precipitate with HCl which was completely unaffected by hot water but dissolved readily and completely in NH_3 solution. On the basis of this much information could you confidently state which Group 1 ions are present and which absent, or might there be some uncertainty?

7. Thallium(I) chloride is also insoluble. Look up the reactions and solubilities of thallium compounds and try to devise an enlarged Group 1 scheme that would allow for the inclusion of Tl^+ in the group.

8. Answer by formula of a reagent or combination of reagents which will precipitate

Hg_2^{+2} but not Hg^{+2}
Hg_2^{+2} but not Ag^+
Hg_2^{+2} but not Pb^{+2}
Pb^{+2} but not Hg^{+2}

9. Answer by formula of a single reagent which you could use to distinguish between the following pairs of substances. Tell what you would observe when the reagent was added to each substance:

Two yellow solids, K_2CrO_4 and $PbCrO_4$
Two white solids, $AgCl$ and $PbCl_2$
Two black solids, Hg and PbS
Two clear solutions, Ag^+, NO_3^- and $Ag(NH_3)_2^+$, Cl^-
Two clear solutions, Pb^{+2}, $2NO_3^-$ and $2H_3O^+$, $PbCl_4^{-2}$
Two yellow solutions, $2K^+$, CrO_4^{-2} and Fe^{+3}, $3Cl^-$

Procedures for Analysis
of Group 2

22

Group 2 is composed of the metal ions that have soluble chlorides but very insoluble sulfides—so insoluble that they precipitate even in the low concentration of sulfide ion present in a $0.5M$ HCl solution. Of the metals we study in the laboratory, eight are included in Group 2. This is the largest group in the qualitative scheme; it is invariably broken down into more manageable subgroups before separating the metals. The reagent we use for this purpose is $2M$ KOH. Those metals which are amphoteric enough that their sulfides dissolve in this solution constitute *Subgroup 2B*; the others comprise *Subgroup 2A*.

PROCEDURE 2.1 / Precipitation of Group 2

A: Preliminary treatment with HCl and H_2O_2. Use 8 drops of a Group 2 known solution or 6 drops of a Group 2 unknown or all of the Group 1 centrifugate of a general unknown. Add 2 drops of $3M$ HCl and 2 or 3 drops of H_2O_2 to the sample in a 5 ml beaker. Boil down to 1 or 2 drops, but *not* to dryness. (Keep the $3M$ HCl handy to add another drop if the solution starts to go dry.) Allow it to cool, then add 6 drops of $6M$ HCl and carefully evaporate to a pasty mass. *Do not bake* (Note 1).

Add concentrated NH_3 until the solution is alkaline to litmus. (If it is already alkaline, omit this step.) Add $3M$ HCl until the solution is just acid. At this point the volume of the solution should be about 15 drops (0.75 ml). If it is noticeably less, add enough water to make it up to this volume. Then add 3 drops of $3M$ HCl and proceed with the precipitation of the group (Note 2).

B: Precipitation of the group. To the material from Part A in a three-inch test tube, add 10 drops of thioacetamide solution and stir. Stopper the test tube with a plug of cotton and place it in a boiling water bath for *at least* 10 minutes. Then add enough water to double the volume of the liquid in the test tube and two more drops of thioacetamide solution. Place the test tube in the boiling water bath for 5 more minutes, then centrifuge and separate by decanting into *Solution 2.1* and *Precipitate 2.1*. Prepare a wash solution by adding 5 drops of $4M$ NH_4Cl and 1 drop of thioacetamide solution to 1 ml of water and heating to boiling (Note 3). Add the first washings to the centrifugate. Wash Precipitate 2.1 twice, using a 10-drop portion of the wash solution each time.

The centrifugate will contain any ions of Groups 3, 4, and 5, but may also contain some unprecipitated material from Group 2. Test for completeness of precipitation by taking about a 1 ml sample of the centrifugate and adding 1 ml of water and 2 drops of thioacetamide and heating in the boiling water bath as before. A yellow, orange, or brown precipitate indicates incomplete precipitation. In that case, dilute all the Group 2 centrifugate with an equal volume of water and heat with thioacetamide, combining any precipitate obtained with Precipitate 2.1. If on your test sample you obtain no precipitate or only a white precipitate (S or ZnS), the precipitation is complete. A black precipitate could be NiS, CoS, or FeS from Group 3; all of the black Group 2 sulfides should have been precipitated already.

If you are doing only a Group 2 known or unknown, the centrifugate may be discarded after testing for complete precipitation. If it is to be saved for analysis of Groups 3, 4, and 5 of a general unknown, heat it in the boiling water bath for ten more minutes to complete the decomposition of thioacetamide and boil off the H_2S (otherwise they would be oxidized to SO_4^{-2} ion with the undesirable effects mentioned in Note 1). Save the centrifugate in a stoppered, *labeled* test tube for the analysis of the later groups.

Group 2

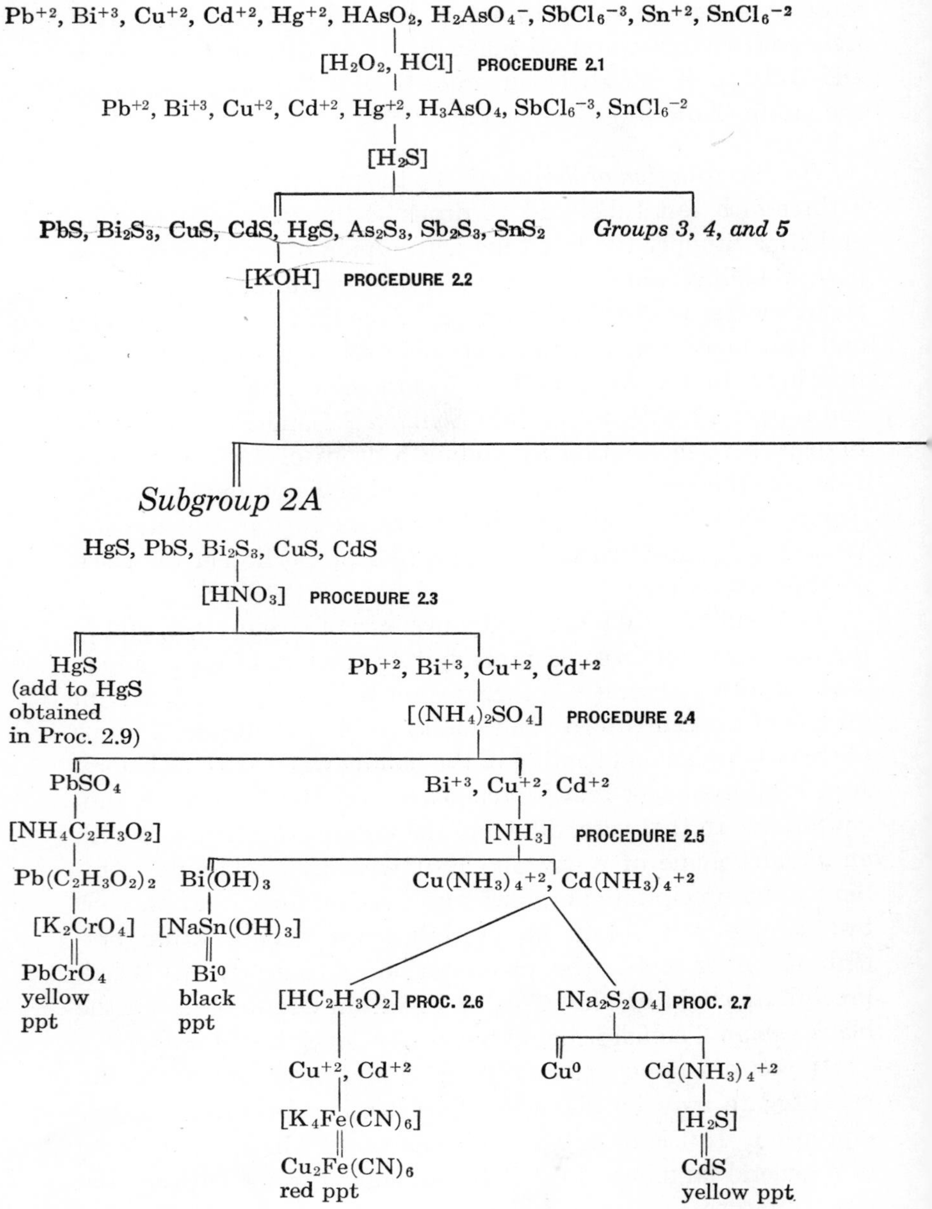

Pb^{+2}, Bi^{+3}, Cu^{+2}, Cd^{+2}, Hg^{+2}, $HAsO_2$, $H_2AsO_4^-$, $SbCl_6^{-3}$, Sn^{+2}, $SnCl_6^{-2}$

$[H_2O_2,\ HCl]$ **PROCEDURE 2.1**

Pb^{+2}, Bi^{+3}, Cu^{+2}, Cd^{+2}, Hg^{+2}, H_3AsO_4, $SbCl_6^{-3}$, $SnCl_6^{-2}$

$[H_2S]$

PbS, Bi_2S_3, CuS, CdS, HgS, As_2S_3, Sb_2S_3, SnS_2 *Groups 3, 4, and 5*

$[KOH]$ **PROCEDURE 2.2**

Subgroup 2A

HgS, PbS, Bi_2S_3, CuS, CdS

$[HNO_3]$ **PROCEDURE 2.3**

HgS
(add to HgS
obtained
in Proc. 2.9)

Pb^{+2}, Bi^{+3}, Cu^{+2}, Cd^{+2}

$[(NH_4)_2SO_4]$ **PROCEDURE 2.4**

$PbSO_4$

Bi^{+3}, Cu^{+2}, Cd^{+2}

$[NH_4C_2H_3O_2]$

$[NH_3]$ **PROCEDURE 2.5**

$Pb(C_2H_3O_2)_2$ $Bi(OH)_3$

$Cu(NH_3)_4^{+2}$, $Cd(NH_3)_4^{+2}$

$[K_2CrO_4]$ $[NaSn(OH)_3]$

$PbCrO_4$ Bi^0
yellow   black $[HC_2H_3O_2]$ **PROC. 2.6** $[Na_2S_2O_4]$ **PROC. 2.7**
ppt   ppt

Cu^{+2}, Cd^{+2} Cu^0 $Cd(NH_3)_4^{+2}$

$[K_4Fe(CN)_6]$ $[H_2S]$

$Cu_2Fe(CN)_6$ CdS
red ppt   yellow ppt

FIGURE 22.1 / THE ANALYSIS OF GROUP 2

Subgroup 2B

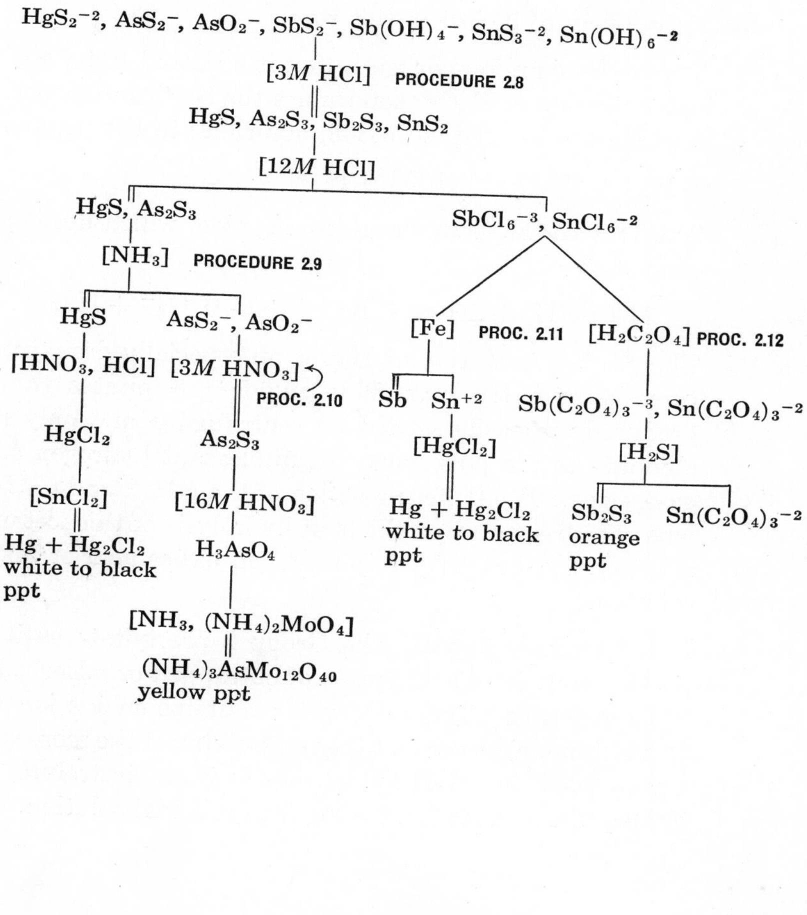

HgS_2^{-2}, AsS_2^-, AsO_2^-, SbS_2^-, $Sb(OH)_4^-$, SnS_3^{-2}, $Sn(OH)_6^{-2}$

[3M HCl]   PROCEDURE 2.8

HgS, As_2S_3, Sb_2S_3, SnS_2

[12M HCl]

HgS, As_2S_3 $SbCl_6^{-3}$, $SnCl_6^{-2}$

[NH$_3$]   PROCEDURE 2.9

HgS AsS_2^-, AsO_2^- [Fe]   PROC. 2.11   [$H_2C_2O_4$] PROC. 2.12

[HNO$_3$, HCl]   [3M HNO$_3$] Sb Sn^{+2} $Sb(C_2O_4)_3^{-3}$, $Sn(C_2O_4)_3^{-2}$

           PROC. 2.10

$HgCl_2$ As_2S_3 [HgCl$_2$]   [H$_2$S]

[SnCl$_2$]   [16M HNO$_3$] $Hg + Hg_2Cl_2$ Sb_2S_3 $Sn(C_2O_4)_3^{-2}$

$Hg + Hg_2Cl_2$ H_3AsO_4 white to black   orange
white to black   ppt   ppt
ppt

[NH$_3$, (NH$_4$)$_2$MoO$_4$]

$(NH_4)_3AsMo_{12}O_{40}$
yellow ppt

Notes

1. Boiling with HCl and H_2O_2 oxidizes $Sn(II)$ to $Sn(IV)$:

$$Sn^{+2} + 2H_3O^+ + 6Cl^- + H_2O_2 \rightarrow SnCl_6^{-2} + 4H_2O$$

Thus SnS_2 is precipitated, rather than SnS. Since SnS is not very soluble in KOH solution while SnS_2 is readily soluble, a much better separation of tin into Subgroup 2B is obtained if tin is first oxidized to the quadrivalent state.

Boiling down with HCl also reduces such ions as CrO_4^{-2} which would otherwise oxidize the thioacetamide to produce sulfate ion, precipitating Ba^{+2}, Sr^{+2}, Ca^{+2}, and Pb^{+2} as insoluble sulfates.

Care must be taken that the HCl solution is not evaporated to complete dryness, or baked, since some of the chlorides of Group 2 elements are volatile. $AsCl_3$ and $SnCl_4$ are especially likely to be lost in this way.

2. The hydronium ion concentration is adjusted to $0.5M$. The concentration of H_3O^+ determines the S^{-2} concentration in a solution saturated with H_2S, according to the equilibrium

$$H_2S + 2H_2O \rightleftharpoons 2H_3O^+ + S^{-2}$$

The H_2S comes from the thioacetamide, which decomposes on boiling:

$$CH_3CSNH_2 + 2H_2O \overset{\rightarrow}{\Delta} NH_4^+ + C_2H_3O_2^- + H_2S$$

The gradual evolution of H_2S is an especially desirable feature, because the crystalline sulfide precipitates that are produced are easily settled by centrifuging, and only slight amounts of the poisonous and unpleasant hydrogen sulfide gas escape. The buffering action of the NH_4^+ and $C_2H_3O_2^-$ ions, which are also products of hydrolysis of thioacetamide, affects the course of precipitation in either acid or alkaline solution.

3. It is necessary to wash the Group 2 precipitate as it may contain considerable amounts of entrapped or adsorbed ions of later groups. The wash water contains sulfide ion (from thioacetamide) to prevent the redissolving of the more soluble Group 2 sulfides. NH_4Cl, because it is an electrolyte, helps to keep the sulfides from going into colloidal solution.

4. The ions of Group 2 as they are present at the beginning of precipitation may be represented as Pb^{+2}, Bi^{+3}, Cu^{+2}, Cd^{+2}, Hg^{+2}, $HAsO_2$, $H_2AsO_4^-$, $SbCl_6^{-3}$, Sn^{+2}, and $SnCl_6^{-2}$. The most abundant or the most significant ionic species for each oxidation state of an element is given. In the case of mercury it is perhaps oversimplified; $HgCl_2$ is a covalent compound which can form ions in two ways in a solution that contains moderate amounts of Cl^-:

$$(1)\ HgCl_2 \rightleftharpoons Hg^{+2} + 2Cl^-$$
$$(2)\ HgCl_2 + 2Cl^- \rightleftharpoons HgCl_4^{-2}$$

The Group 2 solution probably contains $HgCl_2$ in greatest amount, then $HgCl_4^{-2}$, and Hg^{+2} least. However, Hg^{+2} presumably reacts most readily with S^{-2} and, as it is used up in this reaction, more is produced by the equilibrium reaction shown in Equation 1.

Tin(IV) cannot exist as a simple ion. It is found as complex ions such as $SnCl_6^{-2}$ or $Sn(OH)_6^{-2}$ depending on what negative ion is available. With antimony(III) the tendency to form a chloro complex ion is also very marked.

Arsenic(III) forms weak metaarsenious acid, $HAsO_2$, scarcely ionized at all in acid solutions. Arsenic(V) may be expected to be present mainly as H_3AsO_4, which is reduced by H_2S to $HAsO_2$.

5. The sulfides obtained in Procedure 2.1 are

PbS	black
Bi_2S_3	dark brown
CuS	black
CdS	yellow to orange
HgS	black or red (but also may be mixed with substances like $HgS \cdot HgCl_2$, white)
As_2S_3	yellow
Sb_2S_3	orange-red
SnS_2	yellow (there may also be brown SnS)

The first four of these are insoluble in $2M$ KOH solution; they constitute Subgroup 2A. The last three are soluble in $2M$ KOH. HgS is partly soluble, so must be recovered from both subgroups.

PROCEDURE 2.2 / Separation of Subgroups 2A and 2B

Do not start this procedure unless you have 15 minutes of working time available. Once started, it must be finished.

To Precipitate 2.1 from Procedure 2.1 in a 75 mm test tube, add 15 drops of $6M$ KOH, 2 ml of water, and 1 drop of thioacetamide solution (Note 1). Stir up the precipitate and heat in a boiling water bath for 3 minutes with occasional stirring. (Strong KOH or NaOH solutions are likely to bump when heated, especially when there is solid material in the container. Stirring while heating minimizes this danger. Be careful never to let hot alkali spatter into the eyes.) Centrifuge immediately after heating (Note 2). Withdraw the supernatant liquid and wash the residue twice using 5 drops of water for each washing and add the washings to the centrifugate. The residue may consist of the sulfides of Subgroup 2A, PbS, Bi_2S_3, CuS, and CdS plus some HgS, and is to be analyzed according to Procedures 2.3 to 2.7. If there is no time for further work, cover the precipitate with water containing a drop of thioacetamide solution (Note 3), stopper the test tube tightly, and label it 2A. The solution consisting of centrifugate and washings may contain ions of Subgroup 2B: AsO_2^-, AsS_2^-, $Sb(OH)_4^-$, SbS_2^-, $Sn(OH)_6^{-2}$, SnS_3^{-2}, and HgS_2^{-2}. Label it 2B and set it aside in a stoppered test tube to be analyzed by Procedures 2.8 to 2.12.

Notes

1. Thioacetamide is added to maintain sufficient S^{-2} concentration to prevent CuS and PbS from dissolving. The extra sulfide ion also helps dissolve HgS as HgS_2^{-2}.

2. Do not heat the Group 2 precipitate with KOH solution longer than 3 minutes, and do not let the precipitate stand for a long time in contact with KOH, or some of the Subgroup 2A sulfides might dissolve. Copper sulfide is especially apt to dissolve and go into Subgroup 2B.

3. This is done to prevent oxidation of sulfide to sulfate ion, for fear lead would be lost as lead sulfate which would not dissolve in $3M$ HNO_3 in the next procedure but would be left in Precipitate 2.3.

Subgroup 2A: Pb, Bi, Cu, and Cd

PROCEDURE 2.3 / Separation of mercury

This procedure takes 6 or 7 minutes. Don't start unless you have time to finish (Note 1).

Add 1 ml of $3M$ HNO_3 (1.5 ml would be better for a Group 2 known) to the precipitate from Procedure 2.2. Heat it in a boiling water bath for 2 or 3 minutes. Centrifuge and withdraw the solution (which we will call *Solution 2.3*) to a 5 ml beaker for Procedure 2.4. The *Precipitate 2.3* may be black, red, or white or shades in between (Note 2). Wash it with a mixture of 3 drops of water and 2 drops of $3M$ HNO_3, adding the wash water to Solution 2.3. Label Precipitate 2.3 and save it to combine with the HgS of Subgroup 2B, which will be separated in Procedure 2.9.

Notes

1. HNO_3 dissolves the sulfides of Subgroup 2A by oxidizing the sulfide ion so that the $[S^{-2}]$ left is much less than is required to exceed the solubility products of these compounds. CuS, for example, is always in equilibrium with a small amount of Cu^{+2} and S^{-2}:

   (1) $CuS \rightleftharpoons Cu^{+2} + S^{-2}$

   The concentrations present in a saturated solution are represented by the solubility product:

   $$K_{sp} = [Cu^{+2}] \cdot [S^{-2}] = 8.7 \times 10^{-36}$$

   The sulfide ion is oxidized by hot nitric acid in accordance with the equation

   (2) $3S^{-2} + 2NO_3^- + 8H_3O^+ \rightarrow 3S + 2NO + 12H_2O$

   Adding Equations 1 and 2 we get an over-all equation for the dissolving of a sulfide in nitric acid:

   (3) $3CuS + 2NO_3^- + 8H_3O^+ \rightarrow$
   $$3Cu^{+2} + 3S + 2NO + 12H_2O$$

   The K_{sp} of HgS is about 8.6×10^{-53}—much less than that of any of the other sulfides of Subgroup 2A. Therefore it is the last to be dissolved. However, if too strong a solution of HNO_3 is used or if the 3 molar solution is left in contact with the precipitate too long, an appreciable amount of HgS dissolves.

Another reason for avoiding more concentrated HNO_3 is that it is likely to oxidize sulfur to sulfate, giving insoluble $PbSO_4$.

2. Precipitation of mercury(II) with thioacetamide may give either a black or a red form, depending on such factors as temperature and pH. The two forms behave similarly in the reactions used in qualitative analysis, and after treatment with HNO_3, both may give lighter colored or white double salts like white $(HgS)_2 \cdot Hg(NO_3)_2$. A white precipitate at this point is thus not necessarily due to finely divided sulfur. Nor does a dark precipitate prove the presence of mercury, since light colored sulfur may be darkened by adsorbed or entrapped sulfides of Pb, Cu, and Bi.

PROCEDURE 2.4 / Separation and identification of lead

Solution 2.3 may contain Pb^{+2}, Bi^{+3}, Cu^{+2}, and Cd^{+2}, in a nitric acid solution with a total volume of 1.5 ml.

Add 0.4 g $(NH_4)_2SO_4$ (or more or less if the volume of the solution is markedly different from 1.5 ml). Stir thoroughly to dissolve the $(NH_4)_2SO_4$ and let it stand several minutes. Centrifuge and transfer the centrifugate, *Solution 2.4*, to a 75 mm test tube for Procedure 2.5, being careful not to carry over the fine granular *Precipitate 2.4*. Wash Precipitate 2.4 with two 5-drop portions of $1M$ $(NH_4)_2SO_4$, adding the first washing to Solution 2.4.

Even though Precipitate 2.4 may look like a few insignificant specks, assume that $PbSO_4$ is present and proceed as follows, since a barely noticeable amount of $PbSO_4$ may give quite a bulky precipitate of $PbCrO_4$. Add 0.5 ml of $NH_4C_2H_3O_2$ solution and set it in a water bath. Stir while warming for several minutes. To the clear solution (if it is not clear, centrifuge and separate it from the suspended material) add 1 drop of $6M$ acetic acid and 2 drops of K_2CrO_4 solution. A yellow precipitate confirms the presence of Pb^{+2}.

Notes

1. The substances most likely to precipitate along with $PbSO_4$ are $(BiO)_2SO_4$ and $BaSO_4$. Only $PbSO_4$ dissolves in $NH_4C_2H_3O_2$ and gives a yellow precipitate with K_2CrO_4 from a slightly acid solution.

   $PbSO_4$ is quite insoluble but does give an appreciable concentration of Pb^{+2}:

$$PbSO_4 \rightleftharpoons Pb^{+2} + SO_4^{-2} \qquad\qquad K_{sp} = 1.4 \times 10^{-8}$$

   Acetate ion ties up Pb^{+2} either as un-ionized $Pb(C_2H_3O_2)_2$ or as some complex ion so effectively that the $PbSO_4$ all goes into solution in supplying the Pb^{+2} ion for the equilibrium

$$Pb(C_2H_3O_2)_2 \rightleftharpoons Pb^{+2} + 2C_2H_3O_2^-$$

   But CrO_4^{-2} is still better at removing Pb^{+2} ion from solution:

$$PbCrO_4 \rightleftharpoons Pb^{+2} + CrO_4^{-2} \qquad K_{sp} = 2.0 \times 10^{-15}$$

   Thus $PbCrO_4$ can be precipitated even from solutions containing high concentrations of $C_2H_3O_2^-$.

PROCEDURE 2.5 / Separation and detection of bismuth

Solution 2.4 may contain Bi^{+3}, Cu^{+2}, and Cd^{+2}. Add $15M$ NH_3 dropwise with thorough stirring until the solution becomes alkaline, and then 2 drops excess. Be sure the solution is thoroughly mixed so that it is alkaline throughout. A deep blue color indicates copper but does not prove it. A gelatinous precipitate which is not easily noticed may be $Bi(OH)_3$. Centrifuge whether the precipitate is noticed or not and save the centrifugate as *Solution 2.5*, for the next procedure. Wash *Precipitate 2.5* twice with 5-drop portions of water, discarding the washings. Add 6 drops of $6M$ NaOH and 3 drops of $SnCl_2$ solution and stir. An immediate jet-black precipitate proves the presence of bismuth. A brown precipitate is not a positive test (Notes 1 and 2).

Notes

1. The reagent is stannite ion produced when the sodium hydroxide and tin(II) chloride solutions are mixed:

$$3OH^- + Sn^{+2} \rightarrow Sn(OH)_3^-$$

2. $Cu(OH)_2$ and $Cd(OH)_2$ might be present in the white precipitate if insufficient NH_3 was added in the separation.
$Pb(OH)_2$ or $Sn(OH)_2$ might also be present in small amounts.
None of these will be reduced by $Sn(OH)_3^-$ to give black
precipitates. The stannite ion undergoes auto-oxidation-
reduction on standing to give gray or brown metallic tin:

$$2Sn(OH)_3^- \rightarrow Sn(OH)_6^{-2} + \underline{Sn}$$

Since the tin precipitate is neither *immediate* nor *black*, it
does not qualify as a confirmatory bismuth test.

PROCEDURE 2.6 / Detection of copper

Solution 2.5 may contain $Cu(NH_3)_4^{+2}$ and $Cd(NH_3)_4^{+2}$ in ammonia solution. Copper is easily confirmed in the presence of
cadmium, though the reverse is not true. Divide Solution 2.5,
using one-third for this test and two-thirds for the identification
of cadmium, Procedure 2.7. Make the test solution just acid
with $6M$ $HC_2H_3O_2$ and add 2 drops of $K_4Fe(CN)_6$ solution. A
brick-red precipitate or a reddish cloudiness proves the presence
of copper (Note 1). In the absence of copper and the presence
of cadmium, a white precipitate, $Cd_2Fe(CN)_6$, may appear at
this point, but it does not obscure a positive copper test and is
not a suitable confirmation of cadmium.

Notes

1. The deep blue color of $Cu(NH_3)_4^{+2}$ is not by itself a sufficient confirmatory test for copper. Nickel forms a tetraammine complex of similar appearance. To be sure, a student
is not to be congratulated for having precipitated NiS in
Group 2; nevertheless it does happen. Once nickel gets into
Group 2, its behavior mimics copper up to the confirmatory
test in which nickel gives light green $Ni_2Fe(CN)_6$ precipitate.
Also the blue $Cu(NH_3)_4^{+2}$ is not especially sensitive; it will
detect only about one part of Cu^{+2} in 18000 of water. The
$Cu_2Fe(CN)_6$ test is much better. One part of copper in
1,000,000 of water may be detected.

PROCEDURE 2.7 / Detection of cadmium

To two-thirds of Solution 2.5, if copper is present, add a pinch of $Na_2S_2O_4$, sodium dithionite (sometimes called sodium hydrosulfite), about equal in volume to a BB shot. Heat in the hot water bath for 2 or 3 minutes. A black precipitate of finely divided metallic copper forms quickly. Centrifuge and decant the solution into another test tube, discarding the precipitate of free copper. Add 5 drops of thioacetamide solution to the *clear, colorless* centrifugate and heat in the water bath for 2 minutes. A yellow precipitate of CdS confirms the presence of cadmium. If copper is not present, a small amount of $Na_2S_2O_4$ should still be added to remove traces of other ions, especially Hg^{+2} and Bi^{+3}, which darken the CdS (Note 2).

Notes

1. *Alternate test for cadmium using KCN.* (Not to be used unless it is specifically recommended by your instructor!)
   Test the remaining two-thirds of Solution 2.5, containing $Cu(NH_3)_4^{+2}$, $Cd(NH_3)_4^{+2}$, and NH_3, with litmus in the presence of your instructor or the stock clerk who is to add the KCN. Even though you *know* that your solution is alkaline, it must be checked in this way. Add $0.2M$ KCN solution until the blue color disappears, then add 5 drops of thioacetamide solution and heat in the boiling water bath for 2 minutes. As in the other test, a yellow precipitate of CdS confirms the presence of cadmium. Since black CuS would mask the yellow CdS, it is necessary to prevent its formation. This is accomplished in different ways in the two tests for cadmium.
   $Na_2S_2O_4$ reduces copper(II) to the free metal but does not affect Cd^{+2}:

$$(1)\ Cu(NH_3)_4^{+2} + S_2O_4^{-2} + 2H_2O \rightarrow$$
$$Cu^0 + 2SO_3^{-2} + 4NH_4^+$$

   Cyanide ion produces $Cu(CN)_3^{-2}$ and $Cd(CN)_4^{-2}$ ions:

$$(2)\ Cd(NH_3)_4^{+2} + 4CN^- \rightarrow Cd(CN)_4^{-2} + 4NH_3$$
$$(3)\ 2Cu(NH_3)_4^{+2} + 7CN^- + H_2O \rightarrow$$
$$2Cu(CN)_3^{-2} + CNO^- + 6NH_3 + 2NH_4^+$$

Colorless $Cu(CN)_3^{-2}$ is a very stable complex ion and does not dissociate into cyanide and copper(I) ions enough to give a precipitate, even though Cu_2S is very insoluble. $Cd(CN)_4^{-2}$ is much less stable, and the dissociation reaction

$$Cd(CN)_4^{-2} \rightleftharpoons Cd^{+2} + 4CN^-$$

proceeds sufficiently to give an ample supply of cadmium ions to precipitate CdS.

Besides copper, traces of other ions giving dark sulfides may be present. Either the cyanide or dithionite method is effective at removing traces of Hg^{+2}, dithionite is successful with Bi^{+3}, cyanide is fairly effective for Ni^{+2}, and neither is very effective for Pb^{+2}.

2. *What to do if your CdS precipitate is dark* (besides hanging your head in shame).

To remove small amounts of dark sulfides, centrifuge the CdS and discard the solution. Wash with water and reject the washings. Now treat the precipitate with 8 drops of water and 2 drops of $18M$ H_2SO_4. Stir and heat in the water bath. The CdS should dissolve more readily than the dark contaminants. Centrifuge and decant the clear solution to another test tube. Add 5 drops of thioacetamide and heat in the boiling water bath for 2 minutes. Now add $15M$ NH_3 drop by drop from a capillary pipette that delivers small drops. Stir constantly and continue adding the ammonia. When the solution is nearly neutral, yellow CdS will precipitate. Be careful not to add too much NH_3, or a dark precipitate might be obtained again.

Subgroup 2B: Hg, As, Sn, Sb

PROCEDURE 2.8 / Separation of
HgS and As_2S_3 from Sb_2S_3 and SnS_2

Do not start this procedure unless you have at least 15 minutes (Note 1).

The solution labeled 2B obtained in Procedure 2.2 may contain the anions AsO_2^-, AsS_2^-, $Sb(OH)_4^-$, SbS_2^-, $Sn(OH)_6^{-2}$,

SnS$_3^{-2}$, and HgS$_2^{-2}$ in a strongly alkaline solution which also contains some S^{-2} and perhaps S$_2^{-2}$. Transfer the solution—along with any precipitate which may have formed—to a 10 ml beaker and add 3M HCl dropwise with constant stirring until the solution is acid to litmus. (If the Subgroup 2B solution has been set aside for several days, it may be well to add 2 drops of thioacetamide solution at this point and heat in the water bath for 2 or 3 minutes to replace S^{-2} ion which could have been oxidized.) A yellow or brown precipitate may be HgS, As$_2$S$_3$, Sb$_2$S$_3$, and SnS$_2$. If only a white precipitate of S is obtained at this point, the Subgroup 2B elements are absent and no further tests need be made. Transfer the mixture to a 75 mm test tube, washing it in with 2 drops of water. Centrifuge, remove completely the supernatant liquid and discard it (Note 2). Add 10 drops of 12M HCl to the precipitate, mix thoroughly, and heat for 2 minutes in the boiling water bath, stirring constantly. Add 2 drops of thioacetamide solution to reprecipitate any mercury or arsenic that may have dissolved, heat for 2 minutes more, centrifuge, and separate immediately. Wash the precipitate with 3 drops of 12M HCl and 2 drops of water. Transfer the *Solution 2.8* and the acid wash to a 5 ml beaker, label it, and set it aside to test for Sn and Sb in Procedures 2.11 and 2.12 (Note 3). Test *Precipitate 2.8* according to Procedure 2.9.

Notes

1. The separation in this procedure is based on the fact that Sb$_2$S$_3$ and SnS$_2$ dissolve more readily in concentrated HCl. However, active boiling or long standing in this solution may cause some of the As$_2$S$_3$ and HgS to dissolve, especially if atmospheric oxidation of the sulfide ion takes place. The mixture of sulfides is therefore heated with 12M HCl for a limited time in the water bath with a little additional thioacetamide to maintain the sulfide concentration. If the acid solution is then removed promptly, no appreciable amount of arsenic goes into solution.
  No matter what procedure is used, arsenic is probably the most troublesome element to identify in the qualitative scheme. However, if directions are followed carefully and intelligently here, in the preliminary treatment of Group 2 in

Procedure 2.1, and in the confirmatory test, Procedure 2.10, you should have no trouble. (Since many students do have trouble getting an arsenic test, we must conclude that there are students who do not follow the directions carefully and intelligently.)

2. Try to get all the liquid off the mixture of sulfides. If any remains to dilute the $12M$ HCl even slightly, the SnS_2 and Sb_2S_3 will be incompletely dissolved.

3. A yellow or orange precipitate may show up in Solution 2.8, especially if the beaker in which it was received was moist. Don't worry about this; the reactions for dissolving the SnS_2 and Sb_2S_3 are reversible:

$$Sb_2S_3 + 6H_3O^+ + 12Cl^- \rightleftharpoons 2SbCl_6{}^{-3} + 3H_2S + 6H_2O$$

On cooling or diluting, a little precipitate is formed again as there is still some dissolved H_2S present. At the beginning of Procedure 2.11 the excess H_2S is boiled off so that any precipitate dissolves completely.

PROCEDURE 2.9 / Mercury

Separation of mercury in Group 2B. Precipitate 2.8 may contain HgS and As_2S_3. Wash again, this time with water only, and discard the washings. To the residue add 10 drops of $15M$ NH_3 and 2 drops of water and stir thoroughly. Centrifuge and separate *Solution 2.9*, transferring it to a centrifuge tube for Procedure 2.10. *Precipitate 2.9* is usually dark if mercury is present (but see Note 2, Procedure 2.3).

Test for mercury. Combine Precipitate 2.9 with Precipitate 2.3, which contained any HgS from Group 2A. Wash the combined precipitates with 5 drops of water, discarding the washings. Add 5 drops of $12M$ HCl and 1 drop of $16M$ HNO_3 and heat in the water bath till reaction starts. Transfer to a 5 ml beaker, rinsing the tube with a drop or two of water to aid the transfer. Boil down gently under the hood to a few drops, but *not* to dryness. Rinse into a centrifuge tube with 2 drops of water. Centrifuge and separate. To the *clear* solution add 1 or 2 drops of

$SnCl_2$ solution. An opalescent white precipitate which may change to gray or black confirms the presence of mercury. (The reaction may be very slow if the Hg^{+2} is tied up in the $HgCl_4^{-2}$ complex ion, so most of the Cl^- must be removed by boiling off HCl, as directed above.)

PROCEDURE 2.10 / Detection of arsenic

Solution 2.9 may contain AsS_2^- and AsO_2^- in ammonia solution. Add $3M$ HNO_3 until the mixture is decidedly acid. The formation of a yellow precipitate shows the presence of arsenic (Note 1). Centrifuge, discarding the solution. Heat the residue with 5 drops of $16M$ HNO_3 in the water bath for 10 minutes. Add NH_3 carefully with thorough stirring until the solution is alkaline; then allow it to stand for a few minutes. Centrifuge to separate sulfur or any extraneous material such as HgS and decant the solution into a centrifuge tube. Add 4 drops of $(NH_4)_2MoO_4$ solution and acidify strongly with nitric acid. Heat in the boiling water bath for 5 minutes, occasionally scratching the sides of the tube with a stirring rod. A canary yellow precipitate which may be more noticeable after centrifuging proves the presence of arsenic. If no precipitate has formed after 5 minutes but a yellow As_2S_3 precipitate had been obtained earlier in this procedure, add 2 more drops of $(NH_4)_2MoO_4$ and an amount of $16M$ HNO_3 equal in volume to your whole solution, stir, and heat for 5 more minutes (Notes 2 and 3).

Notes

1. The yellow As_2S_3 obtained here gives a better estimate of the amount of arsenic present than does the final confirmatory precipitate. If only a white precipitate of sulfur is obtained, there is no arsenic present at this point. A yellow precipitate, however, may be sulfur, colored by SnS_2 or Sb_2S_3, and a dark precipitate may contain HgS. Since any of these may or may not include some As_2S_3, a confirmatory test is necessary.

2. There are many extremely sensitive tests for arsenic available. Most of these involve the handling of small amounts of very poisonous compounds of arsenic. Some of them require

special apparatus and skillful manipulation. The Gutzeit test described in many larger texts and shown in Figure 13.4, page 147, is quite easy to perform and very sensitive. However, when arsenic is missed in qualitative analysis, it has usually been lost long before the confirmatory test.

3. The yellow confirmatory precipitate, ammonium arseno-molybdate, is commonly written $(NH_4)_3AsO_4(MoO_3)_{12}$. It is now accepted that the formula might better be written

$(NH_4)_3As(Mo_{12}O_{40})$

which would be called ammonium molybdoarsenate. As you will see when you get a balanced formula equation from the word equation for its formation, a large excess of acid is necessary to obtain the precipitate.

PROCEDURE 2.11 / Detection of tin

Solution 2.8 may contain $SbCl_6^{-3}$ and $SnCl_6^{-2}$ in hydrochloric acid solution containing some H_2S. Boil *gently* to drive off all the H_2S. After it has been boiling a minute or so, the steam no longer blackens lead acetate paper. Then dilute the solution with 15 drops of water and divide it, testing one-third for tin and saving two-thirds for antimony in Procedure 2.12.

To the portion to be tested for tin in a test tube, add 1 drop of $12M$ HCl and two *clean* iron brads (Note 1). Heat the tube in the water bath for five minutes. Centrifuge, transfer the clear solution to another tube, and add 1 drop of $HgCl_2$ solution. A white, gray, or black precipitate confirms the presence of tin (Note 2).

Notes

1. If the brads are rusty, remove all the rust with steel wool and HCl, and then wash them thoroughly in water. Better yet, get some new nails.

   In addition to reducing tin(IV) to tin(II), the iron will reduce antimony(III) to black flocks of the metal. Although the formation of black flocks strongly indicates the presence of antimony, it is not a reliable confirmatory test.

2. Observe that the precipitate confirming the presence of tin contains no tin—it is composed of Hg_2Cl_2 and Hg. The reduction of mercury(II), however, is a characteristic reaction of tin(II).

Excess mercury(II) causes the reaction to stop at the formation of white Hg_2Cl_2, and excess tin(II) makes it continue to black Hg. Generally, in the test for mercury (Procedure 2.9), there will be relatively less mercury(II) present than the amount of tin(II) reagent added; therefore, a black precipitate is obtained. Since, in this procedure, there is likely to be less tin(II), a white precipitate is often found. Any shade from white to black is satisfactory.

Sometimes, if much antimony and no tin is present, a white flocculent precipitate of SbOCl is obtained, looking quite unlike the first opalescent white, then darkening, precipitate of Hg_2Cl_2 and Hg. It is easy to determine if this is the case because the SbOCl dissolves easily in concentrated HCl and the Hg_2Cl_2 is unaffected.

PROCEDURE 2.12 / Detection of antimony

To the remainder of Solution 2.8 in a 10 ml beaker, add 0.5 g of oxalic acid and 5 ml of water. Heat and stir until the oxalic acid is dissolved. Add 5 drops of thioacetamide and heat for 2 minutes. An orange-red precipitate of Sb_2S_3 shows the presence of antimony. A slowly forming brown precipitate when tin is present is due to sulfides of tin (Note 1).

Notes

1. Because the trioxalatostannate(IV) complex ion is considerably more stable than the trioxalatoantimonate(III) ion, SnS_2 precipitates only very slowly from this solution.

   Any precipitate that requires as much as 5 minutes to come down is certain to be due to tin and can be ignored.

2. Even if tin was not found to be present it does no harm to add oxalic acid before testing for antimony. Otherwise an erroneous negative test for tin would be certain to spoil the antimony test also.

Word equations for the reactions of Group 2

Lead:

1. Lead ion + sulfide ion → lead sulfide

2. Lead sulfide + hydronium ion + nitrate ion →
   lead ion + sulfur + nitric oxide + water

3. Lead ion + sulfate ion → lead sulfate

4. Lead sulfate + acetate ion → lead acetate + sulfate ion

5.* Lead acetate + chromate ion →
   lead chromate (yellow) + acetate ion

Bismuth:

1. Bismuth ion + sulfide ion → bismuth sulfide

2. Bismuth sulfide + hydronium ion + nitrate ion →
   bismuth ion + sulfur + nitric oxide + water

3. Bismuth ion + ammonia + water →
   bismuth hydroxide + ammonium ion

4.* Bismuth hydroxide + trihydroxostannate(II) ion
   + hydroxide ion →
   bismuth (black) + hexahydroxostannate (IV) ion

Copper:

1. Copper(II) ion + sulfide ion → copper sulfide.
   (If you wish to use the hydrated copper ion, you may, though
   it is unnecessary and professes a knowledge of the degree of
   hydration which we do not really have:
   Tetraaquo copper(II) ion + sulfide ion →
   copper sulfide + water)

2. Copper sulfide + hydronium ion + nitrate ion →
   copper(II) ion + sulfur + nitric oxide + water

3. Copper(II) ion + ammonia → tetraammine copper(II) ion

4. Tetraammine copper(II) ion + hydronium ion →
   copper(II) ion + ammonium ion + water

5.* Copper(II) ion + hexacyanoferrate(II) ion →
   copper(II) hexacyanoferrate(II) (red)

Cadmium:

1. Cadmium ion + sulfide ion → cadmium sulfide
2. Cadmium sulfide + hydronium ion + nitrate ion →
cadmium ion + sulfur + nitric oxide + water
3. Cadmium ion + ammonia → tetraammine cadmium ion
4.* Tetraammine cadmium ion + sulfide ion →
cadmium sulfide (yellow) + ammonia

Mercury:

1. Mercury(II) ion + sulfide ion → mercury(II) sulfide
2. Mercury(II) sulfide + sulfide ion → dithiomercurate(II) ion
3. Dithiomercurate(II) ion + hydronium ion →
mercury(II) sulfide + water + hydrogen sulfide
4. Mercury(II) sulfide + hydronium ion + nitrate ion
+ chloride ion →
mercury(II) chloride + nitrogen dioxide + sulfur + water
5.* Mercury(II) chloride + tin(II) ion + chloride ion →
mercury(I) chloride (white) + hexachlorostannate(IV) ion
6.* Mercury(I) chloride + tin(II) ion + chloride ion →
mercury (black) + hexachlorostannate(IV) ion

Antimony:

1. Hexachloroantimonate(III) ion + sulfide ion →
antimony sulfide + chloride ion
2. Antimony sulfide + hydroxide ion →
tetrahydroxoantimonate(III) ion
+ dithioantimonate(III) ion
3. Tetrahydroxoantimonate(III) ion
+ dithioantimonate(III) ion + hydronium ion →
antimony sulfide + water
4. Antimony sulfide + hydronium ion + chloride ion →
hexachloroantimonate(III) ion + hydrogen sulfide + water
5. Hexachloroantimonate(III) ion + oxalate ion →
trioxalatoantimonate(III) ion + chloride ion
6.* Trioxalatoantimonate(III) ion + sulfide ion →
antimony sulfide (orange) + oxalate ion

Tin:

1. Tin(II) ion + hydrogen peroxide + hydronium ion
     + chloride ion → hexachlorostannate(IV) ion + water

2. Hexachlorostannate(IV) ion + sulfide ion →
                              tin(IV) sulfide + chloride ion

3. Tin(IV) sulfide + hydroxide ion →
        hexahydroxostannate(IV) ion + trithiostannate(IV) ion

4. Hexahydroxostannate(IV) ion + trithiostannate(IV) ion
                + hydronium ion → tin(IV) sulfide + water

5. Tin(IV) sulfide + hydronium ion + chloride ion →
        hexachlorostannate(IV) ion + hydrogen sulfide + water

6. Hexachlorostannate(IV) ion + iron →
                   tin(II) ion + iron(II) ion + chloride ion

7.* Tin(II) ion + mercury(II) chloride + chloride ion →
      mercury(I) chloride (white) + hexachlorostannate(IV) ion

8.* Tin(II) ion + mercury(I) chloride + chloride ion →
          mercury (black) + hexachlorostannate(IV) ion

Arsenic:

1. Metaarsenious acid + hydrogen peroxide →
                                      orthoarsenic acid

2. Orthoarsenic acid + sulfide ion + hydronium ion →
                         metaarsenious acid + sulfur + water

3. Metaarsenious acid + hydronium ion + sulfide ion →
                            arsenic(III) sulfide + water

4. Arsenic(III) sulfide + hydroxide ion →
        metathioarsenite ion + metaarsenite ion + water

5. Metathioarsenite ion + metaarsenite ion + hydronium ion →
                            arsenic(III) sulfide + water

6. Same as 4

7. Same as 5

8. Arsenic(III) sulfide + hydronium ion + nitrate ion →
        orthoarsenic acid + sulfur + nitrogen dioxide + water

9.* Orthoarsenic acid + ammonium ion + molybdate ion
     + hydronium ion →
                ammonium arsenomolybdate (yellow) + water

Questions and problems

1. Give two reasons why a sample should be boiled down with H_2O_2 and HCl before beginning the Group 2 analysis.

2. A certain bemused student analyzed a Group 1 known solution containing the nitrates of Hg_2^{+2}, Ag^+, and Pb^{+2} according to the Group 2 procedures. Suggest the probable behavior of each of these ions in the Group 2 scheme.

3. What undesirable results, if any, would be obtained in each of the following cases?
   a. The Group 2 precipitation was done from a $5M$ instead of a $0.5M$ acid solution
   b. The Group 2 precipitation was done from a $0.05M$ solution instead of a $0.5M$ acid solution
   c. $6M$ NaOH was used instead of $6M$ KOH in separating Subgroup 2A from Subgroup 2B
   d. Subgroup 2A was let stand from one laboratory period to the next exposed to the air, so some S^{-2} was oxidized to SO_4^{-2}
   e. NaOH was used instead of NH_3 in the separation of Bi^{+3}
   f. NH_3 was used instead of NaOH in the confirmatory test for Bi^{+3}
   g. The test solution was not treated with $Na_2S_2O_4$ before testing for Cd^{+2}
   h. $3M$ HCl was used instead of $12M$ HCl in the separation of mercury and arsenic from antimony and tin
   i. A small piece of aluminum wire was used instead of the iron wire in the test for tin
   j. Oxalic acid was omitted in the test for antimony

4. You are given a sample of metal that is known to be one of the following alloys:
   a. Pb, Sn
   b. Pb, Sn, Cu
   c. Sn, Sb, Cu
   d. Sn, Sb
   Devise a quick method based on the procedures of Group 2 to determine which of these alloys you have. For the first step, dissolve a small portion of the metal in aqua regia, which will dissolve any of these alloys fairly easily.

5. List all of the Group 2 ions that answer each of the following descriptions:
   a. Its sulfide is yellow and insoluble in KOH
   b. It gives precipitates with both NaOH and NH_3
   c. Its sulfide is dark and insoluble in KOH
   d. It is reduced to the metal by Sn
   e. It gives a precipitate with K_2CrO_4 solution

6. A colorless Group 2 unknown gave a yellow precipitate with thioacetamide which was completely soluble in $6M$ KOH solution. The KOH solution gave an orange yellow precipitate when treated with 3M HCl and this precipitate was soluble in $12M$ HCl. The solution was divided into two portions. The first was treated with an iron nail, followed by $HgCl_2$ solution, giving a white precipitate. The second portion was treated with oxalic acid, followed by thioacetamide, giving an orange precipitate. Classify all the Group 2 ions in one of the following categories: probably present, probably absent, or completely uncertain.

7. A Group 2 unknown solution was blue and gave a dark precipitate on treatment with H_2S (from thioacetamide). With $6M$ KOH solution, a black precipitate A and a clear centrifugate B were obtained. Precipitate A dissolved readily in HNO_3 giving a blue solution which gave no precipitate with $(NH_4)_2SO_4$. Centrifugate B gave no precipitate when acidified with $3M$ HCl. Classify all of the Group 2 ions, as in Question 6: probably present, probably absent, completely uncertain.

8. Give the formula of a reagent that will dissolve
   a. $Cu(OH)_2$ but not $Bi(OH)_3$
   b. CuS but not HgS
   c. HgS but not CuS
   d. As_2S_3 but not Bi_2S_3
   e. As_2S_3 but not Sb_2S_3
   f. $PbSO_4$ but not $BaSO_4$

9. Give the formula of a reagent that will give a precipitate with
   a. Bi^{+3} but not Al^{+3}
   b. $SbCl_6^{-3}$ but not $SnCl_6^{-2}$
   c. Pb^{+2} but not Cu^{+2}

d. Cu^{+2} but not Cd^{+2}
e. Cd^{+2} but not Cu^{+2}

10. Give the formula of a reagent that will reduce
    a. Cu^{+2} but not Cd^{+2}
    b. $H_2AsO_4^-$
    c. Hg_2Cl_2
    d. $SnCl_6^{-2}$
    e. $Bi(OH)_3$

11. A student is challenged to complete his analysis of Subgroup 2A without using H_2SO_4 or any sulfate. Can you help him devise a scheme for testing for Pb^{+2}, Bi^{+3}, Cd^{+2}, and Cu^{+2} without the use of any SO_4^{-2} ion?

12. The function of the $0.5M$ HCl in the precipitation of Group 2 is, of course, to regulate the equilibrium

$$H_2S + 2H_2O \rightleftharpoons 2H_3O^+ + S^{-2}$$

Assuming that the maximum concentration of H_2S obtainable from thioacetamide is 0.1 molar, what concentration of HCl would be required to prevent any precipitation of CdS from a $0.002M$ Cd^{+2} solution?

Procedures for Analysis
of Group 3

23

Group 3 contains the ions that precipitate in a moderately alkaline buffered solution of NH_3 and NH_4Cl to which $(NH_4)_2S$ has been added. The Group 3 precipitate contains the hydroxides of the tervalent ions, Al^{+3}, Cr^{+3}, and Fe^{+3}, and the sulfides of Co^{+2}, Fe^{+2}, Mn^{+2}, Ni^{+2}, and Zn^{+2}, which, though quite insoluble, were not insoluble enough to precipitate in Group 2. Since several members of this group have more than one relatively stable oxidation state, oxidation-reduction reactions are characteristic of the chemistry of the group. It is assumed that, at the beginning of this group, elements are found only in the oxidation states which survive treatment by HCl and H_2O_2 preliminary to Group 2. These are the states shown at the top of the Group 3 flowsheet, Figure 23.1. Iron is found in the Group 3 precipitate as FeS as well as $Fe(OH)_3$ because it undergoes some reduction by sulfide ion. In the analysis of the group, we follow the rather common practice of subdividing it into an alkali-soluble Subgroup 3B and a non-amphoteric Subgroup 3A before isolating the individual metals.

PROCEDURE 3.1 / Precipitation of the Group

If the solution to be analyzed is a Group 3 known or unknown, proceed directly to Part B, but for a general unknown on which you will be analyzing a Group 2 centrifugate, do Part A first.

A: For a general unknown only. Removal of excess HCl preparatory to precipitating Group 3 in a general unknown. Boil the Group 2 centrifugate down to about 5 drops in a 10 ml beaker. Place the beaker on the wire gauze and heat the gauze an inch or so away from the beaker. Be careful to avoid spattering, and do not evaporate to dryness.

B: Precipitation. Use about 6 drops of Group 3 known or 4 drops of Group 3 unknown or the material from Part A in a 10 ml beaker. Dilute with 5 ml of water and 0.5 ml of $4M$ NH_4Cl solution (Note 1), and heat to boiling. Add $15M$ NH_3 solution until the mixture is neutral, then 2 drops excess NH_3. (On an unknown, note whether a precipitate has formed at this stage. If there is none, Fe^{+3}, Cr^{+3}, and Al^{+3} are absent). Centrifuge and observe the colors of the solution and precipitate (Note 3). Then, with constant stirring, heat the solution again to boiling and add 6 drops of $(NH_4)_2S$ solution, one drop at a time. Centrifuge and add 1 more drop of $(NH_4)_2S$ to see if precipitation is complete. Divide the mixture between two test tubes, using a few drops of cold water to rinse the material into the test tubes, and centrifuge. The centrifugate, which will contain Groups 4 and 5 of a general unknown, should be clear and colorless. If there is an appreciable amount of dark cloudiness due to colloidal cobalt sulfide, repeat Parts A and B on the centrifugate.

If you need to save the clear centrifugate for analysis of later groups, acidify it at once with acetic acid and boil it down to half its volume to remove S^{-2}. Otherwise oxidation to SO_4^{-2} would give insoluble precipitates of Ba^{+2} and Sr^{+2}.

Precipitate 3.1 should be washed with a mixture of 3 drops of concentrated NH_3, 3 drops of $4M$ NH_4Cl, 1 drop of $(NH_4)_2S$ and 1 ml of water for each test tube. Stir up the precipitate in this solution and heat in the water bath before centrifuging. Discard the wash mixture. The precipitate now contains $Al(OH)_3$, $Cr(OH)_3$, $Fe(OH)_3$, FeS, NiS, CoS, MnS, and ZnS. (See Notes 2, 3, and 4 for useful information.)

Notes

1. The addition of NH_4Cl and NH_3 gives a buffer solution in which the OH^- concentration is high enough to precipitate $Al(OH)_3$, $Cr(OH)_3$, and $Fe(OH)_3$, but not high enough to

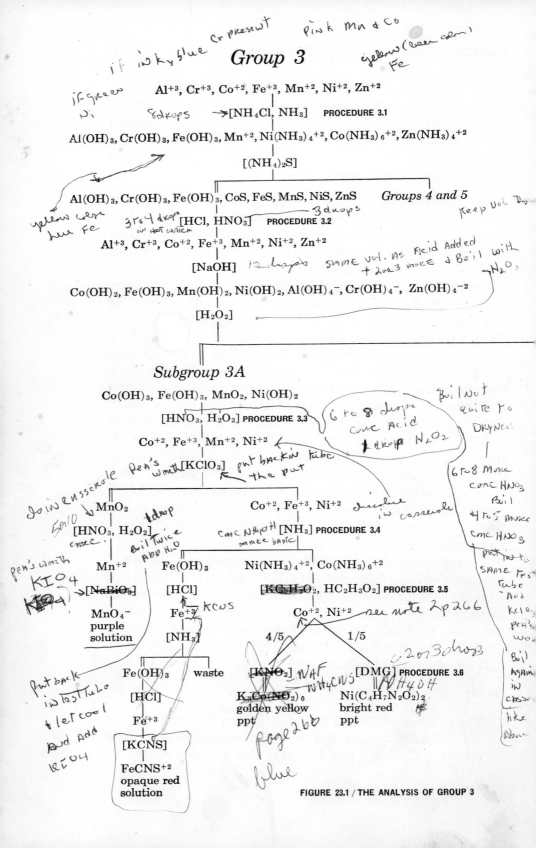

FIGURE 23.1 / THE ANALYSIS OF GROUP 3

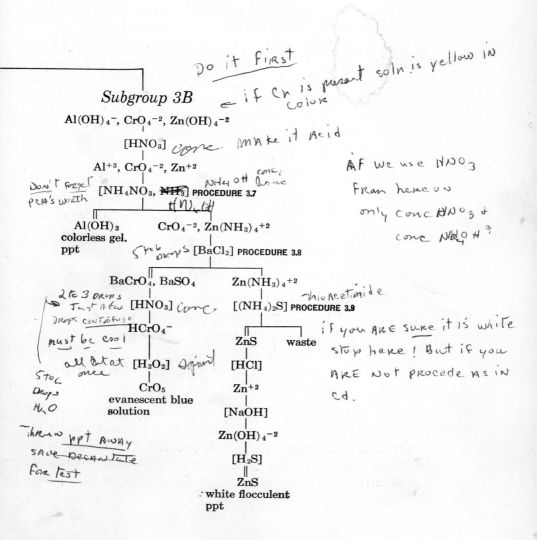

Do it First

if Cn is present soln is yellow in color

Subgroup 3B

Al(OH)₄⁻, CrO₄⁻², Zn(OH)₄⁻²

[HNO₃] *conc* *make it acid*

Al⁺³, CrO₄⁻², Zn⁺²

Don't forget PRA's worth [NH₄NO₃, ~~NH₃~~] PROCEDURE 3.7   *NH₄OH conc. done*

+(NH₄OH

Al(OH)₃
colorless gel.
ppt

CrO₄⁻², Zn(NH₃)₄⁺²

5 to 6 drops [BaCl₂] PROCEDURE 3.8

BaCrO₄, BaSO₄

2 to 3 drops Just a few drops centrifuge [HNO₃] *conc*
must be cool

HCrO₄⁻

all at at once [H₂O₂] *squirt*

stok drops H₂O

CrO₅
evanescent blue
solution

throw ppt away save ~~decantate~~ for test

Zn(NH₃)₄⁺²

Thioacetimide

[(NH₄)₂S] PROCEDURE 3.9

ZnS   waste

[HCl]

Zn⁺²

[NaOH]

Zn(OH)₄⁻²

[H₂S]

ZnS
white flocculent
ppt

if we use HNO₃ from here on only conc HNO₃ & conc NH₄OH ?

if you are sure it is white stop here! But if you are not procede as in cd.

redissolve appreciable amounts of $Al(OH)_3$ and $Cr(OH)_3$ as $Al(OH)_4^-$ and $Cr(OH)_4^-$. Nor is it high enough to precipitate $Mg(OH)_2$, which is not desired in this group. Furthermore, since NH_4Cl is an electrolyte, it helps prevent the precipitates of this group from peptizing; that is, forming colloidal solutions.

2. An unknown mixture containing an alkaline earth ion and such an anion as phosphate, borate, fluoride, or oxalate would give a precipitate at this point, because such combinations of cation and anion are soluble only in somewhat acid solutions. Ordinarily such an unknown will not be given to a student in this course; if one is given, you will also be given directions for the special methods of separation required.

3. The colors observable in a Group 3 unknown may give very helpful hints. Don't disdain to use any help you can get from observing them, but don't report an unknown on basis of color alone. Certain combinations of colored ions can give deceptive hues, and ions that are tied up in complex ions may have their colors modified or changed.

Colored solutions of Group 3 ions:

Fe^{+3}	yellow to orange	Co^{+2}	rose or blue
Fe^{+2}	green to blue-green	Cr^{+3}	green, sometimes violet
Ni^{+2}	green to blue-green	Mn^{+2}	very pale pink
$Ni(NH_3)_4^{+2}$	deep blue	Al^{+3}, Zn^{+2}	colorless

Colored precipitates of Group 3:

$Fe(OH)_3$	red-brown	FeS, CoS, NiS	black
$Cr(OH)_3$	light green	MnS	pink, but turns brown because of oxidation to MnO_2
$Al(OH)_3$	colorless or white		
ZnS	white		

4. Cobalt has a strong tendency to form complex ions, those of cobalt(III) being much more stable than those of cobalt(II). With the concentrations of NH_3 and NH_4^+ which are likely to be present at the various stages of Group 3 analysis, $Co(NH_3)_6^{+2}$, pink, will first be formed. This is oxidized

rather rapidly by air or other oxidizing agent to deep red $Co(NH_3)_6^{+3}$ by the reaction

$$4Co(NH_3)_6^{+2} + O_2 + 2H_2O \rightarrow 4Co(NH_3)_6^{+3} + 4OH^-$$

However, to simplify equation writing, we shall assume that all students carry through their procedures so promptly that there is never time for appreciable amounts of $Co(NH_3)_6^{+3}$ to form.

PROCEDURE 3.2 / Separation of Subgroup 3A from Subgroup 3B

Transfer Precipitate 3.1 from both test tubes to a 10 ml beaker with the aid of 1 ml of $6M$ HCl. Stir well for several minutes. If the precipitate dissolves readily, Ni^{+2} and Co^{+2} are absent from an unknown, and you may skip the rest of this paragraph (Note 1). If any dark precipitate remains, add 5 drops of $16M$ HNO_3 and boil down to about 3 drops. This is best done by suspending the beaker from a triangle or holder of bent wire in an iron crucible to form an air bath. Add 5 drops of water, stir and transfer to a test tube. Use 5 drops more of water to rinse the beaker and add the rinsings to the solution in the test tube. Centrifuge to remove any precipitate of sulfur, and transfer the solution to a crucible. The solution at this point contains Al^{+3}, Cr^{+3}, Fe^{+3}, Co^{+2}, Ni^{+2}, Mn^{+2}, and Zn^{+2}.

Add 1 ml of $6M$ NaOH, stir thoroughly, then add 5 drops H_2O_2 and stir again. Boil gently for 1 minute. (Warning! Strongly alkaline solutions have a tendency to bump, especially when there is extra undissolved solid in the container.) Add 5 drops more H_2O_2 slowly, one drop at a time, and bring to a boil again for at least a minute (Note 2). The whole mess should not amount to more than 1 ml now; if it exceeds that volume, boil it down *carefully*. Transfer to a test tube, rinsing solid material into the test tube with a few drops of hot water, and centrifuge. Separate carefully, withdrawing *Solution 3.2* with a pipette which has a bit of cotton in its tip and transferring to a test tube. Wash the *Precipitate 3.2* with two 10-drop portions of hot water and add the washings to Solution 3.2. *Cautiously* add $16M$ HNO_3 to this Solution 3.2 until it is just acid (Note 3), stopper it, and set it aside for Procedure 3.7. It may contain Al^{+3}, Zn^{+2}, and CrO_4^{-2}.

The Precipitate 3.2 obtained may contain $Fe(OH)_3$, $Co(OH)_3$, $Ni(OH)_2$, and MnO_2. Use it for Procedure 3.3.

Notes

1. Although NiS and CoS do not precipitate from dilute acid solutions (as in the precipitation of Group 2), they are difficult to dissolve once they are formed. The explanation is that the "alpha" forms first precipitated have K_{sp}'s of the order of 10^{-22} (which would make them soluble in dilute HCl). They slowly change into much less soluble "beta" forms with K_{sp}'s of the order of 10^{-27}. (This property can be used as the basis of a quite satisfactory method of separating cobalt and nickel from the other Group 3 ions.)

2. Sufficient H_2O_2 must be added to oxidize all the chromium, manganese, and cobalt present, even though the only major benefit is the removal of Cr^{+3} ions by oxidizing them to CrO_4^{-2}. This is necessary because Cr^{+3} behaves so much like Al^{+3}. The separation of manganese and cobalt is also facilitated slightly, as MnO_2 and $Co(OH)_3$ have less tendency than $Mn(OH)_2$ and $Co(OH)_2$ to be carried into the soluble Subgroup 3B. Excess H_2O_2, however, must be destroyed by boiling before Solution 3.2 is acidified, since it reduces $Cr_2O_7^{-2}$ to Cr^{+3} in acid solution:

$$Cr_2O_7^{-2} + 3H_2O_2 + 8H_3O^+ \rightarrow 2Cr^{+3} + 3O_2 + 15H_2O$$

3. If Solution 3.2 were left standing in strongly alkaline condition for any considerable length of time, it would react with the glass, dissolving enough aluminate and silicate ions to give a gelatinous precipitate in the confirmatory test for aluminum.

4. After Procedure 3.2, the colors of solution and precipitate should be considered again:

Al^{+3}	colorless
Zn^{+2}	colorless
CrO_4^{-2}	yellow
$Co(OH)_3$	black ($Co(OH)_2$ is pink)
$Fe(OH)_3$	red-brown
MnO_2	dark brown, sometimes almost black
$Ni(OH)_2$	light green

You will notice that Subgroup 3B contains only one colored ion, CrO_4^{-2}. The depth of the yellow color should give a good indication of the amount of chromium present. Chromium should not be reported except on the basis of Procedure 3.8, however. (A trace of $Fe(OH)_3$ carried over mechanically in separating Subgroups 3A and 3B would give yellow Fe^{+3}, for example.)

Subgroup 3A: Mn, Fe, Co, and Ni

PROCEDURE 3.3 / Manganese

Separation of manganese. Treat Precipitate 3.2 in the test tube with 5 or 10 drops of $16M$ HNO_3 plus 1 or 2 drops of H_2O_2. Warm in the water bath and transfer the clear solution to a beaker (Note 1). Rinse the test tube with $16M$ HNO_3, adding the washings to the solution in the beaker; if the precipitate was not completely dissolved in the first place, use a drop of H_2O_2 with the HNO_3 and warm the test tube again (Note 2). Make sure that all the precipitate in the beaker is reacted on by the HNO_3-H_2O_2 mixture by stirring the solution, by tilting the beaker with a tongs so that the solution comes in contact with all the solid, or by drawing up some of the reagent with a pipette and washing down the precipitate adhering to the walls.

Boil the solution in the beaker gently until it has evaporated down to about 5 drops or until solid begins to form. Add 10 drops of $16M$ HNO_3 and evaporate it down again to 5 drops to remove the excess H_2O_2. *Do not evaporate to dryness.* Have a little concentrated HNO_3 handy, and if the heat of the beaker continues to evaporate the solution after you have stopped heating, add a drop or two of acid cautiously.

Add $16M$ HNO_3 to bring the volume to 1 ml, heat just below boiling and add $KClO_3$ in many small portions, stirring and heating briefly after each addition, until 0.15 g have been added and *no* more. Measure the $KClO_3$ by volume, not by weight, comparing it with a weighed amount of material. Heat and stir for one half minute, adding HNO_3 if necessary to replace loss by evaporation. A brown or black precipitate may be MnO_2.

Transfer to a test tube. Rinse the beaker with two 5-drop portions of water, adding the washings to the test tube. Centrifuge and separate. *Solution 3.3* may contain Fe^{+3}, Ni^{+2}, and Co^{+2} and is to be used in Procedure 3.4.

Confirmation of manganese. Wash *Precipitate 3.3* in the test tube with several 5-drop portions of hot water, adding the first washing to Solution 3.3. Then dissolve the precipitate in 5 drops of $3M$ HNO_3 and 3 drops of H_2O_2 (more of each may be used if necessary). Heat the test tube several minutes in the water bath to destroy H_2O_2. Cool thoroughly. Add 0.05 g of $NaBiO_3$, stir, and centrifuge. A purple solution of MnO_4^- confirms the presence of manganese (Notes 3 and 4).

Notes

1. The beaker that was used in separating Subgroup 3A from Group 3B may be used, without cleaning. Some Precipitate 3.2 adheres to the sides of the beaker, and by saving it you lessen the mechanical losses which can interfere seriously with the analysis of some of the metals. The precipitate remaining in the beaker must, of course, be washed as thoroughly as that in the test tube.

2. A little H_2O_2 is necessary as a *reducing* agent to aid in the solution of MnO_2 and $Co(OH)_3$, but do not use more than is necessary because the excess must be boiled off in the next step.

3. If, through accident or carelessness, reducing agents such as traces of Cl^- or undecomposed H_2O_2 are present, the purple color will not be obtained or will not persist.

4. A sodium carbonate bead gives another very sensitive test for manganese. Form a loop in a platinum wire. Heat the loop in the bunsen flame, dip it into solid Na_2CO_3, heat it again, and repeat until a drop of molten Na_2CO_3 is produced in the loop. Touch this to the solid substance being tested for manganese and heat again in the oxidizing flame, or touch to an oxidizing agent such as KNO_3 or $KClO_3$ and heat. A green bead containing Na_2MnO_4 is a positive test for manganese.

PROCEDURE 3.4 / Separation and identification of iron

(If white or colorless crystals of KCl have separated from Solution 3.3, centrifuge, wash the precipitate with a few drops of water, adding washings to the centrifugate and discard the residue).

Remove excess acid from Solution 3.3 by transferring it to a 10 ml beaker and evaporating it to about 0.5 ml or until solid separates. *Let it cool.* Meanwhile, put 1 ml of $15M$ NH_3 in a test tube and cautiously add to this the cooled Solution 3.3 *one drop at a time*, with stirring. Rinse the beaker with a few drops of water and add the washings to the test tube. Stir thoroughly. The resulting mixture should be strongly alkaline. If not, add NH_3 until it is alkaline to litmus and 3 drops excess. Stir and centrifuge. The centrifugate, *Solution 3.4*, may contain $Ni(NH_3)_4^{+2}$ and $Co(NH_3)_6^{+2}$ and is to be saved for Procedure 3.5. A reddish brown gelatinous precipitate may be $Fe(OH)_3$. Wash it with a few drops of water, adding the wash to Solution 3.4 (Note 1).

To confirm the presence of iron, dissolve the precipitate in 15 drops of $3M$ HCl and heat in the water bath until the precipitate has dissolved. Then add $3M$ NH_3 with thorough stirring until the solution is alkaline and 10 drops excess NH_3. Centrifuge, wash once with water, and dissolve the precipitate in 10 drops of $3M$ HCl, heating in the water bath to aid solution if necessary. Cool and add several drops of KCNS solution. An opaque red solution containing $FeCNS^{+2}$ confirms the presence of iron. Because this test is extremely sensitive and because a speck of iron can so easily get in by accident, anything less than a strong test is to be regarded with suspicion (Note 2).

Notes

1. The nitric acid solution is neutralized by adding it dropwise to $15M$ NH_3 so that the mixture will go directly from acid to strongly ammoniacal. If ammonia were added to the nitric acid solution, $Ni(OH)_2$ and $Co(OH)_2$ would first precipitate, redissolving as $Ni(NH_3)_4^{+2}$ and $Co(NH_3)_6^{+2}$ when a sufficient excess of NH_3 was present. The precipitates, however, once formed, might become adsorbed on, and entrapped in, the $Fe(OH)_3$, so that they would redissolve with difficulty.

2. The $Fe(OH)_3$ first separated is dissolved, reprecipitated, and redissolved to eliminate adsorbed and entrapped ions as much as possible before performing the confirmatory test. The bulk of the last $Fe(OH_3)$ precipitate is the best index of the amount of iron present.

deliote

PROCEDURE 3.5 / Detection of cobalt

Evaporate Solution 3.4 in a 5 ml beaker down to one drop to remove most of the ammonia, adding water if necessary to prevent its drying up. Add 4 drops of $2M$ $KC_2H_3O_2$ solution and enough $6M$ $HC_2H_3O_2$ to make it just acid to litmus and 2 drops more (Note 1). Set aside one-fifth of this solution for Procedure 3.6. To the remaining four-fifths add an equal volume of $6M$ KNO_2 solution, warm, and let stand for at least 15 minutes. A golden yellow precipitate of $K_3Co(NO_2)_6$, which often forms slowly, confirms the presence of cobalt (Note 2).

Notes

1. The potassium acetate solution is added for two reasons: to buffer the acetic acid solution and to increase the concentration of K^+ to aid in the precipitation of potassium hexanitrocobaltate(III).

2. The formation of blue $Co(CNS)_4{}^{-2}$ ions is a good alternate test for cobalt. Add a little solid NaF *pea's worth* to tie up any Fe^{+3} ions as $FeF_6{}^{-3}$. (Deep red $FeCNS^{+2}$ would, of course, interfere.) Then add about 1 ml of a saturated solution of NH_4CNS in ethyl alcohol. *Bright Blue*

see to

PROCEDURE 3.6 / Detection of nickel

To the remaining one-fifth of the solution which had been set aside in Procedure 3.5, add just 1 drop of $15M$ NH_3 and dilute to 1 ml. Add 5 drops of dimethyl glyoxime and let stand at least 10 minutes. The presence of nickel is confirmed by a red precipitate $Ni(C_4H_7N_2O_2)_2$ (Notes 1 and 2).

Notes

1. Dimethyl glyoxime has the structural formula

$$CH_3—C=N—O—H$$
$$CH_3—C=N—O—H$$

The compound with nickel may be represented by the formula

The nickel(II) ion appears to have a more suitable size and configuration than any other to nestle in the middle of this arrangement. The divalent ions of the neighboring metals of the first transition series, Fe^{+2}, Co^{+2}, Cu^{+2}, interfere slightly. The test is an extremely sensitive one for nickel because the precipitate is very insoluble and brightly colored, and because only a small amount of Ni^{+2} is needed to give a bulky precipitate.

2. Cobalt does not give a precipitate, but in large quantities it interferes by combining with the reagent to form a brown solution. This can be taken care of by adding excess reagent, centrifuging, and washing the nickel dimethylglyoximate precipitate. Or, to the four-fifths which had been used to test for cobalt, a little more KNO_2 solution and 0.2 g of solid KCl can be added to insure precipitation of cobalt. After about 10 minutes the mixture can be centrifuged and dimethylglyoxime reagent added to the cobalt-free centrifugate.

Excess alkalinity brings out the dark soluble cobalt complex, while the red nickel dimethylglyoximate precipitates nicely from a solution that is neutral or slightly alkaline. If you have followed the directions of Procedures 3.5 and 3.6 carefully, you are not likely to be troubled with cobalt interferences.

Subgroup 3B: Al, Cr, and Zn

PROCEDURE 3.7 / Separation and identification of aluminum

To Solution 3.2 which has been saved in a test tube from Procedure 3.2, add 0.1 g powdered NH_4NO_3. Heat in the water bath and stir until the ammonium nitrate is all dissolved. Then add $15M$ NH_3 till the solution is alkaline to litmus and 5 drops excess (Note 1). Warm the solution again and stir thoroughly. The colorless gelatinous precipitate is not easily seen by the inexperienced, although it shows up better when the test tube is held up to the light. It is more easily observed after centrifuging and decanting off the supernatant *Solution 3.7*. Wash the precipitate twice with hot water containing a drop or two of $4M$ NH_4Cl. The $Al(OH)_3$ should be a colorless or whitish gelatinous precipitate remaining in the bottom of the test tube. A dirty or colored precipitate is *not* a satisfactory confirmatory test. (See Notes 2, 3, and 4.)

Notes

1. Zinc is often lost at this point by careless students who fail to add sufficient NH_4NO_3 and NH_3. Instead of soluble $Zn(NH_3)_4^{+2}$ being obtained, gelatinous $Zn(OH)_2$ precipitates and is separated along with the $Al(OH)_3$.

2. A light green or greenish yellow precipitate is caused by $Cr(OH)_3$ owing to incomplete oxidation in Procedure 3.2. It is difficult to distinguish between a precipitate composed just of $Cr(OH)_3$ and one of mixed $Al(OH)_3$ and $Cr(OH)_3$. Repeat all operations beginning with the dissolving in $6M$ NaOH and oxidation with H_2O_2 in Procedure 3.2.

3. A brown or tan discoloration may be attributed to $Fe(OH)_3$ and other colors to adsorbed ions of Subgroup 3A, probably carried over mechanically in the separation of the subgroups. Dissolving the precipitate in $3M$ HCl and reprecipitating with ammonia usually suffices to clear up a dirty gray or brown precipitate; or, if necessary, the separation with NaOH and H_2O_2 may be repeated.

4. A further confirmation is the *aluminon lake* test. Dissolve the $Al(OH)_3$ in 1 or 2 drops of $3M$ HCl, add 2 drops of $3M$ $NH_4C_2H_3O_2$ solution and 2 drops of aluminon (a dye, aurintricarboxylic acid, which gives a distinctive shade of color when it is adsorbed on $Al(OH)_3$). Stir thoroughly, make just alkaline with $3M$ NH_3, stir again, and centrifuge. A bright red precipitate confirms aluminum. (This is really less satisfactory than the colorless $Al(OH)_3$ alone to a careful observer. Similar red colors may be obtained from iron or chromium if they have not been completely removed, and the red lake makes traces of $Al(OH)_3$ show up too well— amounts that might have been dissolved from the pyrex glass.)

The word "lake" used here is derived from the Persian *lak* (compare shellac, lacquer). It refers to any pigment composed of a soluble dye rendered insoluble by adsorption on a gelatinous precipitate, usually a hydroxide of aluminum or tin. What ion in another group is confirmed by a precipitate which is a lake?

PROCEDURE 3.8 / Separation and identification of chromium

Add $BaCl_2$ solution to Solution 3.7 till precipitation is complete. Even with a strongly yellow solution probably no more than 5 drops will be needed. Even if the solution appears colorless, add 1 drop of the reagent. Centrifuge and separate, saving *Solution 3.8* to test for Zn^{+2}. *Precipitate 3.8* may consist of yellow $BaCrO_4$ with perhaps a little white $BaSO_4$ or $BaCO_3$. (SO_4^{-2} from the oxidation of S^{-2} might be carried along this far, and CO_3^{-2} may come from CO_2, which might have been absorbed from the atmosphere by the NH_3 solution.)

To confirm chromium, wash Precipitate 3.8 with hot water. After centrifuging, decant off the water and treat the precipitate with 3 drops of $3M$ HNO_3, stirring thoroughly; then add 10 drops of cold water and stir. Now add just 3 drops of H_2O_2 *all at once* (Note 1). A blue coloration that disappears quickly confirms the presence of chromium (Notes 2 and 3). *Do not do this test on a known except in the presence of your instructor.* The color usually vanishes in a few seconds.

Notes

1. To measure 3 drops of H_2O_2 from a dropper bottle, lift the dropper above the liquid and empty it. Dip it back into the liquid and carefully squeeze the bulb until just 3 bubbles of air come out, then release the bulb. Now simply lift out the dropper and squirt the H_2O_2 into the test tube of chromate solution. We assume that the 3 air bubbles are of essentially the same volume as 3 drops of liquid.

2. The blue substance, perhaps CrO_5, often miscalled *perchromic acid* is very unstable. Since the solution must be acid for its formation, the chromium is originally present as $HCrO_4^-$ or $Cr_2O_7^{-2}$, depending on the acidity of the solution:

   (1) $HCrO_4^- + 2H_2O_2 + H_3O^+ \rightarrow CrO_5 + 4H_2O$

   But high concentrations of acid accelerate its decomposition:

   (2) $4CrO_5 + 12H_3O^+ \rightarrow 2Cr^{+3} + 18H_2O + 7O_2$

   Also, excess H_2O_2 serves as a reducing agent:

   (3) $2CrO_5 + 7H_2O_2 + 6H_3O^+ \rightarrow 2Cr^{+3} + 16H_2O + 7O_2$

   Shaking the solution with ether extracts the CrO_5, which is even more soluble in ether than in water. This concentrates the blue color. Since CrO_5 in the ether layer is separated from H_3O^+ which remains in the water layer, it does not decompose so quickly. However, it often lasts only a few seconds anyway, and those few seconds are better spent observing the blue color in water than in shaking the tube with ether.

3. The exact composition of the blue substance has never been determined to everyone's satisfaction. It seems well established that there are two peroxide groups attached to each chromium atom. The simplest formula would then be $CrO(O_2)_2$ or

   $(O_2)\!\!=\!\!Cr\!\!=\!\!(O_2)$
   $\|$
   O

   It is difficult to determine whether any molecules of water or hydrogen peroxide are attached to this. Substances like blue $K_2Cr_2O_{12}$ can be crystallized and analyzed, so some investigators have concluded that the correct formula of our blue compound is $H_2Cr_2O_{12}$, corresponding to $H_2O_2 \cdot 2CrO_5$, but so far the evidence relating the compounds is flimsy.

Since the peroxide radical has an oxidation number of -2, chromium in CrO_5 must have an oxidation number of $+6$, just as it does in CrO_4^{-2}, $HCrO_4^{-}$, and $Cr_2O_7^{-2}$. Note that Equation 1 then does not represent an oxidation-reduction, but a displacement reaction—the displacement of coordinate-covalently bound oxygens by peroxide groups.

PROCEDURE 3.9 / Detection of zinc

Add 1 drop of $(NH_4)_2S$ solution to Solution 3.8. A white to dirty gray precipitate may be ZnS. Centrifuge, discarding the centrifugate, and wash. Dissolve the precipitate in 1 ml of $3M$ HCl, warming slightly. ZnS dissolves readily under this treatment, but free sulfur does not. Transfer to a 5 ml beaker and boil down to 0.5 ml to remove dissolved H_2S and excess HCl. (If alternate test for zinc is used, proceed according to Note 3 from this point.) Cool and cautiously add $3M$ NaOH with vigorous stirring until the solution is alkaline to litmus, then add 5 drops more (Note 1). Transfer to a test tube. (If there is any cloudiness or any sediment, centrifuge and discard the precipitate.) Add 2 drops of thioacetamide solution, and heat in a boiling water bath for 5 minutes, having the top of the test tube loosely stoppered with a plug of cotton. A white precipitate is ZnS (Note 2).

Notes

1. When the solution is nearly neutral, white gelatinous $Zn(OH)_2$ may be observed to precipitate, then redissolve as excess NaOH is added. However, if ions like Ni^{+2} and Co^{+2} whose hydroxides are colored are completely absent as they should be, and if the amount of Zn^{+2} present is not large, the gelatinous $Zn(OH)_2$ precipitate may well escape notice. Whether it has been observed or not is of no importance to the confirmatory test.

2. The purpose of precipitating ZnS from a moderately alkaline solution is to prevent the precipitation of white, finely divided S, which is easily obtained by oxidation of S^{-2} if the test is carried out in acid solution.

3. *Alternate test for zinc.* Place 3–5 drops of the clear solution to be tested for zinc on a spot plate. Add $3M$ NH_3 solution until it is just alkaline to litmus, then bring it back just to the neutral point with $0.3M$ HCl (1 drop of concentrated acid diluted with 40 drops of water) and add 1 drop excess. To the slightly acid solution, add 1 drop of $0.01M$ $CuSO_4$ solution. Stir, then add 2 drops of ammonium tetrathio-cyanatomercurate(II), $(NH_4)_2Hg(SCN)_4$, reagent. Rub the inside of the spot plate depression with a stirring rod. A *lavender* precipitate, which may develop slowly, indicates Zn^{+2}. A green precipitate is $CuHg(SCN)_4$ *without* zinc.

$$Zn^{+2} + Cu^{+2} + 2Hg(SCN)_4^{-2} \rightarrow \underline{ZnHg(SCN)_4 \cdot CuHg(SCN)_4}$$

coprecipitate   :   lavender

Word equations for the reactions of Group 3

Aluminum:

1. Aluminum ion + water + ammonia →
                 aluminum hydroxide + ammonium ion

2. Aluminum hydroxide + hydronium ion →
                                aluminum ion + water

3. Aluminum ion + hydroxide ion (excess) → aluminate ion

4. Aluminate ion + hydronium ion → aluminum ion + water

5.* Same as 1

It may contribute to an understanding of these reactions if we consider that the aluminum ions are hydrated and assume that the coordination number of aluminum is 6 throughout. Then, using systematic nomenclature for the Werner complexes, we have

1. Hexaaquoaluminum ion + ammonia →
            trihydroxotriaquoaluminum + ammonium ion

2. Trihydroxotriaquoaluminum + hydronium ion →
                       hexaaquoaluminum ion + water

3. Hexaaquoaluminum ion + hydroxide ion →
$$\text{tetrahydroxodiaquoaluminate ion + water}$$

4. Tetrahydroxodiaquoaluminate ion + hydronium ion →
$$\text{hexaaquoaluminum ion + water}$$

5.* Same as 1

We may, if we wish, write the equations for the other metals in similar fashion.

Chromium:

1. Chromium(III) ion + water + ammonia →
$$\text{chromium(III) hydroxide + ammonium ion}$$

2. Chromium(III) hydroxide + hydronium ion →
$$\text{chromium(III) ion + water}$$

3. Chromium(III) ion + hydroxide ion →
$$\text{chromite ion (tetrahydroxochromate(III) ion)}$$

4. Chromite ion + hydrogen peroxide + hydroxide ion →
$$\text{chromate ion + water}$$

5. Barium ion + chromate ion → barium chromate

6. Barium chromate + hydronium ion →
$$\text{barium ion + hydrogen chromate ion + water}$$

7.* Hydrogen chromate ion + hydronium ion
+ hydrogen peroxide → chromium peroxide (CrO_5) + water

Cobalt:

1. Cobalt(II) ion + ammonia → hexaamminecobalt(II) ion

2. Hexaamminecobalt(II) ion + sulfide ion →
$$\text{cobalt(II) sulfide + ammonia}$$

3. Cobalt(II) sulfide + hydronium ion + nitrate ion →
$$\text{cobalt(II) ion + sulfur + water + nitrogen dioxide}$$

4. Cobalt(II) ion + hydroxide ion → cobalt(II) hydroxide

5. Cobalt(II) hydroxide + hydrogen peroxide →
$$\text{cobalt(III) hydroxide}$$

6. Cobalt(III) hydroxide + hydronium ion
+ hydrogen peroxide → cobalt(II) ion + water + oxygen

7. Same as 1

8. Hexaamminecobalt(II) ion + hydronium ion →
$\qquad$ cobalt(II) ion + water + ammonium ion

9.* Cobalt(II) ion + potassium ion + nitrite ion + acetic acid →
$\qquad$ potassium hexanitrocobaltate(III) + nitric oxide
$\qquad$ + acetate ion + water

Iron:

1. Iron(III) ion + water + ammonia →
$\qquad$ iron(III) hydroxide + ammonium ion

2. Iron(III) hydroxide + hydronium ion →
$\qquad$ iron(III) ion + water

3. (Partially at least) iron(III) ion + sulfide ion →
$\qquad$ iron(II) sulfide + sulfur

4. Iron(II) sulfide + hydronium ion + nitrate ion →
$\qquad$ iron(III) ion + sulfur + water + nitrogen dioxide

5. Iron(III) ion + hydroxide ion → iron(III) hydroxide

6, 7, 8, 9, 10. Repeat 2, 1, 2, 1, 2

11.* Iron(III) ion + thiocyanate ion → thiocyanatoiron(III) ion

Manganese:

1. Manganese(II) ion + sulfide ion → manganese(II) sulfide

2. Manganese(II) sulfide + hydronium ion →
$\qquad$ manganese(II) ion + hydrogen sulfide + water

3. Manganese(II) ion + hydroxide ion →
$\qquad$ manganese(II) hydroxide

4. Manganese(II) hydroxide + hydrogen peroxide →
$\qquad$ manganese dioxide + water

5. Manganese dioxide + hydronium ion
$\qquad$ + hydrogen peroxide → manganese(II) ion + oxygen
$\qquad$ + water

6. Manganese(II) ion + chlorate ion →
$\qquad$ manganese dioxide + chlorine dioxide

7. Same as 5

8.* Manganese(II) ion + hydronium ion + bismuthate ion →
$\qquad$ permanganate ion + bismuth(III) ion + water

Nickel:

1. Nickel(II) ion + ammonia → tetraamminenickel(II) ion
2. Tetraamminenickel(II) ion + sulfide ion →
$$\text{nickel sulfide} + \text{ammonia}$$
3. Nickel sulfide + hydronium ion + nitrate ion →
$$\text{nickel(II) ion} + \text{nitrogen dioxide} + \text{water} + \text{sulfur}$$
4. Nickel(II) ion + hydroxide ion → nickel(II) hydroxide
5. Nickel hydroxide + hydronium ion → nickel(II) ion + water
6. Same as 1
7. Tetraamminenickel(II) ion + hydronium ion →
$$\text{nickel(II) ion} + \text{ammonium ion} + \text{water}$$
8. Same as 1
9.* Tetraamminenickel(II) ion + dimethylglyoxime →
$$\text{nickel dimethylglyoximate} + \text{ammonia} + \text{ammonium ion}$$

Zinc:

1. Zinc ion + ammonia → tetraaminezinc ion
2. Tetraamminezinc ion + sulfide ion →
$$\text{zinc sulfide} + \text{ammonia}$$
3. Zinc sulfide + hydronium ion →
$$\text{zinc ion} + \text{hydrogen sulfide} + \text{water}$$
4. Zinc ion + hydroxide ion → tetrahydroxozincate ion
5. Tetrahydroxozincate ion + hydronium ion →
$$\text{zinc ion} + \text{water}$$
6, 7, 8, 9. Repeat 1, 2, 3, 4
10. Tetrahydroxozincate ion + sulfide ion →
$$\text{zinc sulfide} + \text{hydroxide ion}$$

Questions and problems

1. Write formulas illustrating each of the oxidation states found for those elements that display more than one oxidation state in the chemistry of Group 3. In addition, write formulas to illustrate all oxidation states for the Group 3 metals which, though stable, are not exhibited in any of the Group 3 reactions.

2. What is the basis of the separation of Subgroups 3A and 3B?

3. Give the formulas of three substances used as confirmatory tests which are not precipitates.

4. Through an unfortunate misunderstanding, a student analyzed a Group 2 unknown containing Cu^{+2} and Sb^{+3} according to the procedures of Group 3. For the benefit of this poor fellow's relatives and friends, trace the course of this unknown through a Group 3 flowsheet like that of Figure 23.1, giving the formulas of all substances produced.

5. The same befuddled student of Question 4 also tried to analyze his Group 3 unknown containing Al^{+3}, Fe^{+3}, and Ni^{+2} according to the Group 2 procedures. Tell what befell him on this occasion.

6. A Group 3 unknown contained Al^{+3}, Co^{+2}, and Fe^{+3}. Describe the appearance of each precipitate and solution obtained during the analysis.

7. What harmful result, if any, would there be in each of the following cases?
   a. In Procedure 3.1, after the addition of NH_4Cl and NH_3, you neglected to centrifuge before adding $(NH_4)_2S$.
   b. In confirming chromium on a Group 3 known, Procedure 3.8, you added H_2O_2 and then went off to show it to your instructor who was at the far end of the laboratory.
   c. In analyzing a general unknown that contained both Cd^{+2} and Zn^{+2}, you failed to remove the Cd^{+2} completely before starting Group 3.
   d. In analyzing a general unknown containing Mg^{+2}, you neglected to add NH_4Cl in the precipitation of the group, Procedure 3.1.
   e. You failed to oxidize all the Cr^{+3} to CrO_4^{-2}.
   f. On an unknown containing only Al^{+3}, Cr^{+3}, and Fe^{+3}, you tested for iron directly without separating the other ions.

8. A greenish yellow Group 3 unknown solution gave a brown gelatinous precipitate with NH_4Cl and NH_3 which turned black when $(NH_4)_2S$ was added. The precipitate dissolved partially with HCl, completely when boiled with aqua regia.

Treatment with NaOH and H_2O_2 gave a dark precipitate and a colorless solution.

a. Name one Group 3 ion which was probably absent.

b. Name one probably present.

c. Name one about which you could have no information.

9. A green Group 3 solution gave a light green gelatinous precipitate with ammonia which became heavier when $(NH_4)_2S$ was added but changed little in color. It dissolved readily in HCl. Name one ion which you are sure is absent.

10. a. What is the purpose of the H_2O_2 in Procedure 3.2?

b. In Procedure 3.4, why is the $Fe(OH)_3$ dissolved and reprecipitated before the confirmatory test for iron?

c. What is the function of the H_2O_2 in dissolving MnO_2?

d. Why is $KC_2H_3O_2$ added in the confirmatory test for cobalt? Would $NH_4C_2H_3O_2$ or $NaC_2H_3O_2$ be just as satisfactory?

11. Give the formula of the reagents you used in the procedures of this group to

a. Oxidize Cr^{+3} to CrO_4^{-2}

b. Oxidize Mn^{+2} to MnO_2

c. Oxidize Mn^{+2} to MnO_4^-

d. Oxidize Co(II) to Co(III)

e. Reduce MnO_2 to Mn^{+2}

f. Precipitate Fe^{+3} but not Al^{+3}

g. Precipitate Al^{+3} but not Zn^{+2}

h. Precipitate Co^{+2} but not Ni^{+2}

12. Estimating as carefully as you can the amounts of NH_4Cl, NH_3, and $(NH_4)_2S$ solutions which you added in Procedure 3.1, and neglecting the removal of OH^- and S^{-2} ions by precipitates, calculate:

a. The pH of the solution

b. The $[S^{-2}]$ of the solution

13. Calculate the maximum amounts of Al^{+3}, Cr^{+3}, and Fe^{+3} that could be present in one liter of a solution of pH 7.

14. A Group 3 unknown contains just one of these: Al^{+3}, Mn^{+2}, Zn^{+2}. What would you do to demonstrate conclusively which it is?

Procedures for Analysis
of Group 4

The group reagent for Group 4 is $(NH_4)_2CO_3$ added to a solution buffered with NH_3 and NH_4Cl. When the precipitation is carried out as in Procedure 4.1, the carbonates of Ba^{+2}, Ca^{+2}, and Sr^{+2} are precipitated quite completely, In practice, some $MgCO_3$ is likely to be precipitated also, although there is never enough to interfere with the analysis of the Group 4 metals; and enough Mg^{+2} always remains in solution for detection in Group 5. The metals of Group 4 resemble one another closely in most respects, including the solubilities of their salts, as is mentioned in discussion of the solubility product, page 82. Therefore, care must be taken in separating them, as any reagent which will precipitate one will, in larger amount, precipitate them all.

Since there are only the 3 ions in this group, it is customary to study Groups 4 and 5 together, using first a known solution containing all 7 ions of the combined group: Ba^{+2}, Ca^{+2}, Sr^{+2}, Mg^{+2}, K^+, Na^+, and NH_4^+. Afterwards you will analyze an unknown containing perhaps 2 to 5 of these ions. Since so many of the reagents used throughout qualitative analysis are in the form of ammonium salts, the test for the NH_4^+ ion must be made on a sample of the original material.

PROCEDURE 4.1 / Precipitation of Group 4

You will be working on either a Groups 4 and 5 known, a Groups 4 and 5 unknown, or a general unknown. If you are analyzing

Group 4

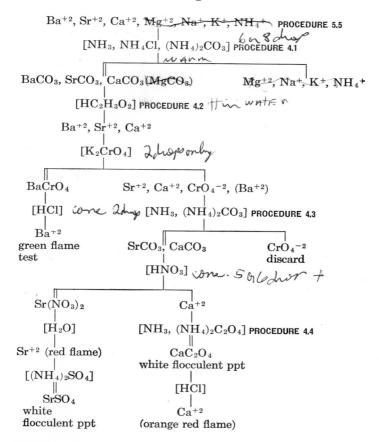

Ba^{+2}, Sr^{+2}, Ca^{+2}, ~~Mg^{+2}, Na$^+$, K$^+$, NH$_4$$^+$~~ PROCEDURE 5.5

[NH$_3$, NH$_4$Cl, (NH$_4$)$_2$CO$_3$] *6 or 8 drops* PROCEDURE 4.1
warm

BaCO$_3$, SrCO$_3$, CaCO$_3$ ~~(MgCO$_3$)~~   Mg^{+2}, Na$^+$, K$^+$, NH$_4$$^+$

[HC$_2$H$_3$O$_2$] PROCEDURE 4.2 *H in water*

Ba^{+2}, Sr^{+2}, Ca^{+2}

[K$_2$CrO$_4$] *2 drops only*

BaCrO$_4$ Sr^{+2}, Ca^{+2}, CrO$_4$$^{-2}$, (Ba^{+2})

[HCl] *conc 2 drops* [NH$_3$, (NH$_4$)$_2$CO$_3$] PROCEDURE 4.3

Ba^{+2}
green flame   SrCO$_3$, CaCO$_3$ CrO$_4$$^{-2}$
test   discard

[HNO$_3$] *conc. 5 or 6 drops +*

Sr(NO$_3$)$_2$ Ca^{+2}

[H$_2$O]   [NH$_3$, (NH$_4$)$_2$C$_2$O$_4$] PROCEDURE 4.4

Sr^{+2} (red flame)   CaC$_2$O$_4$
                            white flocculent ppt

[(NH$_4$)$_2$SO$_4$]   [HCl]

SrSO$_4$ Ca^{+2}
white   (orange red flame)
flocculent ppt

FIGURE 24.1 / THE ANALYSIS OF GROUP 4

a Groups 4 and 5 known or unknown, do Procedure 5.5, the NH$_4$$^+$ test, first, then proceed to Part B of this procedure. If you are doing a general unknown, you will have the centrifugate from Group 3; in that case, begin with Part A.

A: In the analysis of a general unknown. Boil the centrifugate from Group 3 in your crucible (which is supported by a triangle) until crystallization of salts begins to take place. Add 1 ml of 16M HNO$_3$, pouring the acid down the sides of the crucible so that most of the solid material is washed down into the center. Under the hood, heat the crucible again cautiously to dryness, and then more strongly, until no more fumes of NH_4^+ salts are given off. Do not heat beyond the first signs of redness in the crucible, or some of the salts might react with the glaze of the porcelain. After the crucible has cooled thoroughly, add 5 drops of $3M$ HCl and 15 drops of water, stir and transfer to a 75 mm test tube. Use another 15-drop portion of water to rinse the crucible, adding the rinse water to the solution in the test tube. If the solution is cloudy, centrifuge and discard the precipitate.

B: Precipitation. Use the material from Part A above, or take 6 drops of Groups 4 and 5 known solution or 4 drops of a Groups 4 and 5 unknown and dilute to 1 ml in a 75 mm test tube. Add 0.5 ml (10 drops from a standard medicine dropper) of $4M$ NH_4Cl solution. Make alkaline with $15M$ NH_3 and add *1 drop excess*. Add, with stirring, 0.5 ml of $2M$ $(NH_4)_2CO_3$ solution. Heat for several minutes in a water bath held at 60°C, stirring to aid precipitation. Centrifuge and carefully withdraw the liquid with a micropipette, transferring it to a test tube labeled Group 5, and save it for later analysis. It may contain Na^+, K^+, and Mg^{+2} as well as traces of Group 4 ions not precipitated by the Group 4 reagent. The precipitate left in the test tube may contain $BaCO_3$, $SrCO_3$, and $CaCO_3$ (with perhaps some $MgCO_3$).

Notes

1. In a general unknown, the centrifugate from Group 3 contains large amounts of ammonium salts. In Part A of this procedure, the excess which would interfere with the precipitation of Group 4 is destroyed. Nitric acid helps by the reaction

   $$NH_4^+ + NO_3^- \xrightarrow{\Delta} N_2O + 2H_2O$$

   The amount of NH_4^+ which might be present in a Groups 4 and 5 known or unknown is not so large as to cause trouble.

2. Heating to 60° during precipitation lessens supersaturation and aids the growth of large crystals of precipitate, which settle nicely on centrifuging and which have less tendency to adsorb Mg^{+2} ions. A higher temperature than 60° would decompose the $(NH_4)_2CO_3$, which is quite unstable to heat.

PROCEDURE 4.2 / Separation and identification of barium

Wash the Group 4 precipitate with 5 drops of hot water and discard the washings. Then dissolve the precipitate in 5 drops of $6M$ acetic acid, stirring thoroughly. If it does not dissolve completely, add several drops of water and, if necessary, a few more drops of $6M$ acetic acid. Add 2 ml of water and 2 drops of $NH_4C_2H_3O_2$ solution, heat in the boiling water bath, and add 5 drops of K_2CrO_4 solution. Continue to heat and stir for about a minute. Centrifuge and transfer the *Solution 4.2* to another test tube. Label it and save it for Procedure 4.3.

Precipitate 4.2 may be yellow $BaCrO_4$. Confirm it as follows: Wash three times with 5-drop portions of water. (Each time add 5 drops of water to the precipitate, stir it up, then centrifuge and withdraw the water with a capillary pipette or decant it off. Decantation is usually a completely satisfactory method of removing liquid from the heavy, compact precipitates of this group.) Discard the washings, then transfer the $BaCrO_4$ to a crucible, using a microspatula (or a rubber policeman). Add 5 drops of concentrated HCl and heat gently till a green solution is obtained (Note 1). Dip a clean platinum wire into the green solution. A green flame is a positive test for Ba^{+2}. $SrCrO_4$, which might be found in Precipitate 4.2 if a large amount of strontium is present or if the student's technique is poor, would give a crimson flame.

Notes

1. Boiling the $BaCrO_4$ with $12M$ HCl reduces the CrO_4^{-2} ion, leaving the more volatile $BaCl_2$:

$$2BaCrO_4 + 16H_3O^+ + 6Cl^- \rightarrow$$
$$2Ba^{+2} + 2Cr^{+3} + 3Cl_2 + 24H_2O$$

The green color of the reduced solution is due to Cr^{+3}. Of course, it has no connection with the green color of the barium flame; $SrCrO_4$ would give the same green solution but a crimson flame.

2. The platinum wire is cleaned by alternately dipping it in $12M$ HCl and holding it in the flame. Do *not* make a loop

in the wire so that it takes up more solution nor dip the wire in the solid precipitate; barium is hard enough to remove from the wire when it is present only in trace amounts.

PROCEDURE 4.3 / Separation and detection of strontium

Precipitation of $CaCO_3$ and $SrCO_3$. Solution 4.2, in a test tube, may contain Sr^{+2} and Ca^{+2} (with perhaps some Mg^{+2}), CrO_4^{-2}, and an excess of acetic acid. Test for complete precipitation of $BaCrO_4$ by adding a fraction of a drop of K_2CrO_4. If precipitation takes place, add 3 drops more K_2CrO_4, centrifuge, and discard the precipitate, which may contain $BaCrO_4$ and some $SrCrO_4$ (but the amount of either Ba^{+2} or Sr^{+2} you throw away is not enough to interfere with their detection). Make the clear solution basic to litmus by the addition of NH_3 solution. Add 0.5 ml of $(NH_4)_2CO_3$ solution, warm and centrifuge in one or two test tubes, depending on the volume. Discard the supernatant liquid and wash the precipitate twice with hot water, centrifuging and discarding the wash water each time.

Separation of strontium. Dissolve the precipitate of $CaCO_3$, $SrCO_3$, and $MgCO_3$ (as free of liquid as you can get it) by the cautious dropwise addition of $16M$ HNO_3. After effervescence has ceased, add an additional 1.5 ml of concentrated HNO_3. Stir the mixture vigorously for a minute or two, being careful, of course, not to splash any concentrated nitric acid around. Then place the tube in a beaker containing cold water and allow it to stand for 10 minutes with occasional stirring. (Caution: Do not allow any water to get into the tube. It would dilute the acid and render the $Sr(NO_3)_2$ precipitate soluble.) Centrifuge the mixture and decant the supernatant liquid into a 10 ml beaker containing 6 ml of water. Save this *Solution 4.3* in the beaker to test for Ca^{+2} by Procedure 4.4.

Stir the precipitate in the test tube with 6 drops of $16M$ HNO_3, centrifuge, and discard the liquid, which might contain traces of Ca^{+2}.

Identification of strontium. Dissolve the precipitate, $Sr(NO_3)_2$ in 1 ml of hot water. Make a flame test on this solution. (Sr^{+2} gives a crimson flame when the wire is held in the outer edge of the flame about one-half inch above the burner tip. A green flame would indicate incomplete removal of barium.) Add 2 drops of $(NH_4)_2SO_4$ solution to this solution and heat to boiling. The formation of a white flocculent precipitate of $SrSO_4$ confirms the presence of strontium.

Notes

1. HNO_3 must be rinsed out of the dropper because it would attack the rubber bulb, ruining the bulb and contaminating the glass tube.

PROCEDURE 4.4 / Detection of calcium

Solution 4.3 may contain Ca^{+2} and probably some Mg^{+2} dissolved in HNO_3 solution of concentration 3 molar or stronger. Cautiously add concentrated $(15M)$ NH_3 until the solution is alkaline to litmus. The NH_3 solution should be added drop by drop with thorough stirring. Test for neutralization by touching the stirring rod to a piece of litmus resting on a glass or porcelain plate. To the alkaline solution add 1 ml of $0.25M$ $(NH_4)_2C_2O_4$, and allow it to stand for several minutes. A white flocculent precipitate of CaC_2O_4 which sometimes forms quite slowly is the confirmatory test for Ca^{+2}. If a flame test is desirable for greater certainty, transfer the mixture to a test tube and centrifuge. Decant and discard the supernatant liquid unless it is desired to test for Mg^{+2} in Group 4 (see Note 1). Wash the precipitate of CaC_2O_4 by adding 1 ml of water containing a drop of $(NH_4)_2C_2O_4$ solution, stirring, centrifuging, and pouring off the wash water. Acidify the precipitate of CaC_2O_4 with a drop of $12M$ HCl and make a flame test. Observe carefully the difference between the orange-red calcium flame and the crimson strontium flame. If you are undecided about the color of the flame obtained from an unknown, compare the flame with those obtained from known samples of both Ca^{+2} and Sr^{+2} compounds.

Notes

1. If you wish to test for Mg^{+2} in Group 4, the centrifugate separated from the CaC_2O_4 precipitate should be decanted

into a 5 ml beaker and treated with 5 drops of $15M$ NH_3 and 3 drops of $0.25M$ Na_2HPO solution. A fine crystalline precipitate of $MgNH_4PO_4$ is a positive test. The test for Mg^{+2} obtained in Procedure 5.2 is, however, more meaningful.

Word equations for the reactions of Group 4

Barium:

1. Barium ion + carbonate ion → barium carbonate

2. Barium carbonate + hydronium ion →
   barium ion + hydrogen carbonate ion + water

3. Barium ion + chromate ion → barium chromate

4.* Barium chromate + hydronium ion + chloride ion →
   barium ion + chromium(III) ion + chlorine + water

Strontium:

1. Strontium ion + carbonate ion → strontium carbonate

2. Strontium carbonate + hydronium ion →
   strontium ion + hydrogen carbonate ion + water

3. Same as 1

4. Same as 2

5. Strontium ion + nitrate ion $\xrightarrow{\text{(in concentrated HNO}_3\text{)}}$
   strontium nitrate

6. Strontium nitrate $\xrightarrow{\text{(in H}_2\text{O)}}$ strontium ion + nitrate ion

7.* Strontium ion + sulfate ion → strontium sulfate

Calcium:

1. Calcium ion + carbonate ion → calcium carbonate

2. Calcium carbonate + hydronium ion →
   calcium ion + hydrogen carbonate ion + water

3. Same as 1

4. Same as 2

5.* Calcium ion + oxalate ion → calcium oxalate

6. Calcium oxalate + hydronium ion →
   calcium ion + hydrogen oxalate ion + water

Questions and problems

1. What is the basis of the separation of Groups 4 and 5?

2. Look up the separation of strontium and calcium in other qualitative analysis texts. How many different methods of separation do you find? Do you find any separation of barium that is essentially different from the one in this book?

3. You are given a white substance which you know is either $BaCO_3$, $CaCO_3$, $MgCO_3$, or $SrCO_3$. Without using a flame test, how would you quickly identify it?

4. A Group 4 unknown was given out as a solid carbonate. It was completely insoluble in $16M$ HNO_3. Name one cation which was not present.

5. How many reagents can you name that could be used to separate Ba^{+2} and Ca^{+2}? In each case, give the formula of the precipitate and the soluble ion.

6. Tell what trouble, if any, would be observed in each of the following cases:
   a. The Group 4 carbonates were dissolved in $6M$ HCl instead of $6M$ $HC_2H_3O_2$
   b. The Group 4 precipitate was treated with $6M$ H_2SO_4 instead of $6M$ $HC_2H_3O_2$
   c. In the separation of Ca^{+2} and Sr^{+2}, some water was left on the carbonates to which concentrated nitric acid was added
   d. On a general unknown, the centrifugate from Group 3 was not heated with HNO_3 before starting Group 4
   e. On a general unknown, Mn^{+2} was not removed in Group 3, so it was present in the material used for Group 4 analysis

7. How do you account for the fact that no oxidation-reduction reactions are found involving the Group 4 metals?

8. $BaCrO_4$ and $BaSO_4$ are almost equally insoluble—the K_{sp} values are 1.8×10^{-10} and 1.1×10^{-10} respectively. Yet $BaCrO_4$ dissolves readily in acid, while $BaSO_4$ is insoluble in acid. Can you explain this? Does this suggest anything about the acid strength of chromic acid?

Procedures for Analysis of Group 5

25

Group 5 contains all the ions not precipitated by the group reagents of the earlier groups. Besides the ions of the alkali metals (of which Na^+ and K^+ are the only ones commonly considered) it usually includes Mg^{+2} and, invariably, NH_4^+. On the basis of its position in the periodic table, we might have expected Mg^{+2} to be in Group 4. However, its solubilities are rather different from those of the larger alkaline earth ions and most separations place it with the Soluble Group as we do.

While NH_4^+ is not a metal ion, it merits inclusion in our scheme because of the importance of its salts in the laboratory and in commerce. Although in its chemistry NH_4^+ resembles the alkali metal ions, its placement in Group 5 is more formal than actual. Since we find it convenient to add reagents in the form of ammonium salts throughout all the procedures, we must test for the ion on a separate sample to which we have not added any ammonia or ammonium compound. We could, if we wished, add our reagents as the sodium salts. Then we would test for NH_4^+ in the regular procedure and test for Na^+ separately. There are good reasons for the almost universal preference for our way of doing it: most ammonium salts are very soluble; ammonia is a weak base so that the addition of ammonium salts of weak acids does not upset the pH; and excess ammonia is easily removed by heat.

REMEMBER: *Whenever NH_4^+ is a possible ion to be tested for, whether on a known or unknown, go directly to Procedure 5.5 and test for ammonia before testing for any other cation.*

Group 5

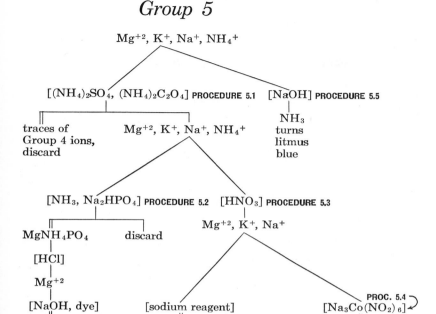

Mg^{+2}, K^+, Na^+, NH_4^+

$[(NH_4)_2SO_4$, $(NH_4)_2C_2O_4]$ PROCEDURE 5.1 $[NaOH]$ PROCEDURE 5.5

traces of Mg^{+2}, K^+, Na^+, NH_4^+ NH_3
Group 4 ions,   turns
discard   litmus
                                                             blue

$[NH_3$, $Na_2HPO_4]$ PROCEDURE 5.2 $[HNO_3]$ PROCEDURE 5.3

$MgNH_4PO_4$ discard Mg^{+2}, K^+, Na^+

$[HCl]$

Mg^{+2}

$[NaOH$, dye]   [sodium reagent]   PROC. 5.4
                                                         $[Na_3Co(NO_2)_6]$

$Mg(OH)_2$ lake $NaMg(UO_2)_3 (C_2H_3O_2)_9 \cdot 5H_2O$ $K_2NaCo(NO_2)_6$
blue ppt   greenish yellow ppt   yellow ppt

FIGURE 25.1 / THE ANALYSIS OF GROUP 5

PROCEDURE 5.1 / Removal of traces of Group 4 ions

In Procedure 4.2, Part B, you saved the centrifugate, labeled Group 5 (see Note 1). To this solution add 1 drop each of $(NH_4)_2SO_4$ and $(NH_4)_2C_2O_4$ solutions. Stir and test with litmus. If the solution is not distinctly alkaline, add enough dilute ($3M$) NH_3 solution to make it so. Then heat to boiling in the water bath. Centrifuge and discard the precipitate (Note 2). *Solution 5.1* contains K^+, Na^+, Mg^{+2}, and NH_4^+ with insignificant amounts of other cations. Take one-third of it in a test tube to test for Mg^{+2} (Procedure 5.2) and save the rest for Procedure 5.3.

Notes

1. A light precipitate of Group 4 carbonates may have settled out from the solution containing Group 5. It is hardly likely

to be heavy enough to indicate that you missed any of the Group 4 ions.

2. Traces of Group 4 ions would interfere with the Mg^{+2} test so they are removed more completely in this procedure.

PROCEDURE 5.2 / Test for magnesium

To the one-third portion of Solution 5.1, add 5 drops of $0.25 M$ Na_2HPO_4 solution. Stir the mixture and let it stand for several minutes. If precipitation is slow, heat it for 5 minutes in a water bath held at 60°, stirring occasionally and rubbing the inside of the test tube with the stirring rod.

A fine crystalline precipitate is $MgNH_4PO_4$. To confirm the presence of Mg^{+2}, wash the precipitate 3 times with hot water (Note 1), dissolve in 5 drops of $3M$ HCl, and add *1* drop of magnesium reagent. Then add $6M$ NaOH with constant stirring until the solution is distinctly alkaline. A sky-blue precipitate confirms the presence of Mg^{+2} (Note 2). The precipitate may be concentrated by centrifuging and, if not too much magnesium reagent has been added, the dye will be entirely in the precipitate, leaving the solution colorless. The purplish color of the magnesium reagent in alkaline solution is not to be confused with the blue lake precipitate.

Notes

1. Since NH_4^+ and PO_4^{-3} ions interfere with the lake test for magnesium, thorough washing is required.

2. The confirmatory precipitate for magnesium is a *lake*—that is, a pigment composed of a precipitate on which is adsorbed a dye. The "magnesium reagent" is a solution of a dye, p-nitrobenzeneazoresorcinol, which is readily adsorbed on gelatinous $Mg(OH)_2$. The alkaline earth ions, which if not completely removed would give phosphate precipitates, do not interfere with this test

PROCEDURE 5.3 / Identification of sodium

(For flame tests for sodium and potassium, see Note 2 after this procedure.)

Transfer the remaining two-thirds of Solution 5.1 to a porcelain crucible. Use a few drops of water as a rinse to insure getting all of the solution possible. Boil the solution carefully down to about 3 drops by placing the crucible on the wire gauze and heating the wire gauze about an inch away from the crucible. The heat conducted through the gauze should be sufficient to give gentle boiling without spattering. Add 10 drops of 16M (concentrated) HNO_3, using the acid to wash solid particles down from the side of the crucible. Boil down to dryness and heat more strongly to drive off fumes of ammonia; *then cool*, add a second portion of HNO_3 to the *cool* crucible and repeat. Finally, support the crucible on the triangle and heat more strongly, heating the sides as well as the bottom of the crucible, but do not *heat to redness* or the salts might react with the glaze of the crucible. Cool and dissolve the residue in 4 drops of water. Stir and warm if necessary to aid solution. Transfer the solution to a centrifuge tube and centrifuge to obtain a *clear Solution 5.3*. Transfer 2 drops of this solution to a *clean* centrifuge tube and add 6 drops of "sodium reagent" (magnesium acetate and uranyl acetate). Stir and scratch the inside of the tube. Within 5 or 10 minutes a crystalline, greenish yellow precipitate of $NaMg(UO_2)_3(C_2H_3O_2)_9 \cdot 5H_2O$ should form. Large amounts of Mg^{+2} give a false test; therefore, unless you are working with an unknown which did not give a test for magnesium, add 5 drops of water and warm in a 50° water bath. If the precipitate persists, it confirms the presence of sodium.

Notes

1. The reason for boiling down with HNO_3 and heating the crucible more strongly afterward is to remove NH_4^+ ion. All ammonium salts are volatile, but ammonium nitrate is especially unstable to heat since it decomposes according to the reaction

$$NH_4NO_3 \xrightarrow{\Delta} N_2O + 2H_2O$$

2. Flame tests for sodium and potassium may be performed on Solution 5.3.

   Acidify the solution with 1 drop of 12M HCl. Use a freshly cleaned platinum wire. The presence of sodium is indicated by a yellow flame of fairly long duration which fluffs out from the wire in all directions. Since sodium is a ubiquitous element and the flame test is very sensitive, a slight yellow coloration of the flame may be obtained from almost anything. Make comparison tests on solutions of NaCl and some shelf chemical like $MgSO_4$ to see what positive and negative flame tests look like. In the absence of sodium, potassium gives a violet flame test (many heavy metals give a pale blue coloration to the flame). If sodium is present, its yellow flame will completely mask the potassium flame. The sodium color may be screened out by viewing the flame through several thicknesses of cobalt glass or through didymium glass such as is used in glass blowers' goggles.

PROCEDURE 5.4 / Identification of potassium

Treat the remainder of Solution 5.3 with $6M$ acetic acid until it is acid to litmus, then decant into a centrifuge tube containing 2 drops of $Na_3Co(NO_2)_6$ solution. Warm it in a 50° water bath for 5 minutes. A yellow precipitate of $K_2NaCo(NO_2)_6$ indicates potassium. However, if NH_4^+ was incompletely removed in Procedure 5.3, a similar precipitate of $(NH_4)_2NaCo(NO_2)_6$ would be obtained, so a confirmatory test is in order. Heat the centrifuge tube in a boiling water bath until the supernatant solution turns pink (Note 1). *Cool* the pink solution, then add 2 more drops of $Na_3Co(NO_2)_6$. A yellow precipitate this second time should be positive confirmation of the presence of K^+.

Notes

1. The pink color of Co^{+2} ion indicates that $Co(NO_2)_6^{-3}$ has been decomposed into Co^{+2} and NO_2^-. The NO_2^- reacts with any remaining NH_4^+:

    $$NH_4^+ + NO_2^- \rightarrow N_2 + 2H_2O$$

PROCEDURE 5.5 / Test for ammonium ion

Tear off a small square of red litmus paper, moisten it with distilled water, and paste it in the center of the convex side of your watch glass. It will adhere readily enough. Now put 1 pellet of solid NaOH in a 5 ml beaker. With a medicine dropper, allow one drop of the solution being tested to fall onto this pellet. Then cover the beaker with the watch glass so that the litmus paper is on the under side of the watch glass and completely inside the beaker. Be careful not to let the litmus paper or the moistened part of the watch glass come in contact with the rim of the beaker. In a few seconds—less than a minute—the litmus paper will turn blue if NH_4^+ is present. The amount of NH_3 liberated here will also be detectable by odor by anyone whose nose is functioning properly. Sometimes *gentle* warming may be necessary, but remember that alkaline solutions bump and spatter when boiled. NaOH spattered on the litmus in this way will certainly turn it blue, but will prove nothing about the composition of the material and too much about the technique of the student.

When the NH_4^+ test is to be made on a solid unknown, proceed as above, but use a pinhead size portion of the solid unknown in the beaker and let fall on it 1 drop of $6M$ NaOH solution.

Any student of qualitative analysis is expected to know that NaOH, either solid or in solution, is to be treated with respect. The pellets are to be transferred with a forceps or spatula, not the fingers, and NaOH is not to be spilled.

Word equations for the reactions of Group 5

Ammonium:

1.* Ammonium ion + hydroxide ion → ammonia + water

Magnesium:

1. Magnesium ion + ammonia
   + monohydrogen phosphate ion →

   $\qquad\qquad\qquad$ magnesium ammonium phosphate

2. Magnesium ammonium phosphate + hydronium ion →
   magnesium ion + ammonium ion + dihydrogen phosphate ion

   $\qquad\qquad\qquad\qquad\qquad$ + water

3.* Magnesium ion + hydroxide ion + dye →

   $\qquad\qquad\qquad$ magnesium hydroxide lake

Potassium:

1.* Potassium ion + sodium ion
   + hexanitrocobaltate(III) ion →

   $\qquad\qquad$ dipotassium sodium hexanitrocobaltate(III)

Sodium:

1. Sodium ion + magnesium ion
   + uranyl ion (dioxouranium(VI) ion) + acetate ion + water →
   $\qquad$ sodium magnesium triuranyl acetate pentahydrate

Questions and problems

1. In Procedure 5.1, you added $(NH_4)_2SO_4$ and $(NH_4)_2C_2O_4$ solutions to remove traces of Group 4 ions. Which of these would be more useful for removing Ca^{+2} ion? Sr^{+2} ion? Ba^{+2} ion?

2. What undesirable result might occur in the following cases:
   a. The Group 4 centrifugate was used directly for the magnesium test without first going through Procedure 5.1
   b. The centrifugate from Procedure 5.2 was used in the test for sodium and potassium
   c. The sodium and potassium tests were made without first boiling the test solution down with HNO_3
   d. In the test for ammonium ion, the mixture of test solution and NaOH was boiled
   e. In the confirmatory test for magnesium, 5 drops of magnesium reagent were used, instead of 1

3. An unknown solution for Groups 4 and 5 gave a white precipitate with $(NH_4)_2CO_3$, NH_4Cl, and NH_3. What do you know about the Group 4 ions that are present? What about Group 5?

4. A flame test was made on a Groups 4 and 5 unknown. Only a violet flame was observed. What ions of Groups 4 and 5 were eliminated?

5. A white solid is known to be either $MgSO_4$, $(NH_4)_2SO_4$, Na_2SO_4, or K_2SO_4. What would be the simplest way to prove conclusively which it is?

6. A white powder is known to be a mixture of just two substances from this list: $BaSO_4$, $MgSO_4$, $(NH_4)_2SO_4$, Na_2SO_4. What would be the simplest procedure to show which two are present?

7. What is the maximum concentration of K^+ ion that can remain in a $0.25M$ solution of $Na_3Co(NO_2)_6$?

Analysis of a Metal
or Alloy

26

Although we are more concerned with the pedagogical implications of qualitative analysis than with its practical aspects, the analysis of alloys is an example of the importance of qualitative methods in modern analytical work. Ordinarily the qualitative procedures would be used to determine what elements are present and to give a rough estimate of their proportions. Quantitative techniques might then be judiciously applied to determine more precisely how much of each metal is present.

Commercial alloys may contain almost any metal, including many we have not included in our qualitative scheme. Since we know that many alloys are important just because of their resistance to chemical attack, it is plain that no ordinary solvent will be satisfactory for dissolving every alloy. Further, commercial alloys may contain only traces of certain ingredients. For those reasons, we shall have to accept certain restrictions in our selection of alloys. We will use alloys made up for qualitative analysis, containing approximately equal amounts of the alloying metals, and not requiring drastic treatment to dissolve.

Although various solvents such as dilute HCl, $HClO_4$ in various concentrations, fused $KHSO_4$, and fused NaOH may be excellent for certain alloys, we shall limit ourselves to $8M$ HNO_3 and aqua regia as solvents and limit our selections of alloys to those soluble with reasonable ease in these reagents.

Alloy

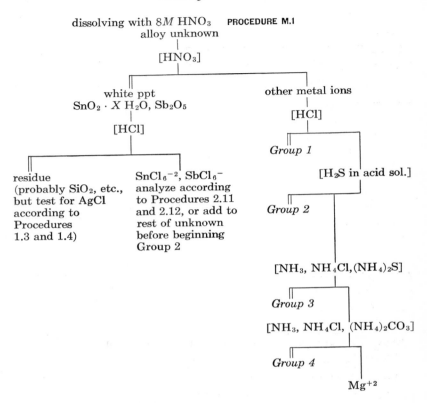

dissolving with $8M$ HNO$_3$ **PROCEDURE M.1**
alloy unknown

[HNO$_3$]

white ppt
SnO$_2$ · X H$_2$O, Sb$_2$O$_5$

[HCl]

other metal ions

[HCl]

Group 1

residue
(probably SiO$_2$, etc.,
but test for AgCl
according to
Procedures
1.3 and 1.4)

SnCl$_6$$^{-2}$, SbCl$_6$$^-$
analyze according
to Procedures 2.11
and 2.12, or add to
rest of unknown
before beginning
Group 2

[H$_2$S in acid sol.]

Group 2

[NH$_3$, NH$_4$Cl,(NH$_4$)$_2$S]

Group 3

[NH$_3$, NH$_4$Cl, (NH$_4$)$_2$CO$_3$]

Group 4

Mg^{+2}

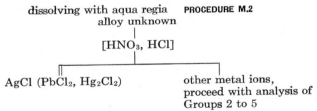

dissolving with aqua regia   **PROCEDURE M.2**
alloy unknown

[HNO$_3$, HCl]

AgCl (PbCl$_2$, Hg$_2$Cl$_2$)

other metal ions,
proceed with analysis of
Groups 2 to 5

FIGURE 26.1 / OUTLINE FOR ANALYSIS OF AN ALLOY

PROCEDURE M.1 / Solution in 8M HNO$_3$

Place about 25 to 50 mg of alloy, in bulk about equal to the
exposed lead in a standard mechanical pencil, in a 5 ml beaker,
add 10 drops (0.5 ml) of $8M$ HNO$_3$, and cover with a small watch
glass. Heat carefully on the wire gauze until reaction is com-

plete. This may require 3 to 5 minutes; in rare instances, it might even require a full laboratory period. It may help to stir the metal occasionally with a glass stirring rod. Add more $8M$ HNO_3 to replace any that boils away, but avoid a large excess.

A. If the alloy dissolves completely, it indicates the absence of tin and antimony. Carefully boil down *almost* to dryness, but do not let it go completely dry, add 10 or 15 drops of $3M$ HNO_3, and boil down to about 5 drops. Transfer to a 75 mm test tube, washing it with water, add more water if necessary, and go through the complete analytical scheme beginning with Procedure 1 of Group 1, saving the centrifugate of each group for the test solution of the succeeding group as shown in the outline, Figure 26.1.

B. If a white or nearly white precipitate remains after long boiling of the alloy with $8M$ HNO_3, it may contain $SnO_2 \cdot XH_2O$ and Sb_2O_5. Boil the mixture down nearly to dryness as above, being very careful not to bake the solid residue. Add $3M$ HNO_3, boil down to 5 drops, transfer to a 75 mm test tube, and centrifuge. Use the solution to test for Groups 1, 2, etc.
Treat the precipitate with 5 drops of concentrated HCl (or enough to cover the solid). Heat in an air bath for 5 minutes or longer, then add 8 drops of water. The precipitate should dissolve, but if any remains, centrifuge and test the residue for AgCl according to Procedures 1.3 and 1.4, Group 1. The solution may contain $SnCl_6^{-2}$ and $SbCl_6^{-3}$ and traces of other metal ions that had been adsorbed on the hydrous oxides of Sn and Sb. It may be tested directly according to Procedures 2.11 and 2.12, Group 2, or better, perhaps, it might be added to the remainder of the unknown immediately before precipitating Group 2. (Procedure 2.1, Part A. See Note 4 after Procedure M.2.)

PROCEDURE M.2 / Solution in aqua regia

If the alloy reacts so slowly with $8M$ HNO_3 that metallic residue (rather than the white or nearly white oxides referred to in Part B) remains after 20 minutes or so, it may be well to try aqua regia. Although HCl may be added directly to the sample that has been boiled with nitric acid, it is probably better to start with a fresh portion of alloy.

Directions for dissolving alloy in aqua regia. Add 8 drops of water, 8 drops of $12M$ HCl, and 3 drops of $16M$ HNO$_3$ to a 25 to 50 mg sample of alloy in a 5 ml beaker. If necessary, heat gently or boil carefully to aid the reaction, adding HCl and HNO$_3$ in the same ratio to replace any liquid that boils away. When the reaction is complete, the alloy will be completely dissolved or converted to a white granular or curdy precipitate. Add a few drops more of concentrated HCl to react with excess nitric acid and boil down to 6 or 7 drops. Allow this to cool, then add an equal volume of water. A precipitate should consist of only Group 1 metal chlorides. Transfer to a test tube, with the aid of a few drops of $3M$ HCl, and centrifuge. Test the precipitate according to the procedures of Group 1, and the centrifugate according to the procedures of the subsequent groups.

Notes

1. Since a number of nitrates, especially Pb(NO$_3$)$_2$ and Bi(NO$_3$)$_3$, are not very soluble in concentrated HNO$_3$, $8M$ acid is more satisfactory.

2. Pure aluminum will not dissolve in $8M$ HNO$_3$ but many of its alloys dissolve readily. Some of the transition metals, particularly Cr, are rendered passive by treatment with nitric acid and thereafter resist other acids. An alloy known to contain the transition metals may be treated with boiling, dilute HCl, though this reagent is not favored for alloys that may contain arsenic, mercury, or other metals that have volatile chlorides. For our purposes, it is better simply not to attempt to analyze stainless steels or other alloys that exhibit passivity.

3. If aqua regia is used to dissolve an alloy, we would expect only the Group 1 chlorides to remain as a precipitate. However, if the reaction of aqua regia with the alloy is continued sufficiently long, any Hg$_2^{+2}$ is oxidized to Hg^{+2}; therefore, Hg$_2$Cl$_2$ is seldom observed. Also the Cl$^-$ concentration is

often high enough to dissolve lead as $PbCl_4{}^{-2}$, so that silver may be the only Group 1 metal observed. The dilution with water before centrifuging should insure that silver will be present as $AgCl$ precipitate rather than as soluble $AgCl_2{}^{-2}$.

4. Whether the alloy was dissolved by Procedure M.1 or M.2, it is not necessary to boil it down with H_2O_2 in Procedure 2.1, Part A. Simply adjust the acidity with concentrated NH_3 and $3M$ HCl and proceed with Part B.

Anion Analysis

Our prime interest in this course is in the chemistry of the metals: to that end we have been devoting ourselves thus far to the analysis of cations. Before we can proceed with the analysis of a salt we must know something also about anion analysis. Although several schemes have been worked out for the systematic analysis of anions similar in principle to the method we have been using for cations, we will find it more satisfactory to identify the various anions by separate tests. One reason for doing it in this simpler way is that we have assumed that you have already had some familiarity with the common anions before you began qualitative analysis. A second reason is that freshmen ordinarily achieve better results more easily by individual tests for anions than by systematic analysis. Also, in the analysis of a salt, if the cation is found first, the number of possible anions may be limited by solubility, color, or other characteristics to a very few choices, which are easily tested for.

We shall limit ourselves to 17 anions divided into 3 groups on the basis of solubility:

Sulfate Group	Chloride Group	Soluble Group
AsO_4^{-3}	Br^-	$C_2H_3O_2^-$
BO_2^-	Cl^-	NO_3^-
CO_3^{-2}	I^-	NO_2^-
CrO_4^{-2}	S^{-2}	
F^-	CNS^-	
$C_2O_4^{-2}$		
PO_4^{-3}		
SO_4^{-2}		
SO_3^{-2}		

(This list may be shortened, if desired, by omitting such anions as acetate, oxalate, and thiocyanate, without affecting the procedures in any way.)

Anion preliminary tests. For preliminary anion tests, on either a known or an unknown, the sodium salts should be used. Ordinarily they are more conveniently stored and distributed as solids than as solutions. Certain of the anion tests are performed on a sample of solid, but for the group tests and for some anion tests, a solution should be made by dissolving an amount of the solid equal in bulk to 2 standard drops, in other words about the size of a grain of rice, in 2 ml of water. The sodium salts of most of these anions should dissolve in this amount of water, but if necessary, add the minimum additional amount of water needed to dissolve substantially all of the solid.

A salt unknown. For analyzing an unknown salt, use the anion test solution obtained in Procedure S.4 or S.5 (pages 317 and 318).

PROCEDURE A.1 / Anion Group tests

A: Test for the Sulfate Group of anions. To a 5-drop portion of the solution to be tested, add 2 drops of $0.5M$ $BaCl_2$ solution. Stir, centrifuge, and add 3 drops of $0.5M$ $CaCl_2$ solution. Notice whether there is any further precipitation. Then add $3M$ HCl till the solution is acid, and 3 drops excess. Does the precipitate redissolve?

Since Ca^{+2} is a better precipitant for $C_2O_4^{-2}$ and F^- than is Ba^{+2}, the barium precipitate is settled by centrifuging to make it easier to observe what happens when $CaCl_2$ is added. If a precipitate does not redissolve in moderately strong acid, it is definite evidence of SO_4^{-2}.

B: Test for the Chloride Group of anions. Besides the salts of the anions listed with this group, most of the silver salts of the Sulfate Group of anions are also insoluble; in fact, only $AgNO_3$ and AgF of the common simple salts are really soluble. Therefore, follow the directions for this test carefully, or you may get a precipitate of one of the so-called soluble salts of silver, such as Ag_2SO_4 or $AgC_2H_3O_2$.

Dilute 4 drops of anion test solution with 1 ml of water, and add 2 drops of $AgNO_3$ solution. Observe the color of any precipitate and then with vigorous stirring add 4 drops of $3M$ HNO_3, 1 drop at a time (the solution should now be strongly acid; if it is not, add more HNO_3). If, after this, there is no precipitate or only a slight turbidity, the Chloride Group anions are absent; a heavy precipitate indicates the presence of a Chloride Group anion.

The possible colors observed before and after acidification may be difficult to interpret even for a simple salt, but here are a few suggestions:

A black precipitate may indicate S^{-2}.

A brown precipitate of Ag_2O may form if the solution being tested is quite basic.

Ag_2CrO_4 is red, and Ag_3AsO_4 tan to brick red.

Ag_3PO_4 and AgI are yellow; $AgBr$ is very faintly yellow— it is usually called cream color.

$AgCl$, $AgCNS$, $AgNO_2$, Ag_2SO_3, $Ag_2C_2O_4$, and $AgBO_2$ are white.

All the precipitates except those of the Chloride Group anions redissolve, perhaps slowly, when the solution is acidified.

If the test solution contains an appreciable amount of NH_3, the formation of $Ag(NH_3)_2^+$ interferes with the precipitation of those silver salts having a fairly large K_{sp}. The dropwise addition of nitric acid decomposes the complex and allows the observation of all the precipitates, including those which redissolve on further acidification.

C: Anions of the Soluble Group. The absence of a test for the Sulfate and Chloride Groups necessitates that a Soluble Group anion be present. When analyzing a mixture it will always be necessary to make tests for Soluble Group ions that have not been otherwise excluded.

D: Volatile anions. Since volatile anions are found in all three solubility groups, a simple test for effervescence combined with the solubility group tests can narrow the possibilities down to a very few anions. This is especially true for a substance known to contain only one anion.

Use the smallest amount of material for which you can observe reactions with the unaided eye. This will be an amount of solid equal in bulk to the head of a pin or to the exposed lead in a mechanical pencil. To this material in a test tube add 2 drops of $3M$ H$_2$SO$_4$. Shake gently and look for effervescence. If you are not sure what to look for, try a sample of Na$_2$CO$_3$ from the reagent shelf. If no bubbling is observed in the cold, heat the mixture.

If effervescence occurs in the cold, it may indicate the presence of CO$_3$$^{-2}$, SO$_3$$^{-2}$, NO$_2$$^-$, or S^{-2}.

A brown gas evolved in the cold is NO$_2$, indicating nitrite (heating may liberate Br$_2$ from bromides).

A colorless gas may be H$_2$S (rotten egg odor) or SO$_2$ (sharp odor) or CO$_2$ (odorless, but a very soluble carbonate may effervesce so vigorously as to expel droplets of sulfuric acid into the air). Perform the confirmatory tests.

On heating, there may be evidence of HCl or HBr (sharp odors, fume in moist air). HC$_2$H$_3$O$_2$ (vinegar odor), NO$_2$ or HNO$_3$ from NO$_3$$^-$, or I$_2$ (violet fumes).

Keep in mind that the behavior of the sodium salt of an anion may be quite different from the salt of another metal with the same anion. Solubilities, hydrolysis reactions, and oxidation-reduction reactions may alter the results.

Procedures A.2 to A.9: Specific Tests for the Sulfate Group of Anions

PROCEDURE A.2 / Test for arsenate, AsO$_4$$^{-3}$, and phosphate, PO$_4$$^{-3}$

Using 2 drops of test solution in a centrifuge tube, add 4 drops of $3M$ HNO$_3$ and 2 drops of (NH$_4$)$_2$MoO$_4$. Stir thoroughly and heat in a 50° water bath. A yellow precipitate, which may form very slowly, shows AsO$_4$$^{-3}$ or PO$_4$$^{-3}$ (Note 3). The precipitate is ammonium arsenomolybdate, usually written as (NH$_4$)$_3$AsO$_4$ · 12MoO$_3$ or ammonium phosphomolybdate, (NH$_4$)$_3$PO$_4$ · 12MoO$_3$.

With a simple salt, the distinction between AsO_4^{-3} and PO_4^{-3} is no problem since arsenic will have already shown up in the cation analysis; also the colors of the silver precipitates obtained in the anion group tests—Procedure A.1—are indicative. In a mixture it will be necessary to remove arsenic by precipitating with H_2S in a strongly acid solution before the phosphate test can be observed.

Removal of the arsenate to test for phosphate. Use a pinhead size portion of the solid (do not use too much), in a test tube with 8 drops $12M$ HCl; heat and stir to dissolve the sample. Add 5 or 6 drops thioacetamide solution and heat in the boiling water bath for several minutes. Dilute with 10 drops of water, stirring thoroughly, and centrifuge. Decant the solution into a 5 ml crucible, discarding the yellow precipitate of As_2S_5. Evaporate the solution just to dryness, being careful not to bake. Cool and dissolve in 4 drops of $3M$ HNO_3 and 4 drops of water. Transfer to a centrifuge tube. If it is not clear, centrifuge and decant into another centrifuge tube. Then treat the solution with several drops of $(NH_4)_2MoO_4$ solution as above and heat.

Notes

1. The familiar orthophosphate ion, PO_4^{-3}, is not the only anion of phosphorus in the $+5$ oxidation state. Metaphosphates having the PO_3^- ion and pyrophosphates having the $P_2O_7^{-4}$ ion hydrate when their water solutions are heated, producing the PO_4^{-3} ion. It is not difficult to distinguish between the different phosphate anions if you wish to. Methods are given in standard reference works on qualitative analysis.

2. Sometimes reducing ions such as S^{-2} or SO_3^{-2} reduce MoO_4^{-2} to a lower oxidation state, giving a mixture with a blue color ("molybdenum blue") which might puzzle the student. Concentrated HNO_3 should prevent this occurrence by oxidizing these ions.

3. Add additional $16M$ nitric acid if necessary, as the $(NH_4)_2MoO_4$ solution is quite strongly ammoniacal. A considerable excess of HNO_3 does no harm.

4. The equation for the reaction for phosphate may be written

$$3NH_4^+ + 12MoO_4^{-2} + H_2PO_4^- + 22H_3O^+ \rightarrow$$
$$(NH_4)_3PO_4 \cdot 12MoO_3 + 34H_2O$$

(See Procedure 2.10, Note 3.)

5. Another satisfactory test involves precipitating $MgNH_4PO_4$ or $MgNH_4AsO_4$ by adding several drops of magnesia mixture to the neutral or slightly alkaline solution to be tested. Carefully wash the white precipitate free of Cl^- and add a drop of $0.2M$ $AgNO_3$. If arsenate is present, red-brown Ag_3AsO_4 will form. If only phosphate is present, the precipitate will be the light yellow Ag_3PO_4.

PROCEDURE A.3 / Test for borate, BO_3^{-3}, BO_2^-, or $B_4O_7^{-2}$

Use a pinhead size portion of the original solid unknown in a crucible on a triangle. Add 3 drops of methyl alcohol and 1 drop of $18M$ H_2SO_4. First stir, then warm gently from below to volatilize the alcohol, and finally bring the burner up to ignite the vapors. If the alcohol vapor contains volatile $(CH_3)_3BO_3$, it will burn with a green flame. Using this procedure, you will not obtain green flame tests from copper or barium salts.

Notes

1. Copper and barium salts also give green flames, but they should give no interference unless the test material is very strongly heated or stirred while being heated. It is possible in this way to get green flashes from copper and barium, but no student has been observed to make this error. However, there can always be a first time; don't let it happen to you.

2. Orthoborate, BO_3^{-3}, metaborate, BO_2^-, and tetraborate, $B_4O_7^{-2}$, all yield orthoboric acid, which combines with methyl alcohol to give a volatile ester $(CH_3)_3BO_3$, methyl borate:

$$3CH_3OH + H_3BO_3 \xrightarrow{H_2SO_4} (CH_3)_3BO_3 \uparrow + 3H_2O$$

Any acid catalyzes the reaction. Sulfuric acid is used because it also helps the reaction go to completion by its dehydrating action.

PROCEDURE A.4 / Test for carbonate

Slip a short piece of rubber tubing over the end of the glass rod
of your platinum wire so it will serve as a loose stopper for a
centrifuge tube into which the wire is inserted. Make a loop
in the end of the wire so that it will hold a drop of liquid. (See
Figure 27.1.)

Use a pinhead size portion of the original solid unknown in a
centrifuge tube. Add 2 drops of $3M$ H_2SO_4. A colorless, odorless gas will be CO_2. Hold the platinum wire loop with a drop

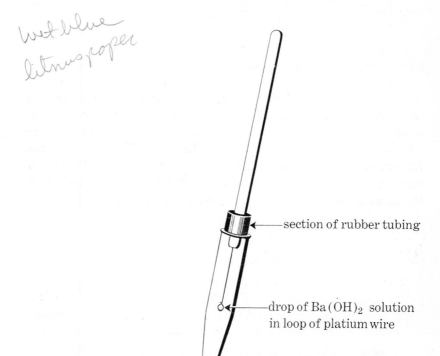

wet blue litmus paper

section of rubber tubing

drop of Ba(OH)$_2$ solution
in loop of platium wire

**FIGURE 27.1 / TEST
FOR CARBONATE**

of fresh, saturated Ba(OH)$_2$ solution, which has been clarified by
centrifuging, above the effervescing solid. The drop becomes
cloudy owing to $BaCO_3$ (see the sulfite test, however).

The less soluble carbonates may have to be heated with acid
before they evolve CO_2.

Notes

1. Naturally, the carbonate test must not be made on an anion test solution prepared by boiling an unknown salt with saturated Na_2CO_3.

2. To test for carbonate in the presence of sulfite, add 2 drops of H_2O_2 to the solid, stir thoroughly, and warm in the water bath for a few minutes before adding the H_2SO_4.

PROCEDURE A.5 / Test for fluoride

Use a portion of solid unknown the size of a standard drop. Mix it thoroughly with an equal volume of fine, pure sand or powdered quartz and put the mixture in a centrifuge tube. Prepare a platinum wire with stopper as in Figure 27.1 and suspend a drop of water in the loop. Add 2 drops of $18M$ H_2SO_4 to the sand-unknown mixture with a capillary pipette and put the platinum wire in position, being careful not to let either the H_2SO_4 or the water drop touch the side of the tube. Warm the tube in the water bath. Fluoride ion is indicated by turbidity of the water drop because of hydrolysis of SiF_4 to H_4SiO_4 (better, $SiO_2 \cdot XH_2O$).

Notes

1. The equations may be written

$$H_3O^+ + F^- \rightarrow HF + H_2O$$

$$SiO_2 + 4HF \rightarrow SiF_4 \uparrow + 2H_2O$$

$$3SiF_4 + 8H_2O \rightarrow \underline{H_4SiO_4} + 4H_3O^+ + 2SiF_6{}^{-2}$$

Although many chemists like to write the formulas of silicic acid to represent definite compounds like H_4SiO_4 (orthosilicic acid) and H_2SiO_3 (metasilicic acid), it is generally agreed that the ratio of water to silicon dioxide varies continuously; thus, $SiO_2 \cdot XH_2O$ is more nearly correct. The drawback of this formula is that, when it is used, balancing the equation becomes a mild algebraic feat:

$$3SiF_4 + (X + 6)H_2O \rightarrow SiO_2 \cdot XH_2O + 4H_3O^+ + 2SiF_6{}^{-2}$$

PROCEDURE A.6 / Test for oxalate

Treat 2 drops of the test solution with 1 drop of $6M$ acetic acid
and 1 drop of $CaCl_2$ solution. Stir and centrifuge, then confirm
that the precipitate is CaC_2O_4 as follows: Dissolve the precipitate by adding 5 drops of $3M$ H_2SO_4 and heating in the water
bath. Now add a drop or two of $0.02M$ $KMnO_4$ solution. The
bleaching effect confirms $C_2O_4^{-2}$.

Notes

1. The equation for the bleaching reaction may be written

$$5C_2O_4^{-2} + 2MnO_4^- + 16H_3O^+ \rightarrow$$
$$10CO_2 + 2Mn^{+2} + 24H_2O$$

PROCEDURE A.7 / Test for sulfite

Effervescence similar to CO_3^{-2} and the sharp odor of SO_2 indicate SO_3^{-2}.

For this test you must use a portion of anion test solution
that has never been acidified. Precipitate 5 drops of test solution
with 20 drops of $BaCl_2$ solution in a test tube. Centrifuge and
wash with 5 drops of water, discarding the centrifugate and the
wash water. The precipitate contains the Sulfate Group anions.
Dissolve all except $BaSO_4$ by adding 5 drops of water and 5 drops
of $3M$ HCl and carefully warming in a 50° water bath for a
minute or so.

Decant the clear solution into a 5 ml beaker and add 2 drops
of H_2O_2 and 2 drops of $BaCl_2$. Heat in the water bath and let
stand for some minutes. A white precipitate of $BaSO_4$ insoluble
in acids shows the presence of SO_3^{-2} in the unknown.

Notes

1. As stated in Procedure A.1, Part A, sulfate is the only anion
   of this group that is not soluble in moderately acid solution.
   Any SO_4^{-2} originally present is removed by the first treatment with $BaCl_2$. Warming with H_2O_2 converts SO_3^{-2} to
   SO_4^{-2}, and the formation of a second portion of acid-insoluble
   $BaSO_4$ is proof of the presence of SO_3^{-2}.

PROCEDURE A.8 / Chromate ion

The presence of CrO_4^{-2} will have been indicated by the color of the original unknown and of the anion test solution, and a test for chromium will have been obtained in cation analysis. If further confirmation is desired, the reaction used as a confirmatory test in Procedure 3.8 may be repeated on the anion test solution:

Use 3 drops of the anion test solution. Make it *just* acid with $3M$ HNO_3 and add 2 drops excess. Then add 8 drops of cold water, stir, and cool by dipping the test tube in a beaker of cold water. Now add 3 drops of H_2O_2 all at once. The evanescent blue color confirms the presence of chromate.

Notes

1. CrO_4^{-2} will not be found in any solution which contains a strong reducing agent such as SO_3^{-2}, S^{-2}, I^-.

PROCEDURE A.9 / Sulfate ion

No further test for SO_4^{-2} is needed beyond that in Procedure A.1, Part A. Only SO_4^{-2} gives a barium precipitate that is insoluble in $3M$ HCl. Be sure to stir the precipitate thoroughly with the HCl so that it has a chance to dissolve. Do not count a mere cloudiness such as might be caused, for example, by the sulfate impurity which is present in almost any sulfite.

Procedures A.10 to A.14: Specific Tests for the Chloride Group of Anions

PROCEDURE A.10 / Test for sulfide

Sulfide ion would be detected in the preliminary tests for volatile acids with dilute H_2SO_4 in Procedure A.1. The colors and solubilities of sulfides are likely also to give indication of its presence.

However, some sulfides are so insoluble that they evolve little H_2S and are not easily reacted on by saturated Na_2CO_3 solution. (Procedure S.5.) If this seems to be the case, a bit of the solid unknown may be warmed with $3M$ HCl and a pinch of granulated zinc. (Beware of H_2S produced by reduction of a sulfate.) In addition to detection by its characteristic odor, H_2S gas may be tested for with slightly moistened lead acetate paper. Instead of commercial lead acetate paper, a strip of filter paper moistened with $0.2M$ $Pb(C_2H_3O_2)_2$ solution may be used.

Method: Place a pinhead size portion of the solid unknown in a 5 ml beaker with 4 or 5 drops of $3M$ HCl. Warm the beaker gently if necessary. Hold the moistened lead acetate paper at the mouth of the beaker, or *better*, cover the beaker with a watch glass that has a small square of moist lead acetate paper on its under or convex side. (The technique is similar to that used in the test for ammonia, Procedure 5.5.) A brown to shiny black precipitate of PbS indicates sulfide.

Notes

1. The results of the cation tests will have told you whether or not to use a little granulated zinc in the sulfide test. The sulfides of Co^{+2} and Ni^{+2} and most of the Group 1 and Group 2 metal ions are insoluble enough so that they do not give off H_2S. Zinc with hydrochloric acid reduces the sulfides of these metals:

$$Zn + 2H_3O^+ + Ag_2S \rightarrow Zn^{+2} + H_2S + 2Ag$$

2. If you desire variety, filter paper moistened with dilute cadmium acetate solution may be used. A yellow precipitate of CdS is a positive test for sulfide ion.

3. If sulfide ion is present in a mixture, it must be removed before testing for the other ions of the group. $0.5M$ $Zn(NO_3)_2$ solution may be used to remove S^{-2} from the test solution. First add $6M$ acetic acid, if necessary, to make the test solution acid to litmus, then add 10 drops of $Zn(NO_3)_2$ solution, stir for a minute, and centrifuge. Test for complete precipitation with another drop of $Zn(NO_3)_2$ solution.

PROCEDURE A.11 / Test for thiocyanate

In a centrifuge tube mix a drop of the test solution with 5 drops of water, 1 drop of $3M$ HCl and 1 drop of $0.5M$ FeCl$_3$. The familiar opaque red color of FeCNS^{+2} shows the presence of CNS$^-$.

Notes

1. If thiocyanate ion is present in a mixture it will interfere with subsequent tests for Cl$^-$, Br$^-$, and I$^-$. CNS$^-$ ion may be removed by precipitating the halide with AgNO$_3$ solution and carefully heating the precipitate in a crucible to dull red heat to burn off the thiocyanate. Redissolve the Ag precipitate in 10 drops of $3M$ H$_2$SO$_4$ with 0.1 g of granulated zinc.

2. Another method of analyzing for halide ions in a mixture that contains CNS$^-$ is to add sodium hypochlorite solution to some of the anion test solution which has been made *just* acid with $6M$ acetic acid. This oxidizes I$^-$ to I$_2$ and destroys CNS$^-$ without affecting Br$^-$. After extracting with CCl$_4$ to remove I$_2$ (see Note 1, Procedure A.13) add several drops of $3M$ HNO$_3$ and more of the diluted sodium hypochlorite solution 1 drop at a time with shaking. Br$^-$ is oxidized to Br$_2$ in the more acid solution.

PROCEDURE A.12 / Test for iodide

Since iodide is much more easily oxidized than Br$^-$ or Cl$^-$, it is quite easily tested for. Besides, it is usually indicated during preliminary tests and anion group tests.

Use 2 drops of the test solution with 3 drops of $3M$ HNO$_3$, 1 drop of H$_2$O$_2$, and 2 drops of CCl$_4$, in a centrifuge tube. A brown color in water is due to I$_2$ which is extracted by the CCl$_4$ as a violet solution on vigorous shaking. Since it is desired to *concentrate* the color so that it will show up better, there is no point in using a large amount of CCl$_4$.

Notes

1. Many other oxidizing agents are equally satisfactory. A drop of Cl$_2$ water may be used if it is known that only a single

anion is present. For testing for iodide in the presence of bromide and chloride, hypochlorite ion in a solution buffered with acetic acid (Note 2, Procedure A.11) or iron(III) ion ($0.5M$ $Fe(NO_3)_3$) in a solution made acid with $3M$ HNO_3 is suitable. These oxidizing agents are strong enough to to oxidize I^- to I_2 but not to oxidize Br^- to Br_2.

PROCEDURE A.13 / Test for bromide

If there was no positive test for iodide, the same portion of test solution may be used; otherwise acidify 2 drops of the anion test solution with $3M$ HNO_3. Add NaClO solution *drop by drop* with stirring. A yellow color, which may be concentrated by shaking with two drops of CCl_4, is a positive test. Sometimes a test is obtained which is genuinely red-brown in color, but a modest yellowing is a positive test. If you are uncertain, compare your test with a blank. Excess oxidizing agent may oxidize the Br^- past Br_2 to BrO_3^-, decolorizing the solution again. That is the reason for the dropwise addition of the reagent.

Notes

1. To test for bromide in the presence of iodide, first oxidize the I^- to I_2 with one of the weaker oxidizing agents (Note 2, Procedure A.11, and Note 1, Procedure A.12), extract with carbon tetrachloride, and carefully remove the globule of CCl_4 with a capillary pipette. Then heat the water solution for several minutes in a boiling water bath to drive off the remaining I_2, and test the colorless solution for bromide ion.

2. If you plan to test for Cl^- on the same sample later, a good oxidizing agent to use for Br^- is $16M$ HNO_3. To 2 drops of the test solution in a centrifuge tube, add an equal amount of $16M$ HNO_3 and heat in the boiling water bath for just half a minute, then quickly cool and add 2 drops of CCl_4. Stir vigorously.

3. Apparently most of the difficulty with the bromide test stems from its failure to come up to the student's expectations. When he does not get as definite a test as with iodide, he assumes that bromide is not present. Actually, the test for bro-

mide is considerably less sensitive, principally because bromine is much less soluble in CCl_4 and gives a less brilliant color in CCl_4 than does I_2.

PROCEDURE A.14 / Test for chloride

On an unknown that is known to contain only one anion, negative tests for the other members of the group leave chloride as the anion present.

To test for Cl^- in a mixture, use the solution that has been tested for Br^- with $16M$ HNO_3 (Note 2, Procedure A.13). Dilute with 10 drops of water, stir, and add 2 drops of $0.2M$ $AgNO_3$ solution. A silver precipitate obtained after the other ions of the group have been destroyed must be AgCl. This precipitate redissolves readily in $7.5M$ NH_3 solution (concentrated NH_3 diluted with an equal volume of water). AgBr requires concentrated NH_3 to dissolve it completely, and AgI is insoluble in NH_3 solution.

Notes

1. Another effective procedure for the separation and detection of chloride, bromide, and iodide involves the use of $K_2S_2O_8$ in acetic acid solution to oxidize I^- and in strongly acid solution to oxidize Br^-. Details of this and additional methods may be found in more advanced texts.

Procedures A.15 to A.17: Specific Tests for the Soluble Group of Anions

PROCEDURE A.15 / Test for acetate

Ethyl acetate is prepared by a method similar to that used in preparing methyl borate, Procedure A.3, and is detected by odor.

A pinhead size sample of solid unknown is mixed with 1 drop of $18M$ H_2SO_4 in a crucible. Add 2 drops of *ethyl* alcohol (stockroom) and stir up the mixture. Then warm gently and notice the fruity odor of ethyl acetate, often compared to orange blossoms. If you have occasion to test for acetate, run two comparison tests—one known to contain acetate ion and one without —so that you will be able to distinguish the sharp odor of ethyl alcohol from the fruity odor of ethyl acetate.

PROCEDURE A.16 / Test for the nitrite ion

Nitrite ion is generally indicated by the preliminary tests. It gives the usual nitrate tests along with tests for a reducing agent. A simple test to distinguish NO_2^- from NO_3^- is the oxidation of I^- in slightly acid solution:

Dilute 2 drops of test solution in a centrifuge tube with 4 drops of water, 2 drops of $6M$ acetic acid, and 2 drops of $2M$ $KC_2H_3O_2$. Add 1 drop of $0.5M$ KI solution. If NO_2^- is present, I^- is oxidized to I_2, which may be extracted with a few drops of CCl_4 to give a violet solution.

Notes

1. The solution is buffered with $KC_2H_3O_2$ to lessen interference by other oxidizing ions, particularly CrO_4^{-2}. Nitrate does not interfere.

PROCEDURE A.16 / Test for the nitrate ion

The brown ring test for nitrate is interfered with by CrO_4^{-2}, I^-, and Br^-, which give similar dark layers, though not the sharp brown line at the junction of the two solutions that is the mark of a good brown ring test.

Removal of interfering anions (necessary only in analysis of mixtures). Use 4 drops of test solution in a test tube, add $0.2M$ $Pb(C_2H_3O_2)_2$ solution dropwise until precipitation is complete, centrifuge and decant the solution into another test tube, and add 4 drops of saturated Ag_2SO_4 solution. Stir and centrifuge, then use the supernatant solution for the nitrate test.

Brown ring test. Put 3 drops of the anion test solution in a centrifuge tube. If the solution is not acid to litmus, add $3M$ H_2SO_4 until it is. Then *carefully* add 5 drops of concentrated H_2SO_4, mix, and cool the tube under the cold water tap or in a beaker of ice water. Now prepare a solution of 1 drop $18M$ H_2SO_4 and a drop size portion of $FeSO_4 \cdot 7H_2O$ in 1 ml H_2O. Hold the centrifuge tube in an inclined position (about 45°) and carefully add 5 drops of this $FeSO_4$ solution so that it will layer over the heavier solution in the tube. Then set the tube upright and allow it to stand for as much as 15 minutes without shaking. A sharp brown line, due to $FeNO^{+2}$, at the junction of the two liquids shows the presence of nitrate (or nitrite). Of course, you would not make the test on a portion of your sodium carbonate test solution which you have acidified with HNO_3. (Some students do!)

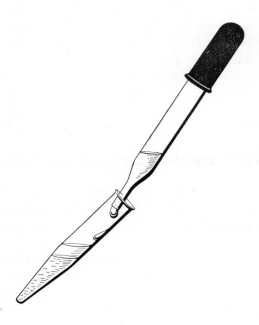

FIGURE 27.2 / THE BROWN RING TEST

Analysis of Salts

28

We will concern ourselves primarily with the analysis of a substance that is known to be a simple salt. By the application of a little common sense and chemical knowledge you can apply these same procedures to the analysis of an acid or oxide, to a complex salt such as an alum, or to a simple mixture of salts. You may assume that at least your first two solid unknowns will be simple salts. As soon as you have obtained good tests for one cation and one anion, you should feel justified in reporting your unknown. On the other hand, a faint test may mean an impurity in a commercial salt, or it may result from a trace of contaminant that you have inadvertently introduced.

PROCEDURE S.1 / Physical examination

Observe and record whether the sample is *white* or *colored, powdered* or *crystalline, heterogeneous* or *homogeneous, hard* or *soft, efflorescent, hygroscopic* or *unaffected by humidity changes.*

Color. Most of the ions included in cation and anion analysis are colorless, and their salts would be expected to be colorless too. Certain combinations of cation and anion result in compounds that are largely covalent, however, so we have yellow CdS, red HgI_2, black PbS. Table 28.1 summarizes some useful information on color. It may be augmented by the use of a handbook or by observations of the salts on the shelves of the laboratory.

Remember, however, that many substances have isomorphous forms and others have several hydrates which vary in color, and that shades of color depend on state of subdivision. Thus a sample of a salt on the reagent shelf and your unknown may be identical substances of equal purity, yet they may appear quite different. It would be equally foolish to ignore physical appearance when reporting an unknown or to base your report mainly on physical appearance. We suppose you would think twice before reporting a red salt as $BaCl_2$, but there are available several forms of such things as CdS, Sb_2S_3, and many chromium salts, which have wide differences in appearance.

TABLE 28.1 / COLORS OF COMMON INORGANIC SOLIDS

Black:	Sulfides of Ag(I), Co(II), Cu(II), Fe(II), Hg(II), Ni(II), Pb(II)
	Oxides: CuO, FeO, Fe_3O_4, MnO_2, NiO
	Finely divided metals and carbon
Brown:	Sulfides of Sn(II), Bi(III)
	Oxides: Ag_2O, Bi_2O_3, CdO, hydrated Fe_2O_3, PbO_2, $CuCrO_4$
Red:	Sulfides of As(III), Hg(II), Sb(III)
	Oxides: Fe_2O_3, HgO, Pb_3O_4
	HgI_2, $(NH_4)_2Cr_2O_7$, certain other dichromates and iodides, some cobalt salts
Pink:	Mn salts (light pink), hydrated cobalt salts (pinkish red)
Orange:	Sb_2S_3, some dichromates, CdS
Yellow:	Sulfides of As(III), As(V), Cd, Sn(IV)
	Some oxides, such as PbO, some iodides, such as AgI
	Iron(III) salts, most chromates
	Sulfur
Green:	Nickel salts, hydrated iron(II) salts, some copper(II) and some chromium(III) salts
Blue:	Hydrated copper(II) salts, anhydrous cobalt salts
Purple:	Permanganates and some chromium(III) salts

Many of these substances listed in Table 28.1 are not soluble; others, such as the anhydrous cobalt(II) salts, will change in color as they are dissolved; therefore, a second table giving the colors of the solutions that are included in our cation and anion analysis may be even more useful. A solution containing more than one of these colored ions might have unexpected shades of color, and complexing groups such as NH_3 or Cl^- may decidedly alter the colors.

TABLE 28.2 / COLORS OF IONS IN DILUTE SOLUTION

Yellow or orange: Chromates and dichromates, iron(III)
Pink: Cobalt(II), manganese(II) (faint)
Green or blue: Nickel(II), iron(II), chromium(III), copper(II).

PROCEDURE S.2 / Sampling

If the substance is in the form of relatively large crystals, or if it is not homogeneous, grind it to a fine powder before taking a sample for the preliminary tests or for cation or anion analysis. If this is not done, the sample may not be representative; moreover, solution of a fine powder is more rapid than that of large crystals. Occasionally an unknown mixture will be made up of crystals that are obviously different in nature; it is perfectly legitimate to separate them with a forceps or micro spatula and analyze them separately, but it is not necessarily advantageous to do so. If you decide to try this, scatter the material on a piece of glazed paper and use a hand lens.

If you consider it necessary to grind your sample, a very clean small mortar and pestle may be used, but most substances can be powdered by placing them in a spot plate depression or in a crucible and tapping them with the blunt end of a stirring rod.

PROCEDURE S.3 / Preliminary tests

Depending on circumstances, many preliminary tests might be advisable. Flame tests, borax bead tests, char tests for organic material, and tests with various acids, alkalies, and other reagents all are useful. We will limit ourselves to testing for volatile anions with dilute H_2SO_4, as described in Procedure A.1, Part D. (If ClO_3^- were given in unknowns we would have to use HCl.)

PROCEDURE S.4 / Solubility

Use a pinhead size sample with 10 drops of water in a test tube, and shake the tube for *several minutes* (some quite soluble substances dissolve slowly). If solution does not take place readily in the cold, try heating in the water bath.

A. If the substance dissolves completely or leaves only a very faint cloudiness, test the solution with 10 drops of saturated Na_2CO_3, using more if necessary to make the solution alkaline to litmus.

If a precipitate forms, prepare test solutions by boiling with Na_2CO_3 solution as in Procedure S.5.

If no precipitate forms, only Na^+, K^+, or NH_4^+ can be present as cations in a simple salt. To test for these cations, use a bit of the solid unknown to test for NH_4^+ (Procedure 5.5) and dissolve a pinhead size portion of the solid in 10 drops of water to test for Na^+ and K^+ according to the procedures of Group 5. For the anion tests, dissolve a proportionately larger amount, equal in bulk to 1 or 2 standard drops, in 1 ml of water and use as the *anion test solution.*

B. If the substance is not soluble in water, go on to Procedure S.5. However, you may, if you wish, try the solubility of the unknown in $3M$ HCl. If it is soluble, such a solution may be used for cation tests, though the solution for anion tests must still be prepared according to Procedure S.5. Before proceeding in this way consult your instructor about the "interfering anions" referred to in the note after precipitation of Group 3.

PROCEDURE S.5 / Separation of cation and anion with Na₂CO₃

Use an amount of the solid unknown equal in bulk to 2 standard drops (or about the size of a grain of rice) in a test tube. Add 2 ml of saturated Na_2CO_3 solution and heat with stirring in a boiling water bath for at least 3 minutes. Centrifuge and separate by decantation:

A. The solid residue should contain the carbonate of the cation with very little of the original anion. For cation tests, try dissolving a portion in $3M$ HCl. If it dissolves, Group 1 is not present; therefore, go directly to Procedure 2.1 and continue through the analysis of Group 2 and the later groups till the cation is found. If dilute HCl does not dissolve the residue, try $3M$ HNO_3 and hot $6M$ acetic acid on successive portions till a suitable solvent is found (Note 1). A small amount of material not dissolving might indicate incomplete substitution of carbonate for the salt anion. In a simple salt, a bit of the precipitate remaining undissolved may be ignored; for a mixture, it would be necessary to resume treatment with Na_2CO_3 (Note 2).

B. The centrifugate obtained after Na_2CO_3 treatment contains sodium as the cation along with carbonate and the unknown anion. This is called the *anion test solution* and should be reserved for anion tests. (For salts of alkali metals, see Part A of Procedure S.4).

Notes

1. If the carbonate is insoluble in $3M$ HCl but soluble in $3M$ HNO_3, a Group 1 cation is probably present.

2. Of course, many substances, such as glass, resist treatment with Na_2CO_3, and require special reagents not used in this course. Some very insoluble sulfides are not easily separated with Na_2CO_3. If such a sulfide is suspected, the anion may be detected using Procedure A.10, and the cation test solution obtained with hot $16M$ HNO_3.

3. Aluminum salts may dissolve completely in Na_2CO_3 solution, but on dilution the aluminum reprecipitates:

$$AlO_2^- + 2H_2O \rightarrow \underline{Al(OH)_3} + OH^-$$

PROCEDURE S.6 / Analyze for the cation
according to Procedures 1.1 to 5.5

PROCEDURE S.7 / Do the Anion Group tests, Procedure A.1

PROCEDURE S.8 / Stop to think

With the information you have at this point you should have a very definite idea what anion or anions may be present in a simple salt or mixture.

Compile the results of your observations of solubility, color, anion group tests, and so forth, and list the possible anions that may be present. For a simple salt, there will usually be very few possibilities; for a mixture, the number of possible anions will seldom be large. Then, make the necessary specific anion tests as in Procedures A.2 to A.16.

TABLE 28.3 / SOLUBILITIES

Salts of the anions of the Sulfate Group:

Arsenates, borates, and carbonates are insoluble, except those of NH_4^+, Na^+, and K^+. The bicarbonates of these three and of Ba^{+2}, Ca^{+2}, Fe^{+2}, Mg^{+2}, Mn^{+2}, and Sr^{+2} are soluble. Many borates are soluble in NH_4Cl solution, and all are soluble in hot dilute acids. Any salts of these ions with tervalent or quadrivalent metals are so completely hydrolyzed that they may be considered as not existing. AsO_4^{-3} should be detected in cation analysis.

Fluorides are insoluble, except those of Na^+, K^+, NH_4^+, Ag^+, and Sn^{+2}. FeF_3 is slightly soluble, but like many other metals, iron forms a very soluble complex ion with excess F^-.

Phosphates are insoluble, except those of NH_4^+, Na^+, and K^+. Phosphates of alkaline earth metals are soluble in acid but insoluble in neutral or alkaline conditions. Hence alkaline earth phosphates will give a precipitate with Group 3 of the metal analysis; for example, $CaNH_4PO_4$ precipitates from a solution containing Ca^{+2} and PO_4^{-3}. Fluorides and others behave somewhat similarly and are not readily removed by treatment with saturated Na_2CO_3 solution. They require special treatment; ask your instructor.

Oxalates are insoluble, except those of Na^+, K^+, NH_4^+, and Fe^{+3}. A number of oxalate complexes of other metals are soluble.

Chromates are insoluble, except those of Na^+, K^+, NH_4^+, Ca^{+2}, Mg^{+2}, Zn^{+2}, and Fe^{+3}. They should give a chromium test in cation analysis.

Sulfates are soluble, except $BaSO_4$, Hg_2SO_4, $PbSO_4$, and $SrSO_4$. Ag_2SO_4 and $CaSO_4$ are slightly soluble. Some basic sulfates are insoluble; for example, $(BiO)_2SO_4$.

Sulfites are generally similar to carbonates. $MgSO_3$ is slightly soluble.

Salts of the anions of the Chloride Group:

Chlorides and bromides of Ag^+ and Hg_2^{+2} and iodides of Ag^+, Hg_2^{+2}, Hg^{+2}, and Pb^{+2} are insoluble. $PbCl_2$, $PbBr_2$, and $HgBr_2$ are slightly soluble. Some basic halides are insoluble; for example, $SbOCl$.

Thiocyanates are soluble, except Ag^+, Pb^{+2}, Hg_2^{+2}, and Hg^{+2}.

Sulfides are insoluble, except Na_2S, K_2S, and $(NH_4)_2S$. Slightly soluble sulfides are BaS, SrS, CaS, and MgS.

Salts of the anions of the Soluble Group:

Nitrates are soluble, except a few basic salts like $BiONO_3$.
  Nitrates do not exist for arsenic or tin(IV).

Nitrites are soluble, except $AgNO_2$, slightly soluble.
  Nitrites are very unstable to oxidation or reduction.

Acetates are soluble, except a few sparingly soluble ones like $AgC_2H_3O_2$ and $Hg_2(C_2H_3O_2)_2$. Acetates char when strongly heated. (Many inorganic substances change to dark oxides when heated; for example, $CuSO_4$.)

part FOUR

APPENDIX

Chemical Arithmetic

I

I.1 / SIGNIFICANT FIGURES

Physical measurements of distance, volume, time, and the like can be made only with limited accuracy. The accuracy of a particular measurement can be stated at the same time we record its value, by use of the proper number of significant figures. Thus, if a sportswriter observing a forward pass in a football game estimates its distance at 40 yards, he is justified in using only one significant figure in giving the distance. The rule to follow is to include the trustworthy figures and the first somewhat doubtful figure. A temperature on a good thermometer graduated in degrees may be read as 112.8°, with the final figure a doubtful one obtained by estimation. If the thermometer is considered unreliable, the temperature would better be given as 113°, or even 110°, depending on what is considered to be the first doubtful digit.

In calculations based on physical measurements, the *least* precise measurement determines the number of significant figures that may be used. For example, if a screw weighing 1.2 grams drops off a Volkswagen weighing 750 kilograms, the weight of the car is still 750 kilograms, or $750. - 0.0012 = 750$.

Also, if the track for a 220-yard race is measured by simply pacing it off, the accuracy could scarcely be better than two significant figures. Then, even though an electronic timer accurate to the thousandth of a second is used, the time of a race should not be expressed to more than two significant figures. The precision of measurement would be equally poor if the distance is measured to a fraction of an inch with the finest surveying equipment, and an alarm clock used to time the race. But if both the distance and the time are accurately measured to five significant figures, the same number of figures should be used in expressing the result.

As has been stated in the text, the measurements of solubility products and other values used in qualitative analysis are seldom accurate to more than two significant figures. There is no justification for carrying out an answer to a problem to a greater degree of precision than the data on which it is based. If several steps of calculations are needed in working out a problem, you can avoid the accumulation of errors in rounding off numbers by carrying one extra figure through the intermediate steps. Thus, if the answer is to be expressed to two significant figures, you would use three figures up to the last step, but use only two in the answer.

I.2 / EXPONENTIAL NUMBERS

The very large and very small numbers used in chemistry are conveniently written in exponential form; for example, the Avogadro number is invariably written as 6.02×10^{23} rather than 602,000,000,000,000,000,000,000. The exponential method of writing numbers is illustrated by these examples:

$$
\begin{aligned}
10000 &= 10^4 \\
1000 &= 10^3 \\
100 &= 10^2 \\
10 &= 10^1 \\
1 &= 10^0 \\
0.1 &= 10^{-1} \\
0.01 &= 10^{-2} \\
0.001 &= 10^{-3} \\
0.0001 &= 10^{-4} \\
22000. &= 2.2 \times 10^4 \\
0.178 &= 1.78 \times 10^{-1} \quad or \quad 17.8 \times 10^{-2} \quad or \quad 178 \times 10^{-3}
\end{aligned}
$$

The exponent, it will be seen, represents the number of places the decimal point has been moved; if the exponent is negative, it means the decimal point has been moved that many places to the right; if positive, to the left. The preferred way of writing an exponential number is with just one digit to the left of the decimal point; in the last example, 1.78×10^{-1} would be the usual form.

Besides permitting brief statements of extremely large or small numbers, exponential numbers may help in showing the number of significant figures in a measurement. For example, the precision of the value 1300 centimeters is uncertain, but 1.3×10^3, 1.30×10^3, and 1.300×10^3 express different degrees of precision. Also, calculations involving very large or very small numbers are much easier when exponential numbers are used.

Addition and subtraction of exponential numbers. Exponential numbers may be added or subtracted if the exponential terms are of the same power of ten.

Examples:

1. Add 5.23×10^{-5} and 6.0×10^{-6}

   Solution:
   $$\begin{array}{r} 5.23 \times 10^{-5} \\ +0.60 \times 10^{-5} \\ \hline 5.83 \times 10^{-5} \end{array}$$

2. Subtract 6.0×10^{-6} from 5.23×10^{-5}

   Solution:
   $$\begin{array}{r} 5.23 \times 10^{-5} \\ -0.60 \times 10^{-5} \\ \hline 4.63 \times 10^{-5} \end{array}$$

Multiplication and division of exponential numbers. To multiply exponential numbers, add the exponents of the exponential term; to divide, subtract the exponents. The other terms of the exponential numbers are multiplied or divided as usual.

Examples:

1. Multiply 1.78×10^3 by 3.5×10^8

   Solution: $(1.78 \times 10^3)(3.5 \times 10^8) = 1.78 \times 3.5 \times 10^3 \times 10^8$
   $$= 1.78 \times 3.5 \times 10^{11} = 6.2 \times 10^{11}$$

(Note the number of significant figures in the answer.)

2. Multiply 4.968×10^3 by 2.532×10^{-2} and divide the product by 1.4×10^{-4}

   Solution: $\dfrac{(4.968 \times 10^3)(2.532 \times 10^{-2})}{1.4 \times 10^{-4}}$

   $$= \frac{4.968 \times 2.532}{1.4} \times \frac{10^3 \times 10^{-2}}{10^{-4}}$$

   $$= \frac{4.968 \times 2.532}{1.4} \times \frac{10^1}{10^{-4}} = 8.98 \times 10^5 = 9.0 \times 10^5$$

Powers of exponential numbers. The exponent is multiplied by the power desired; the other term is multiplied by itself as usual.

Example:

Cube 3.95×10^{-2}

Solution: $(3.95 \times 10^{-2})^3 = (3.95)^3 \times (10^{-2})^3 = 61.6 \times 10^{-6}$
$$= 6.16 \times 10^{-5}$$

Roots of exponential numbers. The exponent is divided by the root desired. If necessary, change the form of the number so that the exponent can be divided evenly by the root.

Examples:

1. Find the square root of 3.8×10^{-7}

    Solution: $\sqrt{3.8 \times 10^{-7}} = \sqrt{38 \times 10^{-8}} = \sqrt{38} \times 10^{-4}$
    $$= 6.2 \times 10^{-4}$$

(The square root of 38 may be quickly approximated by interpolation. The nearest square below 38 is 36, the nearest one above is 49; they differ by 13. Therefore $\sqrt{38}$ is approximately $6\frac{2}{13}$ or about 6.2. The result is accurate enough for most K_a and K_{sp} calculations.)

2. Find the cube root of 8.07×10^{-11}

    Solution: $\sqrt[3]{8.07 \times 10^{-11}} = \sqrt[3]{80.7 \times 10^{-12}} = \sqrt[3]{80.7} \times 10^{-4}$
    $$= 4.3 \times 10^{-4}$$

I.3 / LOGARITHMS

The common logarithm of a number is the power to which 10 must be raised to equal the number. For example:

log of $1000 = $ log of $10^3 = 3$
log of $0.001 = $ log of $10^{-3} = -3$ (usually written $7.0 - 10$)

The logarithm of any number which is not an even multiple of 10 is not an integer. Such a logarithm consists of two parts: an integer called the *characteristic* and a decimal portion called the *mantissa*. The mantissa is determined by the digits of the number and is obtained from a table of logarithms. The characteristic of the logarithm of a number greater than 1 is one less than the number of digits to the left of the decimal point. For a number less than 1, the characteristic is a negative number one unit greater than the number of zeros between the decimal point and the first digit other than zero. Examples of logarithms are:

$$\log 3480 = \log (3.48 \times 10^3) = 3.5416$$
$$\log 85.50 = \log (8.55 \times 10^1) = 1.9320$$
$$\log 3.480 = \log (3.48 \times 10^0) = 0.5416$$
$$\log 0.0855 = \log (8.55 \times 10^{-2}) = 0.9320 - 2 \; or \; 8.9320 - 10$$
$$\log 0.000348 = \log (3.48 \times 10^{-4}) = 0.5416 - 4 \; or \; 6.5416 - 10$$

Notice that in the last two examples, only the characteristic is negative; the mantissas are positive. Sometimes the negative characteristic is represented by writing the logarithm as $\bar{2}.9320$ or $\bar{4}.5416$. In certain problems, some involving pH for example, it may be necessary to convert the whole logarithm to a negative number by subtracting the positive mantissa from the negative characteristic:

$$8.9320 - 10 = -1.0680$$
$$6.5416 - 10 = -3.4584$$

The number corresponding to a given logarithm is called its antilogarithm. It is obtained by looking up the mantissa in a log table and using the characteristic to locate the decimal point. For example:

$$\text{antilog} \quad 3.8463 = 7020$$
$$\text{antilog} \quad 8.6556 - 10 = 0.04525$$

Since logarithms are exponents, multiplication requires only the addition of logarithms, division requires subtraction, raising a number to a power requires multiplying its logarithm by the power, and extracting a root requires dividing the logarithm by the desired root.

A *slide rule* is essentially a graphic logarithmic scale, accurate to three places. Actually, a three-place table of logarithms is satisfactory for almost all the calculations of this book, but the four-place table permits computations to three significant figures whenever they seem to be justified.

LOGARITHMS

No.	0	1	2	3	4	5	6	7	8	9	1	2	3	4	5	6	7	8
10	0000	0043	0086	0128	0170	0212	0253	0294	0334	0374	4	8	12	17	21	25	29	33
11	0414	0453	0492	0531	0569	0607	0645	0682	0719	0755	4	8	11	15	19	23	26	30
12	0792	0828	0864	0899	0934	0969	1004	1038	1072	1106	3	7	10	14	17	21	24	28
13	1139	1173	1206	1239	1271	1303	1335	1367	1399	1430	3	6	10	13	16	19	23	26
14	1461	1492	1523	1553	1584	1614	1644	1673	1703	1732	3	6	9	12	15	18	21	24
15	1761	1790	1818	1847	1875	1903	1931	1959	1987	2014	3	6	8	11	14	17	20	22
16	2041	2068	2095	2122	2148	2175	2201	2227	2253	2279	3	5	8	11	13	16	18	21
17	2304	2330	2355	2380	2405	2430	2455	2480	2504	2529	2	5	7	10	12	15	17	20
18	2553	2577	2601	2625	2648	2672	2695	2718	2742	2765	2	5	7	9	12	14	16	19
19	2788	2810	2833	2856	2878	2900	2923	2945	2967	2989	2	4	7	9	11	13	16	18
20	3010	3032	3054	3075	3096	3118	3139	3160	3181	3201	2	4	6	8	11	13	15	17
21	3222	3243	3263	3284	3304	3324	3345	3365	3385	3404	2	4	6	8	10	12	14	16
22	3424	3444	3464	3483	3502	3522	3541	3560	3579	3598	2	4	6	8	10	12	14	15
23	3617	3636	3655	3674	3692	3711	3729	3747	3766	3784	2	4	6	7	9	11	13	15
24	3802	3820	3838	3856	3874	3892	3909	3927	3945	3962	2	4	5	7	9	11	12	14
25	3979	3997	4014	4031	4048	4065	4082	4099	4116	4133	2	3	5	7	9	10	12	14
26	4150	4166	4183	4200	4216	4232	4249	4265	4281	4298	2	3	5	7	8	10	11	13
27	4314	4330	4346	4362	4378	4393	4409	4425	4440	4456	2	3	5	6	8	9	11	13
28	4472	4487	4502	4518	4533	4548	4564	4579	4594	4609	2	3	5	6	8	9	11	12
29	4624	4639	4654	4669	4683	4698	4713	4728	4742	4757	1	3	4	6	7	9	10	12
30	4771	4786	4800	4814	4829	4843	4857	4871	4886	4900	1	3	4	6	7	9	10	11
31	4914	4928	4942	4955	4969	4983	4997	5011	5024	5038	1	3	4	6	7	8	10	11
32	5051	5065	5079	5092	5105	5119	5132	5145	5159	5172	1	3	4	5	7	8	9	11
33	5185	5198	5211	5224	5237	5250	5263	5276	5289	5302	1	3	4	5	6	8	9	10
34	5315	5328	5340	5353	5366	5378	5391	5403	5416	5428	1	3	4	5	6	8	9	10
35	5441	5453	5465	5478	5490	5502	5514	5527	5539	5551	1	2	4	5	6	7	9	10
36	5563	5575	5587	5599	5611	5623	5635	5647	5658	5670	1	2	4	5	6	7	8	10
37	5682	5694	5705	5717	5729	5740	5752	5763	5775	5786	1	2	3	5	6	7	8	9
38	5798	5809	5821	5832	5843	5855	5866	5877	5888	5899	1	2	3	5	6	7	8	9
39	5911	5922	5933	5944	5955	5966	5977	5988	5999	6010	1	2	3	4	5	7	8	9
40	6021	6031	6042	6053	6064	6075	6085	6096	6107	6117	1	2	3	4	5	6	8	9
41	6128	6138	6149	6160	6170	6180	6191	6201	6212	6222	1	2	3	4	5	6	7	8
42	6232	6243	6253	6263	6274	6284	6294	6304	6314	6325	1	2	3	4	5	6	7	8
43	6335	6345	6355	6365	6375	6385	6395	6405	6415	6425	1	2	3	4	5	6	7	8
44	6435	6444	6454	6464	6474	6484	6493	6503	6513	6522	1	2	3	4	5	6	7	8
45	6532	6542	6551	6561	6571	6580	6590	6599	6609	6618	1	2	3	4	5	6	7	8
46	6628	6637	6646	6656	6665	6675	6684	6693	6702	6712	1	2	3	4	5	6	7	7
47	6721	6730	6739	6749	6758	6767	6776	6785	6794	6803	1	2	3	4	5	5	6	7
48	6812	6821	6830	6839	6848	6857	6866	6875	6884	6893	1	2	3	4	4	5	6	7
49	6902	6911	6920	6928	6937	6946	6955	6964	6972	6981	1	2	3	4	4	5	6	7
50	6990	6998	7007	7016	7024	7033	7042	7050	7059	7067	1	2	3	3	4	5	6	7
51	7076	7084	7093	7101	7110	7118	7126	7135	7143	7152	1	2	3	3	4	5	6	7
52	7160	7168	7177	7185	7193	7202	7210	7218	7226	7235	1	2	2	3	4	5	6	7
53	7243	7251	7259	7267	7275	7284	7292	7300	7308	7316	1	2	2	3	4	5	6	6
54	7324	7332	7340	7348	7356	7364	7372	7380	7388	7396	1	2	2	3	4	5	6	6
	0	1	2	3	4	5	6	7	8	9	1	2	3	4	5	6	7	8

OGARITHMS

.	0	1	2	3	4	5	6	7	8	9	1	2	3	4	5	6	7	8	9
	7404	7412	7419	7427	7435	7443	7451	7459	7466	7474	1	2	2	3	4	5	5	6	7
	7482	7490	7497	7505	7513	7520	7528	7536	7543	7551	1	2	2	3	4	5	5	6	7
	7559	7566	7574	7582	7589	7597	7604	7612	7619	7627	1	2	2	3	4	5	5	6	7
	7634	7642	7649	7657	7664	7672	7679	7686	7694	7701	1	1	2	3	4	4	5	6	7
	7709	7716	7723	7731	7738	7745	7752	7760	7767	7774	1	1	2	3	4	4	5	6	7
	7782	7789	7796	7803	7810	7818	7825	7832	7839	7846	1	1	2	3	4	4	5	6	6
	7853	7860	7868	7875	7882	7889	7896	7903	7910	7917	1	1	2	3	4	4	5	6	6
	7924	7931	7938	7945	7952	7959	7966	7973	7980	7987	1	1	2	3	3	4	5	6	6
	7993	8000	8007	8014	8021	8028	8035	8041	8048	8055	1	1	2	3	3	4	5	5	6
	8062	8069	8075	8082	8089	8096	8102	8109	8116	8122	1	1	2	3	3	4	5	5	6
	8129	8136	8142	8149	8156	8162	8169	8176	8182	8189	1	1	2	3	3	4	5	5	6
	8195	8202	8209	8215	8222	8228	8235	8241	8248	8254	1	1	2	3	3	4	5	5	6
	8261	8267	8274	8280	8287	8293	8299	8306	8312	8219	1	1	2	3	3	4	5	5	6
	8325	8331	8338	8344	8351	8357	8363	8370	8376	8382	1	1	2	3	3	4	4	5	6
	8388	8395	8401	8407	8414	8420	8426	8432	8439	8445	1	1	2	2	3	4	4	5	6
	8451	8457	8463	8470	8476	8482	8488	8494	8500	8506	1	1	2	2	3	4	4	5	6
	8513	8519	8525	8531	8537	8543	8549	8555	8561	8567	1	1	2	2	3	4	4	5	5
	8573	8579	8585	8591	8597	8603	8609	8615	8621	8627	1	1	2	2	3	4	4	5	5
	8633	8639	8645	8651	8657	8663	8669	8675	8681	8686	1	1	2	2	3	4	4	5	5
	8692	8698	8704	8710	8716	8722	8727	8733	8739	8745	1	1	2	2	3	4	4	5	5
	8751	8756	8762	8768	8774	8779	8785	8791	8797	8802	1	1	2	2	3	3	4	5	5
	8808	8814	8820	8825	8831	8837	8842	8848	8854	8859	1	1	2	2	3	3	4	5	5
	8865	8871	8876	8882	8887	8893	8899	8904	8910	8915	1	1	2	2	3	3	4	4	5
	8921	8927	8932	8938	8943	8949	8954	8960	8965	8971	1	1	2	2	3	3	4	4	5
	8976	8982	8987	8993	8998	9004	9009	9015	9020	9025	1	1	2	2	2	3	4	4	5
	9031	9036	9042	9047	9053	9058	9063	9069	9074	9079	1	1	2	2	3	3	4	4	5
	9085	9090	9096	9101	9106	9112	9117	9122	9128	9133	1	1	2	2	3	3	4	4	5
	9138	9143	9149	9154	9159	9165	9170	9175	9180	9186	1	1	2	2	3	3	4	4	5
	9191	9196	9201	9206	9212	9217	9222	9227	9232	9238	1	1	2	2	3	3	4	4	5
	9243	9248	9253	9258	9263	9269	9274	9279	9284	9289	1	1	2	2	3	3	4	4	5
	9294	9299	9304	9309	9315	9320	9325	9330	9335	9340	1	1	2	2	3	3	4	4	5
	9345	9350	9355	9360	9365	9370	9375	9380	9385	9390	1	1	2	2	3	3	4	4	5
	9395	9400	9405	9410	9415	9420	9425	9430	9435	9440	0	1	1	2	2	3	3	4	4
	9445	9450	9455	9460	9465	9469	9474	9479	9484	9489	0	1	1	2	2	3	3	4	4
	9494	9499	9504	9509	9513	9518	9523	9528	9533	9538	0	1	1	2	2	3	3	4	4
	9542	9547	9552	9557	9562	9566	9571	9576	9581	9586	0	1	1	2	2	3	3	4	4
	9590	9595	9600	9605	9609	9614	9619	9624	9628	9633	0	1	1	2	2	3	3	4	4
	9638	9643	9647	9652	9657	9661	9666	9671	9675	9680	0	1	1	2	2	3	3	4	4
	9685	9689	9694	9699	9703	9708	9713	9717	9722	9727	0	1	1	2	2	3	3	4	4
	9731	9736	9741	9745	9750	9754	9759	9763	9768	9773	0	1	1	2	2	3	3	4	4
	9777	9782	9786	9791	9795	9800	9805	9809	9814	9818	0	1	1	2	2	3	3	4	4
	9823	9827	9832	9836	9841	9845	9850	9854	9859	9863	0	1	1	2	2	3	3	4	4
	9868	9872	9877	9881	9886	9890	9894	9899	9903	9908	0	1	1	2	2	3	3	4	4
	9912	9917	9921	9926	9930	9934	9939	9943	9948	9952	0	1	1	2	2	3	3	4	4
	9956	9961	9965	9969	9974	9978	9983	9987	9991	9996	0	1	1	2	2	3	3	3	4
	0	1	2	3	4	5	6	7	8	9	1	2	3	4	5	6	7	8	9

I.4 / THE QUADRATIC FORMULA

Most quadratic equations used in the calculations of qualitative analysis can be simplified by approximations to the form

$$x^2 = n$$

but in some cases, such simplifications would result in serious error. The quadratic formula may then be used. Writing the equation in the form

$$ax^2 + bx + c = 0$$

the value of x is obtained from the formula

$$x = \frac{-b \pm \sqrt{b^2 - 4ac}}{2a}$$

There will be no difficulty deciding which of the two possible roots is the proper one to choose.

Questions and problems

1. In the logarithms 3.4823 and 9.5569 − 10, what are the characteristics? What are the mantissas?

2. Change to exponential form and then perform the indicated operations:
   a. $0.0098 + 0.00062$
   b. 22400×78.54
   c. $3.1416 \div 850$
   d. $(0.000031)^5$
   e. $\sqrt[3]{0.000075}$

3. By means of logarithms perform the indicated operations:
   a. 370×8.15
      Method: log 370 = 2.5682
               log 8.15 = 0.9112
                          3.4794
            antilog of 3.4794 = 3015

   But only three significant figures are justified; therefore the answer is 3020.

b. $\sqrt[3]{3.87 \times 10^{-5}}$

c. $\frac{4}{3} \times 3.1416 \times (8.52)^3$

d. $8011 \div 613$

e. $\dfrac{6503 \times 562}{946}$

4. Use a slide rule to obtain the logarithms of the following numbers:

a. 273

b. 1.8×10^{-7}

c. 113

5. On the slide rule, find the antilogs of:

a. 0.903

b. $8.508 - 10$

c. 4.115

Organization of the Laboratory

II

II.1 / APPARATUS

Suggested equipment for student lockers

4	5 ml beakers	1	tongs
4	10 ml beakers	2	vials litmus, red and blue
1	100 ml beaker	1	watch glass
1	150 ml beaker	1	metal water bath top
1	250 ml beaker	1	platinum wire, 5 cm
6	30 ml dropping bottles	1	bunsen burner
4	dropper bulbs	1	microburner
1	crucible with cover	1	wing top
1	graduated cylinder, 10 ml	1	wire gauze
1	nickel spatula	1	triangle
1	thermometer	1	file
10	test tubes, 10×75 mm	1	sponge
4	centrifuge tubes, 2 ml	1	test tube cleaner
1	test tube holder	1	pkg pipe cleaners
1	test tube rack		

In addition to these items, there should be available in the laboratory: ring stands, 7 mm glass tubing, 3 mm glass rod, iron crucibles, corks, labels, rubber bands, matches, cobalt glasses, and spot plates. A triple-beam balance of 0.01 g sensitivity is adequate for the weighings required. There should be about one centifuge for each half dozen students.

Each student should supply himself with an apron and towels.

Gp II $\underline{As^{3+}, As^{5+}}$, $\underline{Sb^{3+}, Sb^{5+}}$, $\underline{Sn^{2+}, Sn^{4+}}$,

①　　②　　③

Hg^{2+}, Pb^{2+}, Bi^{3+}, Cu^{2+}, Cd^{2+}

④　　⑤　　⑥　　⑦　　⑧

Arsenic subgp

Copper   "

2B

3M HCl

12m HCl

NH_3 Fe $H_2C_2O_4$

HNO_3 3m HNO_3 $HgCl_2$ H_2S

HCl   16m HNO_3

$SnCl_2$ NH_3

            $(NH_4)_2MoO_4$

GP II Reagents

H_2O_2

3M HCl & 6M HCl

H_2S 1M THIO ACE CH_3CSNH_2

KOH

2A ――――――――――――――――――――――――― 2A

HNO_3

$(NH_4)_2SO_4$

lvl $\begin{cases} NH_4C_2H_3O_2 \\ K_2CrO_4 \end{cases}$

NH_3

$HC_2H_3O_2$ $Na_2S_2O_4$

$K_4Fe(CN)_6$ H_2S

II.2 / **REAGENTS**

Acids:

Acetic acid	$6M$
Hydrochloric acid, concentrated	$12M$
Hydrochloric acid, dilute	$3M$
Nitric acid, concentrated	$16M$
Nitric acid, dilute	$3M$
Sulfuric acid, concentrated	$18M$
Sulfuric acid, dilute	$3M$

Bases:

Ammonia solution, concentrated	$15M$
Ammonia, dilute	$3M$
Potassium hydroxide	$6M$
Sodium hydroxide	$6M$

Other reagents, solutions:

Reagents marked by an asterisk are used only for special tests or for alternate methods. Those marked by a dagger do not keep well; only a small amount should be prepared at a time and they should be replaced periodically.

Reagent	Concentration	Formula	Grams per liter
*Aluminon	0.1%		1
Ammonium acetate	$3M$	$NH_4C_2H_3O_2$	231
Ammonium carbonate	$2M$	$(NH_4)_2CO_3$	
	Dissolve 192 g in 400 ml $3M$ NH_3 and dilute to 1 liter.		
Ammonium chloride	$4M$	NH_4Cl	214
†Ammonium molybdate	$0.5M$	$(NH_4)_2MoO_4$	
	Dissolve 90 g $(NH_4)_2Mo_7O_{24} \cdot 4H_2O$ in 100 ml $6M$ NH_3. Add 240 g NH_4NO_3. Stir, then dilute to 1 liter.		
Ammonium oxalate	$0.25M$	$(NH_4)_2C_2O_4 \cdot H_2O$	35
Ammonium sulfate	M	$(NH_4)_2SO_4$	132

Reagent	Concentration	Formula	Grams per liter
Ammonium sulfide		$(NH_4)_2S$	
1 volume reagent grade ammonium sulfide, 1 volume concentrate NH_3, and 1 volume water.			
*Ammonium tetra-thiocyanato-mercurate		$(NH_4)_2[Hg(CNS)_4]$	
300 g $HgCl_2$ and 330 g NH_4CNS per liter of solution			
Barium chloride	$0.5M$	$BaCl_2 \cdot 2H_2O$	122
Barium hydroxide	saturated	$Ba(OH)_2$	
Calcium chloride	$0.5M$	$CaCl_2 \cdot 2H_2O$	73
Carbon tetrachloride		CCl_4	
*Copper sulfate	$0.01M$	$CuSO_4 \cdot 5H_2O$	2.5
Dimethyl glyoxime	1%	$(CH_3)_2C_2N_2O_2H_2$	
10 g in 1 liter 95% ethyl alcohol			
Ethyl alcohol	95%	C_2H_5OH	
†Hydrogen peroxide	3%	H_2O_2	
Iron(III) chloride	$0.5M$	$FeCl_3 \cdot 6H_2O$	135
*Iron(III) nitrate	$0.5M$	$Fe(NO_3)_3$	120
Lead acetate	$0.2M$	$Pb(C_2H_3O_2)_2 \cdot 3H_2O$	76
*Magnesia mixture			
Dissolve 55 g $MgCl_2 \cdot 6H_2O$ and 140 g NH_4Cl in 500 ml water. Add 131 ml concentrated NH_3 and dilute to 1 liter.			
Magnesium reagent	0.01%	p-nitrobenzeneazoresorcinol	
0.1 g in 1 liter $0.025M$ NaOH			
Mercury(II) chloride	$0.2M$	$HgCl_2$	54
Methyl alcohol		CH_3OH	
Potassium acetate	$2M$	$KC_2H_3O_2$	196
Potassium chromate	$0.5M$	K_2CrO_4	97
*Potassium cyanide	$0.2M$	KCN	13
Potassium hexa-cyanoferrate(II)	$0.5M$	$K_4Fe(CN)_6 \cdot 3H_2O$	211
Potassium iodide	$0.5M$	KI	83
Potassium nitrite	$6M$	KNO_2	510
Potassium permanganate	$0.02M$	$KMnO_4$	3
Potassium thiocyanate	$0.5M$	$KCNS$	49

Reagent	Concentration	Formula	Grams per liter
Silver nitrate	0.2M	$AgNO_3$	34
Sodium carbonate	saturated	Na_2CO_3	
†Sodium hexanitro-cobaltate(III)	0.25M	$Na_3Co(NO_2)_6$	100
Disodium hydrogen phosphate	0.25M	Na_2HPO_4	35
Sodium hypochlorite	5%	$NaClO$	

Use Clorox, Hi-lex or other commercial bleach.

Sodium reagent

Warm together 30 g $UO_2(C_2H_3O_2)_2 \cdot 2H_2O$, 100 ml glacial acetic acid and 120 ml water until the salt dissolves; then add 220 ml glacial acetic acid. Prepare another solution by slowly stirring 148.5 g $Mg(C_2H_3O_2)_2 \cdot 4H_2O$ into a hot mixture of 320 ml glacial acetic acid and 40 ml water. Mix the two warm solutions. Let the mixture stand overnight and then clarify it by centrifuging or filtering through cotton.

†Thioacetamide	10%	CH_3CSNH_2	100
†Tin(II) chloride	0.25M	$SnCl_2 \cdot 2H_2O$	56

56 g in 3M HCl. Keep in a stoppered bottle containing several grams of granulated tin.

*Zinc nitrate	0.5M	$Zn(NO_3)_2 \cdot 6H_2O$	148

Solid reagents:

Ammonium nitrate	NH_4NO_3
Ammonium sulfate	$(NH_4)_2SO_4$
Iron, clean, rust-free brads	Fe
Iron(II) sulfate	$FeSO_4 \cdot 7H_2O$
Lead acetate paper	
Oxalic acid	$H_2C_2O_4$
Potassium chlorate	$KClO_3$
Potassium chloride	KCl
Sodium bismuthate	$NaBiO_3$
Sodium dithionite	$Na_2S_2O_4$
Sodium hydroxide pellets	$NaOH$
Zinc, granulated	Zn

II.3 / TEST SOLUTIONS

In general, solutions to be tested should be about 0.2 molar with respect to each of the ions being tested for. Exceptions are a few ions which are easily tested for or have limited solubility. The concentration of an individual ion should be the same in known and unknown solutions.

Ion	Compound	Molarity	Grams per liter	Solvent
Group 1:				
Ag^+	$AgNO_3$	0.1	17	$0.6M$ HNO_3
Pb^{+2}	$Pb(NO_3)_2$	0.1	33	$0.6M$ HNO_3
Hg_2^{+2}	$Hg_2(NO_3)_2 \cdot 2H_2O$	0.03	17	$0.6M$ HNO_3
	The $Hg_2(NO_3)_2 \cdot 2H_2O$ dissolves very slowly. Stir and heat.			
Group 2, Part 1:				
Pb^{+2}	$PbCl_2$	0.05	14	$0.1M$ HCl
Cd^{+2}	$2CdCl_2 \cdot 5H_2O$	0.2	46	$0.1M$ HCl
Cu^{+2}	$CuCl_2 \cdot 2H_2O$	0.2	34	$0.1M$ HCl
Hg^{+2}	$HgCl_2$	0.2	54	$0.1M$ HCl
Group 2, Part 2:				
As(III)	As_2O_3	0.05	10	$3M$ HCl
As(V)	$Na_2HAsO_4 \cdot 7H_2O$	0.2	62	$3M$ HCl
Sb(III)	$SbCl_3$	0.2	45	$3M$ HCl
Sn(IV)	$SnCl_4 \cdot 5H_2O$	0.2	70	$3M$ HCl
Bi^{+3}	$BiCl_3$	0.2	63	$3M$ HCl
	The Group 2 known solution should be made and stored in two parts as divided above, and combined immediately before use.			
Group 3:				
Al^{+3}	$AlCl_3 \cdot 6H_2O$	0.2	48	$0.1M$ HCl
Cr^{+3}	$CrCl_3 \cdot 6H_2O$	0.2	53	$0.1M$ HCl
Fe^{+3}	$FeCl_3 \cdot 6H_2O$	0.2	54	$0.1M$ HCl
Co^{+2}	$CoCl_2 \cdot 6H_2O$	0.2	48	$0.1M$ HCl
Ni^{+2}	$NiCl_2 \cdot 6H_2O$	0.2	48	$0.1M$ HCl
Mn^{+2}	$MnCl_2 \cdot 4H_2O$	0.2	40	$0.1M$ HCl
Zn^{+2}	$ZnCl_2$	0.2	27	$0.1M$ HCl

Ion	Compound	Molarity	Grams per liter	Solvent
Groups 4 and 5:				
Ba^{+2}	$BaCl_2 \cdot 2H_2O$	0.2	48	Water
Ca^{+2}	$CaCl_2 \cdot 2H_2O$	0.2	29	Water
Sr^{+2}	$SrCl_2 \cdot 6H_2O$	0.2	53	Water
Mg^{+2}	$MgCl_2 \cdot 6H_2O$	0.2	40	Water
Na^+	NaCl	0.2	12	Water
K^+	KCl	0.2	15	Water
NH_4^+	NH_4Cl	0.3	16	Water

Anion knowns are better given out as solid salts, but if desired, $0.2M$ solutions of anions may be employed.

Tables

TABLE III.1 / STANDARD OXIDATION POTENTIALS (ACTIVITY SERIES)

Half-cell reaction	E, volts
$Li \rightleftharpoons Li^+ + e$	3.02
$K \rightleftharpoons K^+ + e$	2.92
$Ba \rightleftharpoons Ba^{+2} + 2e$	2.90
$Ca \rightleftharpoons Ca^{+2} + 2e$	2.87
$Na \rightleftharpoons Na^+ + e$	2.71
$Mg \rightleftharpoons Mg^{+2} + 2e$	2.37
$Al \rightleftharpoons Al^{+3} + 3e$	1.67
$Zn \rightleftharpoons Zn^{+2} + 2e$	0.76
$S^{-2} \rightleftharpoons S + 2e$	0.51
$Fe \rightleftharpoons Fe^{+2} + 2e$	0.44
$Cd \rightleftharpoons Cd^{+2} + 2e$	0.40
$Co \rightleftharpoons Co^{+2} + 2e$	0.28
$Ni \rightleftharpoons Ni^{+2} + 2e$	0.24
$H_2SO_3 + 6H_2O \rightleftharpoons SO_4^{-2} + 4H_3O^+ + 2e$	0.17
$Sn \rightleftharpoons Sn^{+2} + 2e$	0.15
$Pb \rightleftharpoons Pb^{+2} + 2e$	0.13
$H_2 + 2H_2O \rightleftharpoons 2H_3O^+ + 2e$	0.00
$H_2S + 2H_2O \rightleftharpoons S + 2H_3O^+ + 2e$	−0.14
$Cu^+ \rightleftharpoons Cu^{+2} + e$	−0.17
$Cu \rightleftharpoons Cu^{+2} + 2e$	−0.34
$2I^- \rightleftharpoons I_2 + 2e$	−0.55
$Fe^{+2} \rightleftharpoons Fe^{+3} + e$	−0.77
$Ag \rightleftharpoons Ag^+ + e$	−0.80
$NO + 6H_2O \rightleftharpoons NO_3^- + 4H_3O^+ + 3e$	−0.96
$2Br^- \rightleftharpoons Br_2 + 2e$	−1.07
$Au \rightleftharpoons Au^{+3} + 3e$	−1.48
$Cl^- + 2H_2O \rightleftharpoons HClO + H_3O^+ + 2e$	−1.49

TABLE III.2 / IONIZATION CONSTANTS AT 25°C   339

TABLE III.2 / IONIZATION CONSTANTS AT 25°C

Acid		K_a
Acetic	$HC_2H_3O_2$	1.8×10^{-5}
Arsenic	H_3AsO_4	K_1 5×10^{-3}
	$H_2AsO_4^-$	K_2 8.3×10^{-8}
	$HAsO_4^{-2}$	K_3 1×10^{-12}
Hydrated aluminum ion	$Al(H_2O)_n^{+3}$	K_1 1.2×10^{-5}
Benzoic	$HC_7H_5O_2$	6.5×10^{-5}
Carbonic	H_2CO_3	K_1 4.2×10^{-7}
	HCO_3^-	K_2 4.8×10^{-11}
Cyanic	$HCNO$	2.0×10^{-4}
Formic	$HCHO_2$	2.1×10^{-4}
Hydrazoic	HN_3	2.0×10^{-5}
Hydrocyanic	HCN	4.0×10^{-10}
Hydrofluoric	HF	7.0×10^{-4}
Hydrogen peroxide	H_2O_2	2.4×10^{-12}
Hydrogen sulfide	H_2S	K_1 1.0×10^{-7}
	HS^-	K_2 1.2×10^{-15}
Hypobromous	$HBrO$	2.0×10^{-9}
Hypochlorous	$HClO$	3.5×10^{-8}
Nitrous	HNO_2	4.4×10^{-4}
Oxalic	$H_2C_2O_4$	K_1 4.5×10^{-2}
	$HC_2O_4^-$	K_2 5.5×10^{-5}
Phenol	HC_6H_5O	1×10^{-10}
Phosphoric	H_3PO_4	K_1 7.5×10^{-3}
	$H_2PO_4^-$	K_2 6.2×10^{-8}
	HPO_4^{-2}	K_3 1×10^{-12}
Phosphorous	H_3PO_3	K_1 2×10^{-2}
	$H_2PO_3^-$	K_2 6×10^{-7}
Propionic	$HC_3H_5O_2$	1.3×10^{-5}
Sulfuric	H_2SO_4	K_1 very large
	HSO_4^-	K_2 1.2×10^{-2}
Sulfurous	H_2SO_3	K_1 1.5×10^{-2}
	HSO_3^-	K_2 6.2×10^{-8}
Hydrated zinc ion	$Zn(H_2O)_n^{+2}$	3×10^{-10}

Base		K_b
Ammonia	NH_3	1.8×10^{-5}
Aniline	$C_6H_5NH_2$	4.0×10^{-10}
Methylamine	CH_3NH_2	5.0×10^{-4}

TABLE III.3 / SOLUBILITY PRODUCT CONSTANTS AT 25°C

Substance		K_{sp}
Aluminum hydroxide	$Al(OH)_3$	3×10^{-33}
Antimony(III) sulfide	Sb_2S_3	2.9×10^{-59}
Barium carbonate	$BaCO_3$	5.0×10^{-9}
Barium chromate	$BaCrO_4$	1.8×10^{-10}
Barium fluoride	BaF_2	1.0×10^{-5}
Barium oxalate	BaC_2O_4	1.7×10^{-7}
Barium sulfate	$BaSO_4$	1.1×10^{-10}
Bismuth sulfide	Bi_2S_3	6.8×10^{-97}
Cadmium carbonate	$CdCO_3$	2.2×10^{-13}
Cadmium hydroxide	$Cd(OH)_2$	2.2×10^{-14}
Cadmium sulfide	CdS	7.8×10^{-27}
Calcium carbonate	$CaCO_3$	7.5×10^{-9}
Calcium chromate	$CaCrO_4$	7.1×10^{-4}
Calcium fluoride	CaF_2	9.6×10^{-11}
Calcium oxalate	CaC_2O_4	2.0×10^{-9}
Calcium phosphate	$Ca_3(PO_4)_2$	1×10^{-25}
Calcium sulfate	$CaSO_4$	2.4×10^{-5}
Cobalt(II) hydroxide	$Co(OH)_2$	2.5×10^{-16}
Cobalt(II) sulfide	CoS	5.9×10^{-21}
Cobalt(III) hydroxide	$Co(OH)_3$	3.0×10^{-43}
Chromium(III) hydroxide	$Cr(OH)_3$	7×10^{-31}
Copper(I) chloride	$CuCl$	4×10^{-7}
Copper(I) iodide	CuI	1×10^{-12}
Copper(I) sulfide	Cu_2S	1.6×10^{-48}
Copper(II) iodate	$Cu(IO_3)_2$	1.4×10^{-7}
Copper(II) sulfide	CuS	8.7×10^{-36}
Iron(II) hydroxide	$Fe(OH)_2$	2.0×10^{-15}
Iron(II) sulfide	FeS	4.9×10^{-18}
Iron(III) hydroxide	$Fe(OH)_3$	6.0×10^{-38}
Lead(II) bromide	$PbBr_2$	5.0×10^{-6}
Lead(II) carbonate	$PbCO_3$	1.2×10^{-13}
Lead(II) chloride	$PbCl_2$	1.6×10^{-5}
Lead(II) chromate	$PbCrO_4$	2×10^{-15}

All solubility products for sulfides are from Waggoner, *J. Chem. Educ.*, **35**, 339 (1958). Averaged values from the literature are used for other compounds.

Substance		K_{sp}
Lead(II) fluoride	PbF_2	3.0×10^{-8}
Lead(II) hydroxide	$Pb(OH)_2$	2×10^{-15}
Lead(II) iodate	$Pb(IO_3)_2$	1.9×10^{-13}
Lead(II) iodide	PbI_2	9.6×10^{-9}
Lead(II) phosphate	$Pb_3(PO_4)_2$	3×10^{-44}
Lead(II) sulfate	$PbSO_4$	1.4×10^{-8}
Lead(II) sulfide	PbS	8.4×10^{-28}
Lithium phosphate	Li_3PO_4	3.5×10^{-13}
Magnesium ammonium phosphate	$MgNH_4PO_4$	2.5×10^{-13}
Magnesium carbonate	$MgCO_3$	4×10^{-5}
Magnesium fluoride	MgF_2	8×10^{-8}
Magnesium hydroxide	$Mg(OH)_2$	1.2×10^{-11}
Magnesium oxalate	MgC_2O_4	8.6×10^{-5}
Manganese(II) carbonate	$MnCO_3$	8.8×10^{-11}
Manganese(II) hydroxide	$Mn(OH_2)$	6×10^{-14}
Manganese(II) sulfide	MnS	5.1×10^{-15}
Mercury(I) bromide	Hg_2Br_2	1.0×10^{-22}
Mercury(I) chloride	Hg_2Cl_2	1.3×10^{-18}
Mercury(I) iodide	Hg_2I_2	3.3×10^{-25}
Mercury(I) sulfide	Hg_2S	5.8×10^{-44}
Mercury(II) sulfide	HgS	8.6×10^{-53}
Nickel carbonate	$NiCO_3$	1.4×10^{-7}
Nickel hydroxide	$Ni(OH)_2$	2×10^{-16}
Nickel sulfide	NiS	1.8×10^{-21}
Dipotassium sodium hexanitrocobaltate(III)	$K_2Na[Co(NO_2)_6]$	2×10^{-11}
Silver acetate	$AgC_2H_3O_2$	2.5×10^{-3}
Silver arsenate	Ag_3AsO_4	1×10^{-22}
Silver bromide	$AgBr$	4.8×10^{-13}
Silver carbonate	Ag_2CO_3	8×10^{-12}
Silver chloride	$AgCl$	1.2×10^{-10}
Silver chromate	Ag_2CrO_4	2.2×10^{-12}
Silver cyanide	$AgCN$	1.5×10^{-14}
Silver iodide	AgI	1.4×10^{-16}
Silver nitrite	$AgNO_2$	2.5×10^{-4}
Silver phosphate	Ag_3PO_4	1.0×10^{-18}
Silver sulfide	Ag_2S	6.8×10^{-50}
Silver thiocyanate	$AgCNS$	1×10^{-12}

Substance		K_{sp}
Sodium diammonium hexanitrocobaltate(III)	$Na(NH_4)_2[Co(NO_2)_6]$	1.5×10^{-12}
Strontium carbonate	$SrCO_3$	1.0×10^{-9}
Strontium chromate	$SrCrO_4$	3.6×10^{-5}
Strontium fluoride	SrF_2	7.9×10^{-10}
Strontium oxalate	SrC_2O_4	5.6×10^{-8}
Strontium sulfate	$SrSO_4$	3.0×10^{-7}
Tin(II) hydroxide	$Sn(OH)_2$	5×10^{-26}
Tin(II) sulfide	SnS	1.2×10^{-25}
Zinc carbonate	$ZnCO_3$	1×10^{-10}
Zinc hydroxide	$Zn(OH)_2$	4×10^{-17}
Zinc sulfide	ZnS	1.1×10^{-21}

TABLE III.4 / INSTABILITY CONSTANTS OF COMPLEX IONS

Ion	K_{inst}
$Ag(NH_3)_2^+$	6.8×10^{-8}
$Cd(NH_3)_4^{+2}$	1×10^{-7}
$Co(NH_3)_6^{+2}$	1.3×10^{-5}
$Co(NH_3)_6^{+3}$	2.2×10^{-34}
$Cu(NH_3)_4^{+2}$	2.6×10^{-13}
$Zn(NH_3)_4^{+2}$	2.6×10^{-10}
$HgBr_4^{-2}$	2.3×10^{-22}
$HgCl_4^{-2}$	8.0×10^{-16}
$Ag(CN)_2^-$	1.7×10^{-19}
$Au(CN)_2^-$	5×10^{-39}
$Cd(CN)_4^{-2}$	1.6×10^{-19}
$Cu(CN)_3^{-2}$	1×10^{-35}
$Fe(CN)_6^{-4}$	1×10^{-35}
$Fe(CN)_6^{-3}$	1×10^{-42}
$Zn(CN)_4^{-2}$	1×10^{-18}
AlF_6^{-3}	1×10^{-21}
FeF_5^{-2}	4×10^{-16}
HgI_4^{-2}	5×10^{-31}
$FeSCN^{+2}$	8×10^{-3}
$Hg(SCN)_4^{-2}$	1×10^{-21}
$Ag(S_2O_3)_2^{-3}$	6×10^{-14}

index

Index

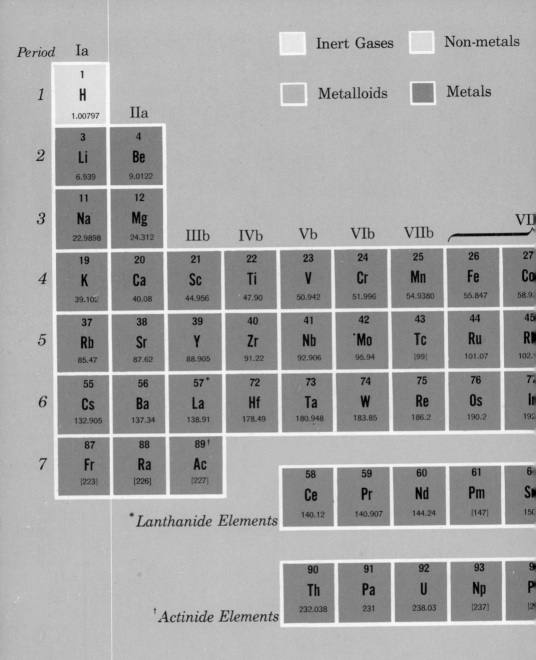

Periodic Table
of the Elements